GIMME GIMME GIMME

B⬛XTREE

First published in 2002 by Boxtree
an imprint of Pan Macmillan Ltd
Pan Macmillan, 20 New Wharf Road, London, N1 9RR
Basingstoke and Oxford
Associated companies throughout the world
www.panmacmillan.com

ISBN 0 7522 7268 3

Produced under license from Tiger Aspect Productions

9 8 7 6 5 4 3 2 1
A CIP catalogue record for this book available from the British library.

Design by designsection
Main Illustrations by Triffic pictures
Other Illustrations by designsection
All photographs © BBC Picture Archive
Printed by Mackays of Chatham plc.

Dedication

I would like to dedicate this book to Liddy 'Clear As Mud?'
Oldroyd, who directed series 1 and 2. For keeping
everyone's spirits up, for laughing longest and loudest at
my jokes, and for having a unique ability to pass on HUGE
pieces of gossip during a take – and still give notes to
actors and crew afterwards. I love you Liddy.

A huge thank you to Bernie Darnell, the script supervisor
on all three series, for overseeing all the changes to the
scripts, while maintaining the disposition of Mary Poppins.
Cheers Bern.

I would also like to give a special mention to my friend Sue
Evans. Sue's spirit is in these pages because she liked a
laugh, and she liked to be filthy. Sue was one of the
funniest people I ever met and she gave me some of my
best lines. I am particularly grateful for the 'refugee from
the People's Republic of Lesbania: National Costume –
checked shirt and clompy boots.' I miss you Sue.

Cast List

LINDA	Kathy Burke
TOM	James Dreyfus
BERYL	Rosalind Knight
SUZE	Beth Goddard
JEZ	Brian Bovell

Contents

INTRODUCTION

It was the summer of 1996 and my film *Beautiful Thing* was on at the pictures. As it was quite a funny film, and had started off as quite a funny play, my agent kept sending me up for meetings with TV producers who said things like 'We've got a really good idea. A sitcom about people working in a bank...' or 'We've got a really good idea. A sitcom based on *Priscilla, Queen of the Desert...*' or 'We've got a really good idea. A sitcom about teachers in the staff room of a comprehensive school...' Actually, I started writing that one.

Anyway, none of these ideas really got me excited so I asked my agent, politely, to stop sending me to meet sitcom people. Then he sent me to see Sue Vertue – another bloody sitcom person! But he promised me I'd like her. She'd done things like *Mr Bean* and *Vicar of Dibley*, both of which I loved. In fact, in my teaching days my nickname amongst the kids was Mr Bean – kids are great, aren't they?

Sue and I hit it off immediately. I was struck at the time by how pretty she was – sort of Zoë Ball's slightly elder sister, she'll love me for that – and we had a real laugh. She said she thought there was mileage in doing a sitcom about a straight woman and a gay man sharing a flat together. For the first time in my S.M.E. (Sitcom Meeting Experience) I got excited. Not only did I think it could work, but – more excitingly – I wouldn't have to do any research. I wouldn't have to go and work in a bank. Or go back to teaching, undercover. Or even become an Australian drag queen. Damn!

Sue told me to jot down some ideas on a piece of paper and she'd bung it in to the BBC. So I did. This is what I came up with:

LINDA and TOM have just moved in together. They're not lovers. They share everything except bodily fluids. LINDA is a single heterosexual woman. TOM is a single gay man.

LINDA works for a temping agency, with a view to meeting people. She has a lovely telephone manner and always has an adventurous packed lunch. She is a working class Londoner with a family living just round the corner. Her mum, MAUREEN, thinks Tom is the ideal man for her, and can't get her head around the fact that he's gay.

TOM works as a waiter in a nearby Italian restaurant.

GIMME GIMME GIMME

A middle class Londoner, his mum DAPHNE thinks that at last
he has found the perfect woman in Linda, who can 'straighten
him out'.

Upstairs lives their landlady BERYL. A stern woman in her
fifties, with a voice like a foghorn, she is lonely and
desperate to look on her lodgers as long lost children.
This idea is entertained by neither Tom nor Linda.

Linda and Tom are both on the lookout for Mr Right. They
have similar tastes in most things. They like the same old
music: Patsy Cline, ABBA, Ella Fitzgerald. They like the
same sort of movies: *Who Will Love My Children?* This all
bodes well for living together.

They also go for the same sort of man!

Their bedsit is bohemia-meets-kitsch. *Hollywood Wives-
meets-Coronation Street*. They have a huge framed photograph
of Jackie Collins on their main living room wall, as she's a
woman who knows a thing or two about finding the right man.
The series would follow their various attempts to lure men
back to the flat, win them over, make them stay the night,
and then sign them up for a six or seven month relationship.
Problems do arise, however, because the bedroom is Linda's
designated area whilst Tom's is the living room which boasts
a shabby sofa-bed. Whoever lures a man back though is
allowed the bedroom for that night. It's murder if they've
both found one.

Much comedy mayhem ensues as we
follow the loves and lives of
Linda and Tom!!

If you are at all familiar with *Gimme
Gimme Gimme* – and I'm assuming as
you've picked this book up at all then you
must have at least heard of it – then you'll
probably realise that the preceding pitch bears
little resemblance to the series that followed.
You may even wonder how on earth the
show was commissioned on the basis of one
slightly dull document. Well, if I tell you
that the following eleven words were added
at the top, you will realise why it was taken
seriously by the BBC.

Linda will be played by Kathy Burke,
Tom by James Dreyfus.

Kathy had recently won the Best Actress award at the Cannes Film Festival for *Nil By Mouth*, and James had just won Most Promising Newcomer at the British Comedy Awards. So the Beeb were keen. What's more, those eleven words were true. Well, kind of. I had telephoned Kathy and James to ask, 'Would you mind if I put your names on this document? It'll probably never get made. You don't have to do it if you don't want to. It's just it might get it read quicker.' Kindly they both said they didn't mind.

Oh and by the way, I didn't just look up their telephone numbers in the directory. I had worked with Kathy before. She directed my play *Boom Bang-a-Bang* at the Bush Theatre in 1995, and had become a close friend. James had played a small, though scene-stealing, part in a reading of a script of mine *Love Junkie* at the BBC. Also, at the time, Tiger Aspect had come to Kathy asking what she'd like to do. Fortunately for me she'd answered 'Something by Jonathan Harvey.' Our previous working relationship meant that I trusted Kathy's judgement on scripts implicitly, so that made her perfect – not only as a star of the show – but as the script editor too.

A year or so of meetings followed, with Kathy and James talking about how they saw the characters and the sorts of things they were keen on portraying. I had umpteen meetings also with Jon Plowman, Head of Comedy at the BBC. It was during these meetings that the slant changed slightly, and Linda and Tom transmogrified into the monsters we know and loathe today. I think Sue always saw the programme as being much more tasteful than the show it turned out to be, but I kind of knew that with Kathy and James on board things would never be... safe!

Things changed as I wrote more and more sample material. Parents were ditched. A 'couple next door' were created to play off against the leads: always shagging, the perfect people to drive Linda and Tom up the wall. They were of course Jez and Suze!

When I was training to be a teacher, many moons ago, I had worked with a woman who was convinced that all the boys in her class fancied her. She was continually moaning about how they were always trying to look up her skirt while she was illustrating her clematis on the blackboard. (My advice? Wear pants!). She complained that they phoned her at home asking her to describe her underwear. This woman was, shall we say, no oil painting and the rest of us thought she was making it all up. I would always encourage her to talk at

GIMME GIMME GIMME

length about how sexy she was, as the writer in me knew that one day this would make something pretty amusing. And I was right: with a few other irritating habits thrown into the mix, Linda emerged.

Tom of course changed from being a waiter to being an out-of-work actor – in fact, the worst actor in the country. Although he remained quite posh, I pushed his snobbish tendencies only to reveal that he was, in fact, from very humble origins in Manchester.

Kathy in particular was keen to make her character quite dark, and to play up the grotesquery of the situation. The more we all played around with it, the more the show became like a living cartoon.

Eventually we did a reading of the first episode for the then controller of BBC2, Mark Thompson, and we got the final go-ahead to make the series. It was so exciting for me to write the first series, though I do look back on that first episode and cringe slightly – well, a lot actually. I had never written for television before and I now realise that sitcom is one of the hardest disciplines to get right. I found it really difficult to imagine what it was all going to look like taking place in that small box in the corner of the living room. I had written plays before, even a film, so I could picture everything when writing for the stage or big screen, but this time I really couldn't picture it all in my head.

We were very lucky with our set designer James Dillon. I was sick of seeing shows where the characters were on low incomes yet had six grand sofas. I was adamant that Linda and Tom's flat should be grubby and vile, and that their sofa should look as though Yootha Joyce had farted on it. Nice!

The first series was not to everybody's taste. I soon realised that with this show people either loathed it or loved it. That suits me fine (he said through gritted teeth). There can be no greater insult, surely, than 'Yeah, it was okay'.

SERIES

WHO'S THAT BOY?

Perhaps not the best half hour of television comedy ever aired. I still remember a friend of mine asking 'Does it get any better?' Hopefully it did. I think opening episodes are hard to write – well, that's my excuse and I'm sticking to it! You have to introduce the characters and the tone of the series, so it can all be a bit expository (if there is such a word). However it's not all doom and gloom. This episode houses one of my favourite ever lines:

BERYL: Is he a ventriloquist?
LINDA: Well I wouldn't mind him sticking his hand up me skirt and making me lips move.

That certainly set the tone for the show!

THE BIG BREAK

An attempt to get Jez and Suze involved in the story. This episode features our first appearance by the inspirational Sir Simon Shepherd. I seem to recall James's Phil Mitchell impersonation was very funny – though as I can't be bothered to watch the video, I might be imagining this.

LEGS AND CO.

This was certainly a very enjoyable episode to film. My old mate Morgan Jones played the terminally depressed Shirley, and Adrian Bowers knocking about in a pair of leather slacks certainly made the time fly by. The sight of Kathy bending over in her pink cat suit brings a smile to my face even now.

ONE

DO THEY TAKE SUGAR?

The first pre-EastEnders appearance by Miss Elaine Lordan. She hadn't worked for a while so I created the role for her. This was, in fact, the first episode we ever filmed, to fit in with Miss Lordan's schedule. You see, she was appearing in one of my plays at the National Theatre, so we had to work round her. In fact, she only ever seemed to work in my things. And where is she now? Hobnobbing with those Slaters round Albert Square. And do I get a phone call, ever? Do I buffalo! The bitch!

SATURDAY NIGHT DIVA

At last Linda manages to throw herself at Jez, after sniffing her own knickers and identifying them by the whiff of her Bounce.

I DO, I DO, I DO, I DO, I DO

Costume designer Chris Marlowe excelled himself on this episode. The wedding dress and bridesmaid's frocks were ever so slightly camp. I was an extra in the wedding scene of this episode which took an age to film. So long in fact that although we started at 8.30am, not only did I miss my friend's real wedding that same day at 3pm, but I also missed her celebratory boat disco which left Westminster Pier at 8pm. And those dogs on mine and my boyfriend's knees were rank!

Episode One
WHO'S THAT BOY?

LINDA'S BEDROOM

linda wakes up with a stonking hangover. she kisses her liam gallagher posters.

♀ LINDA: My lovely Liam! My lovely Liam!

she sticks a pin in a doll with blonde hair.

♀ LINDA: My vile Patsy!

TOM'S BEDROOM

tom wakes up with the same hangover.

♂ TOM: Oh my eyes!

LIVING ROOM

jez stands in his underpants doing the washing up. linda comes in looking for cigarettes and finds none. she clocks jez and hurries out.

GARDEN

beryl is strimming her hedge. linda comes out.

♀ LINDA: Were we making a noise last night?
BERYL: Why? Going to apologise?
♀ LINDA: No, I just can't remember.
BERYL: Ambient trip-hop I can put up with, but when you stuck on Acker Bilk I was sick.
♀ LINDA: I think Tom's pulled. There's some bloke in my lounge.
BERYL: Is he nice and menacing?
♀ LINDA: I don't know, I've only seen him from the back. What are you doing that for?
BERYL: I take a pride in my dwellings, unlike some. The basement flat's empty so that only leaves me and you and since when have you been green fingered?

♀ LINDA: I'd rather not say. I need fags.
BERYL: There's two in your flat at the moment, isn't there?
♀ LINDA: Ha bloody ha. Lesbian.

LIVING ROOM

tom comes in also on the search for cigarettes. he sees jez and rushes out too.

STREET

linda walks down the street behind a busty blonde. some workmen wolfwhistle at her. linda is delighted. linda heading for the checkout with 2 pints of milk. she walks past the busty blonde.

♀ LINDA: Lesbian.

linda observes her reflection in a mirror. tom comes up behind her.

♂ TOM: Do you feel as bad as I do?
♀ LINDA: Don't speak to me in public.
♂ TOM: Have you got a spot?
♀ LINDA: No, just wondering what I'd look like with a blonde streak like Ginger Spice.
♂ TOM: Oh God rest her soul.
♀ LINDA: What you come for, milk?
♂ TOM: Yes.
♀ LINDA: Right. Some lesbian's just tried to get hold of me.
♂ TOM: What again?

linda grabs tom's arm.

♀ LINDA: On my life. They're like flies round shit today. Well bees round honey. (Seeing the busty blonde). Whoa, Lesbo alert, pretend to be my husband.
♂ TOM: Get off me.

♀ LINDA: Oh look it's little Sultana. Olright Sult?

♂ TOM: Do you mind!

♀ LINDA: Watch it!

they fight.

♂ TOM: Don't you dare hit me. No, not the face.

♀ LINDA: How's your mother Sult? All right? SULTANA: Yeah.

♀ LINDA: Oh good. I was at Borstal with her.

♂ TOM: Really?

♀ LINDA: This is my husband Tom.

♂ TOM: I'm not your husband.

♀ LINDA: Ain't he naughty, Sult? Oh you got something in your eye Sult? Your little magic eye?
SULTANA: I was doing a cabbage earlier.

♀ LINDA: They're marvellous them little magic eyes, ain't they? I'm surprised to see you here actually. Leaving the trade indoors. Or did he get off?

♂ TOM: Trade?

♀ LINDA: Some gay tart in a pair of boxers farting around in my living room.

♂ TOM: Well he's bugger all to do with me.

♀ LINDA: Well he didn't come round to sort out my plumbing.

♂ TOM: I've never seen him before in my life.

♀ LINDA: Hurry up Sult!

♂ TOM: No, wait, wait, are you honestly telling me that you know absolutely nothing about that man in our flat? What if he's broken in?

♀ LINDA: What in a pair of Calvin's? Do me a favour.

♂ TOM: He had a very nice back.

♀ LINDA: And an arse like two eggs in an hankie. What did we get up to last night?

♂ TOM: I've no idea.

STREET

tom and linda running home. behind the busty blonde the workmen whistle again. linda is delighted again.

SHARED HALL

linda & tom entering house out

of breath. beryl stands there pruning some plants.

♀ LINDA: Oh I shouldn't have run like that.

♂ TOM: Wait, wait, wait. Wait, wait, wait. Could we just have five minutes to think this through please.

♀ LINDA: Look there is a bloke in there and one of us must have slept with him.

♂ TOM: Well how did we get home?

♀ LINDA: In a taxi.

♂ TOM: Oh you remember do you?

♀ LINDA: No, but we always go home in a taxi.

♂ TOM: Oh, oh it's the taxi driver. You've gone and paid him in kind. Poor man. I tell you what I remember about the evening. I wore my velour look combat slacks and Baby Spice pumps.

♀ LINDA: Oh shut up. We went to Cheeky Charlie's to celebrate you getting an agent for your crappy acting and me getting another evening job.

tom sees beryl earwigging.

♂ TOM: What are you looking at?
BERYL: I'm just pruning my bush, dear.

♀ LINDA: We must have met him in the club. I mean what am I talking about? He's got to be yours!

♂ TOM: Why?

♀ LINDA: It was a gay club.

♂ TOM: Ah, ah, ah, ah, ah. Gay friendly. There's a difference.

♀ LINDA: Do you mean to tell me that some of the blokes in that club last night were straight?!!

♂ TOM: Yes.

♀ LINDA: You bastard Tom! Why didn't you tell me that before? Some of them blokes were really gorgeous!

♂ TOM: So that man in there could be Arthur or Martha.

beryl comes closer.

♀ LINDA: What do you want?
BERYL: If you want the advice of an ex-prostitute.

♂ TOM: Well we don't.

BERYL: Check the bedrooms for evidence.

LINDA: I bet there's loads in mine. Miss Marple'd have a field day. She'd say, 'These knickers have been ripped off in the heat of passion. I spy love on the sheets'. She'd also conclude that suspect A (Points to herself) is far better looking than suspect B (Points to him). Stands to reason, he's mine.

TOM: Oh. Oh, and I look like the back end of a bus do I?

LINDA: If buses mince.

she goes in. he follows.

LINDA'S BEDROOM

linda comes in and spies her bed. she pulls back the duvet and has a good look at the sheets. nothing.

LINDA: Bugger!

TOM'S BEDROOM

tom comes in and goes through his condom box to see if there are any missing.

TOM: Oh let it be me, let it be me. One, two, three, oh pooh!

LIVING ROOM

they come in to an empty room, tidied immaculately.

TOM: Oh, oh well there we go. Proves my point doesn't it? Had to be gay. No straight man would ever leave a place this spotless. There's probably a quiche in the oven. Where is he?

LINDA: Here, he's having a dump isn't he? He's in our toilet having a dump.

TOM: Is he?

LINDA: Yeah come on.

HALLWAY

linda approaches the bathroom door.

LINDA: Hello, this is Linda La Hughes here. The Ginger Jerry Hall.

TOM: Are you all right in there?

LINDA: Isn't he quiet? Ain't you quiet.

I'm quiet when I'm on the lav. I've got the functions of an angel.

TOM: Maybe he's shy. Oh no maybe he's deaf.

LINDA: I can do sign language. (Indicates) That's a pint of lager. I am fantastic with the physically challenged.

TOM: Yes, I wonder why.

linda calls through.

LINDA: Are you deaf?!!

TOM: Maybe it's unlocked.

tom pushes open the door.

LINDA: Here, how would you like it if you were parking your breakfast and a load of people walked in on you?

they go in

TOM: Hello!

LINDA: Oh bugger!

it's empty.

LIVING ROOM

tom and linda watching telly.

TOM: We should never have left him here on his own you know, never. He'll think we're so, so rude. That is, if he was ever here at all. You know I mean maybe we imagined him. Maybe he was some sort of an illusion. Maybe he was...

LINDA: Maybe I'm trying to watch the television, so maybe you should shut up.

TOM: Well in the immortal words of Toyah 'the voice' Wilcox. 'It'ths a myth-stery'. Actually that was bloody good wasn't it? It's a mythstery. I must put that down on my C.V. Special skills, lisping.

LINDA: Tom.

TOM: I wonder if he lisped.

LINDA: Where's my cup of tea?

TOM: He was very rugged wasn't he? I wonder if people say that about me. You know for all I know I could be walking down the street doing something quite banal. I don't know, like taking a library book back or something, the latest Sue Townsend. Or the Two Fat Ladies cookery book. And then maybe a bus is going past and one passenger looks down, clocks me and says to their friend. "Look at him, isn't he rugged?"

♀ LINDA: Tom!

♂ TOM: All right, all right, all right. I'll get your tea. Okay what do you want, what do you want? Do you want Darjeeling, raspberry zinger or pyramids?

♀ LINDA: I'd rather do a Sarah Miles and drink my own piss.

♂ TOM: Don't be so . . . Linda!

♀ LINDA: What?

♂ TOM: Linda, come here please. There's a note. There's a note there. Is it from him? Oh my God. You read it. No I'll read it. No I think I'm having a panic attack.

she picks up the note.

♀ LINDA: All right, keep your hair on. Oh he's got nice big capitals.

♂ TOM: Just read it bitch!

♀ LINDA: Hi cats.

♂ TOM: Oh, what's he calling us cats for? What's that all about?

♀ LINDA: Look do you want me to read it or not?

♂ TOM: Yes I do, I do.

♀ LINDA: Hi cats. (Has trouble reading it) Thanks you, thanks. Thanks for last night. Peto.

♂ TOM: Peto?

♀ LINDA: Want a butchers?

♂ TOM: Peto!

♀ LINDA: Oh. I've just worked it out.

♂ TOM: What, what, what?

♀ LINDA: Peto is a Nigerian name isn't it? It was the cab driver. "Hello my name is Peto. I'm your cab driver for the evening." See? It makes perfect sense dunn it? Hi cats, thanks for last night. Peto. Stands to reason.

♂ TOM: Does it?

♀ LINDA: Yeah. You see them Nigerians mate, they love a good scar. (Points to hers) He probably took one look at this right, and thought I was a warrior queen.

♂ TOM: Yes but why does he call us cats?

♀ LINDA: Well it's Nigerian isn't it? For oh dusky maiden and dusky maiden's homosexual flatmate.

♂ TOM: All right, now I know you're just making that up and that is so racist.

♀ LINDA: What with the amount of ethics I've slept with? Do me a favour.

LINDA'S BEDROOM

linda lies on her bed watching zoe ball on the tv. the door opens and tom pops his head round.

♂ TOM: Can I come in?

♀ LINDA: You're not going to talk are you?

tom finds linda's massive mobile phone.

♂ TOM: No. Oh what's this?

♀ LINDA: What's it look like?

♂ TOM: A house brick.

♀ LINDA: It's my mobile phone for my new evening job.

♂ TOM: Oh I don't see why you think that you have to have two jobs.

♀ LINDA: I work in the media mate. It ain't well paid. A lot of people in the media have two jobs just to help pay the lecky bill. You can find that Kate Adie down the pubs in Hackney of a Wednesday selling whelks.

♂ TOM: Don't you dare bracket yourself with Saint Kate of the Troubled Spots. You're just a bloody little receptionist. Okay? Oh look it's Zoe Ball! Oh Zoe Ball! Lovely, lovely, lovely Zoe Ball! Mirror, mirror on the wall! The fairest TV kids presenter of them all has to be... Miss Zoe Ball!

♀ LINDA: Shut up!

♂ TOM: Of course I was a huge fan of her father's. Do you remember, Johnny 'Think Of A Number' Ball? Do you remember? Oh, very talented family all round. Michael Ball entered the Eurovision Song Contest. Oh and as for Kenny Ball...

♀ LINDA: Oh will you get out of my bedroom you overgrown streak of piss.

♂ TOM: Well I find it very funny that you're so dismissive of the fact that we woke this morning with a strange man in our flat.

♀ LINDA: Do you know what you are? Desperate mate. So we got a bit pissed last night. So we can't remember much about the

> ## LINDA
> **'I'm quiet when I'm on the lav. I've got the functions of an angel.'**

end of the evening. So get over it!

♂ TOM: Aren't you intrigued?

♀ LINDA: I'm too hung over to be intrigued. Anyone would think you'd never seen a man in a pair of undies before.

♂ TOM: Well I haven't seen as many as you and I went to an all boys boarding school.

♀ LINDA: I bet you were the sort of wimp who always had a note from his mother.

♂ TOM: Well at least my mother could read and write.

♀ LINDA: Peto was mine.

♂ TOM: How do you know that?

♀ LINDA: Well I weren't going to tell you before but I found a hair in my bed and it weren't auburn.

♂ TOM: Show me this instant.

♀ LINDA: No, no I didn't want to show you because I knew you'd be heartbroken.

♂ TOM: I don't believe you, I found a hair in my bed this morning and it was a really big one.

♀ LINDA: Well he was a bit of a slapper then wasn't he?

♂ TOM: Well I just don't understand how we can wipe out part of our memory like that. I mean the human body is a nightmare. Oh, oh, oh maybe last night we had our minds removed. Now there's a scary thought.

♀ LINDA: Not half as scary as the thought of me punching you out if you don't shut up.

♂ TOM: You know what we should do? We should get drunk.

♀ LINDA: Oh no.

♂ TOM: Yes we should because if we get drunk we'll be in the same psychological state as we were last night and therefore we might remember what happened.

he heads for the door.

♀ LINDA: Where you going?

♂ TOM: Why are you going to miss me?

♀ LINDA: Like a cat with no neck misses licking his own arsehole.

♂ TOM: Is that a yes or a no?

♀ LINDA: Haven't a clue!

LIVING ROOM

tom, beryl & linda enter room. beryl carries a tray of alcohol.

BERYL: Why didn't you tell me earlier? An actor with an agent, Tom, is respectable. Like a prozzy when she gets her first pimp.

♀ LINDA: What's going on?

♂ TOM: Bloody Mary, look.

BERYL: You should have told me last night, then Beryl would have slipped into her boob tube and mashed potatoed till dawn.

♂ TOM: Don't be revolting.

♀ LINDA: Do you know what? I really don't think I could touch a drop.

**LIVING ROOM,
TWENTY MINUTES LATER**

♀ LINDA: No the thing is right, he was bloody gorgeous Beryl, weren't he Tom?

♂ TOM: From behind, he had perfect buns.

BERYL: Well I saw him from the front.

♀ LINDA: Yeah course you did. When you were trimming your hedge.

BERYL: He put me in mind of a young Shirley Porter. Sidney Poitier.

♂ TOM: Beryl, when he walked past you did he mince?

♀ LINDA: Do it for her.

♂ TOM: Shall I act it? I'll act it for you.

tom minces for her.

♂ TOM: Was he like this?

he swaggers like a macho man.

♂ TOM: Or, or, was he like this?

♀ LINDA: What's the difference?

♂ TOM: Oh you bitch.

BERYL: Walking interpretation isn't one of my strong points.

♀ LINDA: Well didn't he say anything to you?

BERYL: Oh yes.

♂ TOM: Well what?

BERYL: Morning.

♂ TOM: Yeah but was it (Camp) morning! Or (Butch) morning!?

BERYL: Well my strimmer was going full pelt so I had to lip read.

♀ LINDA: So he didn't say nothing like... Tell Linda I love her?

BERYL: Oh if he did then he ventriloquised it. Is he a ventriloquist?

♀ LINDA: Well I wouldn't mind him sticking his hand up my skirt and making me lips move, do you know what I mean?

TOM: Oh it's tragic Beryl. And all we've got to show for it is one lousy letter he left.

BERYL: Well why didn't you say? I could phone my great pal Reeney. When she came off the game she took up handwriting analysis.

LINDA: Oh hang on I'll get it.

TOM: But won't she actually have to see the handwriting?

BERYL: No she knew my niece Janet in Joburg was a lesbian just by me describing the apostrophes in her suicide note.

TOM: Oh that's fantastic.

beryl is on the phone now.

BERYL: Reeney. Gag the Chinchilla I want a consultation. Okay. Have you got a copy of this week's Bella handy? Right okay. Page three. The first letter be-eth H and it's twice the size of Anthea Turner's head. What? Oh all right I'll read it, it says 'Hi cats, thanks for last night, P.T.O. (She turns the page over) I'll be back at lunchtime tomorrow, see you then Jez.'

TOM: No Peto.

BERYL: Jez.

LINDA: Peto.

TOM: P.T.O. It's P.T.O. P.T.O.

LINDA: Well he ain't put a dot in between each letter. Mummy always said you have to put a dot in between each letter.

TOM: Oh you bloody stupid woman! I'll bloody well kill you!!

LINDA: Well it ain't my fault. I can't help being visibly disabled. Anyway Peto's coming back to me.

she heads for her bedroom.

BERYL: Do you want this consultation or don't you?

LINDA: I've got to get my beauty sleep.

TOM: A century of sleep wouldn't be enough.

suddenly linda kicks and screams.

LINDA: Where's my bed? You put my bed back you!!

BERYL: Try the bedroom love.

LINDA: Oh.

tom tries to get past her.

TOM: Come here you. Get out of my bloody way.

they fight their way out of the room.

BERYL: (On phone) No Rene, keep talking. It's their bill.

LINDA'S BEDROOM

linda, drunk, cold calling on her mobile phone.

LINDA: Mr Adams? Hello it's Linda La Hughes here from Mattress Blasters. Were you aware that there are millions of parasites eating away daily at your divan? But fear not help is at hand. We at Mattress Blasters can offer you a cleansing service for only seventy-four ninety-nine. Yes seven four nine nine. Mr Adams? What you got on? Mr Adams? I think I'm going to be sick.

KITCHEN, NEXT MORNING

linda sits in a nigerian head-dress going through the yellow pages. tom comes in.

TOM: Morning. You haven't um, made any special effort for Jez have you?

LINDA: No, I just threw on the first thing that fell out of my wardrobe.

TOM: Oh I forgot to ask, he did say he'd be back sort of around lunch time didn't he?

LINDA: Did he? I don't know I didn't pay much attention really.

TOM: No me neither. Me neither. What time would you say lunch was?

LINDA: I don't know, whenever you're peckish, I suppose.

TOM: Well being a thespian...

LINDA: Tom, can't you see I'm moonlighting here?

TOM: Sorry, sorry. I'll be fingering through Richard The Third until he comes.

tom goes to the lounge with his script.

LINDA: (On Phone) Mr Armitage? Well put your husband on then.

tom puts some music on. it sends him into a flashback the night before.
tom and linda forming a human bump 'n' grind sandwich with jez
we snap back to:

LIVING ROOM, AS BEFORE

linda snapping the stereo off.

♀ LINDA: Tom I'm trying to supplement my earnings in there!!

♂ TOM: I've remembered what he looks like!

the doorbell goes.

♂ TOM: He's early.

♀ LINDA: Oh that's so heterosexual!

♂ TOM: Ow!

linda pushes tom out of way.

HALLWAY

linda and tom drag jez through towards the living room.

JEZ: Hit cats.

♀ LINDA: Puddycat.

LIVING ROOM

they bring him through.

♂ TOM: Hey Jez. How's it hanging boy?

JEZ: Fine, fine. Hey, what a night eh? Did we have a night or what?

♂ TOM: Yes didn't we? Didn't we?!

♀ LINDA: Yeah I'm black and blue all over. Do you know what I'm saying?

JEZ: I really should remember that break dancing's a very eighties thing. Still, you're both quick learners!.

♂ TOM: Jez, Jez, Jez. Pop quiz. Village People, great or shite?

JEZ: Erm. . . .

♀ LINDA: Jez, Jez, Judy Garland. Torch song icon or draggy old corpse with a couple of talentless kids?

JEZ: Sorry?

♂ TOM: So what you been up to then Jez my old sparring partner?

JEZ: Oh packing up my old kit bag you know.

♂ TOM: Yes and smile, smile, smile!

♀ LINDA: So what are you moving Jez? Are you moving?

JEZ: Yes, yes today. Don't you remember?

♀ LINDA: Yeah course we do. Course we do.

♂ TOM: Yeah moving.

they haven't a clue what he's on about.

JEZ: Well I can't wait too long. I want to start bringing my stuff in. You did say the other night you'd give us a hand.

♀ LINDA: In Jez boy, in?

♂ TOM: Bringing stuff in?

JEZ: Yes, yes in. I knew this was going to happen. You don't remember a thing, do you?

♀ LINDA: I remember your face vaguely.

JEZ: So it's not all right for me to move in then? It's just that the other night you, they warned me. Never get pally with the clients.

♂ TOM: Clients?

JEZ: You hired me from the escort agency. Big Boys. You phoned. I came over. Well had a little bit of fun. Nothing too heavy, no ropes.

♀ LINDA: Oh I think I'm going to be sick.

♂ TOM: (To Linda) Tell me you didn't touch me!

suze enters beaming.

SUZE: Jez? Jez! Are you with those kind of people? Hi cats!! Tom and Linda? Suze. We're so looking forward to moving in below you.

♀ LINDA: You just watch it now Lesbo.

♂ TOM: Jez?!

JEZ: Guess what city this is? Windupsville U.S.A.!!

SUZE: Oh you didn't wind them up?

JEZ: Yes I did. They couldn't remember a thing. So I told them I was their escort.

♀ LINDA: So yous two are moving into the flat downstairs?

SUZE: Got it in one Linds!

♂ TOM: So what the hell were you doing in our flat?

JEZ: Will you tell them or shall I?

SUZE: Well you tell them. He's so talented orally.

JEZ: You tell them kitten-mitten.

SUZE: No you tell them big daddy.

TOM: Oh just spit it out bitch!

SUZE: Jez came over Friday night to do some last minute painting. He locked himself out. I've been in Lytham St-Anne's all week. So he had absolutely nowhere to go. You two came home roaring drunk and said that he could sleep on the settee. He said you were jolly good fun. That trick you can do with a pint glass Linda. Ooh! Come on Jez. Let's leave these two party animals to do their thing.

JEZ: Thanks for the other night.

SUZE: Ciao Linda. Ciao Tom. Must do supper one night.

suze and jez leave.

LINDA: Do supper one night? Oh we must do supper one night? I'd rather chew the cud with Rosemary West.

LINDA'S BEDROOM

linda puts a sign round her barbie. it reads suze. she sticks a pin in it.

LIVING ROOM

tom watching 'the other half' on tv. linda comes in.

LINDA: Dale Winton on a Sunday?

TOM: I taped it.

LINDA: Why?

TOM: I had my reasons.

a knock at the door.

LINDA: Go away!

BERYL: It's Beryl.

LINDA: What do you want?

beryl enters.

BERYL: He's back.

LINDA: Oh tell us something we don't know.

BERYL: He's wheedled his way in with her downstairs. That new girl.

LINDA: Piss off, we're busy having a life.

BERYL: Anyone ever tell you you're fickle?

LINDA: No I don't hang around long enough.

BERYL: I'm going to phone Reeney.

beryl exits.

LINDA: Is that programme where couples go on and you have to guess who's going out with who?

TOM: It might be.

LINDA: We could go on that.

TOM: We're not a couple. No we're not. Why don't you go and chat someone up on the phone.? It's the only way you'll ever meet anybody. And anyway I'm not talking to you.

LINDA: Bet I can get you to. Bet you I can. Let's play Casualty.

TOM: Oh fabulous. All right, okay, okay, okay. You be the paramedic and I'll be the relative, okay?

LINDA: Okay.

linda goes out.

TOM: All right, all right I just need to prepare so don't be too quick.

LINDA: Okay. You ready?

TOM: No, not yet, I'm preparing. Okay I'm ready now, I'm ready now.

linda rushes in.

LINDA: Holby General, where is she?

TOM: She's over there and I think she's dead.

LINDA: Yes she is. (She claps) I've got it, I've got it. I've got it. The Bill.?

TOM: Yes the Bill, okay.

LINDA: Okay?

TOM: Okay we'll do the Bill. I need to prepare so don't be too quick.

LINDA: Are you ready? DCI Snatch, Sun Hill.

TOM: Oh I suppose I'm nicked ain't I?

LINDA: Yes you are. (She claps) I got it, I got it, Championship Boxing.

TOM: Championship Boxing, that's oh, oh, oh, hang on, hang on, we haven't played that before. How do they do it?

linda punches tom.

LINDA: Like this.

freeze on linda punching tom out.

Episode Two
THE BIG BREAK

KITCHEN / LIVING ROOM

linda is mascara-ing her hair. tom lies on the floor in his underwear with his feet tied to the door handle. jez and suze are having noisy sex downstairs.

♀ LINDA: Listen to that! They're at it again. I don't know why Jez is wasting his time on a boiler like Suze when he's got the likes of me bang on top of him.

♂ TOM: You wish, you big wench, now shut up. I'm visualising.

♀ LINDA: You're what?

♂ TOM: Visualising. I read about it in a magazine. What you do is you turn upside down and you let all the blood rush to your head and then you imagine something that you'd really want to happen and it happens, and it's true that.

♀ LINDA: What you imagining then? Leonardo DiCaprio running about on top of you, with nothing but a smile?

♂ TOM: No. If you must know I was imagining myself on the set of Peak Practice. Getting a bed bath from Sir Simon Shepherd. Well I've been with my new agent a month now and not a dickie bird, so I've decided to take up positive thinking and make things happen.

♀ LINDA: You couldn't make that kettle boil could you? Me tea's gone cold.

the phone rings.

♂ TOM: Who's ringing at this bloody time in the morning?

♀ LINDA: I don't know I'm not psychic.

♂ TOM: Well pick it up then.

♀ LINDA: You pick it up.

♂ TOM: I'm a little bit tied up at the moment.

♀ LINDA: I'm mascararing my hair!

we hear norma, tom's agent, leaving a message.

NORMA: Hi Tom, Norma here. Sorry to ring so early...

♂ TOM: It's my agent! It's my agent!

NORMA: ...just to let you know we've got you an audition, it's tomorrow, it's ten thirty and it's for a show called Crimewatch U.K. You're up for the part of a suspected granny basher in a reconstruction, and you're to wear navy slacks. It's cockney, it's working class, and it's real life. I know it's a stretch darling, but think EastEnders and be butch. Phone the office this afternoon for more info. Ciao darling. Get me Su Pollard on line five!

♂ TOM: Linda! Linda it worked. I'm going to play a cokerny!

♀ LINDA: Right. I'm going to check the post. And will you put some clothes on please. You're bringing up my toast.

HALLWAY

linda opens the door to jez who was just about to knock.

♀ LINDA: Oh were you reaching for my knocker there Jez?

JEZ: Hi Linda. There's some post here for you.

♀ LINDA: Oh I should get myself a slot, then you could slip it through on a regular basis.

tom comes along doing a dreadful cockney accent.

♂ TOM: Morning then Jez me ole china!

JEZ: What an hilarious accent. Liverpool?

suze comes out of their flat.

♂ TOM: I've got an audition you see, so I'm just practising my oral technique. Oright Suze me old bird, how's it going!

JEZ: Geordie right?

SUZE: Well not totally tickerty boo actually.

♂ TOM: Oh yes, whatever's the matter?

JEZ: Bloody Smeg's on the blink.

♀ LINDA: Didn't sound like it earlier.

SUZE: Smeg cooker, Linda.

♀ LINDA: Oh. (Laughs)

SUZE: It's no laughing matter. Have you tried heating Pop Tarts on a set of Carmen rollers? We'll be lucky to be out of the house by twelve.

♂ TOM: Oh jolly bad luck, strike a light.

JEZ: Glasgow?

linda turns to go back in.

♀ LINDA: Get out me way please.

♂ TOM: (Trying to mimic her) Get out my way please. (She punches him) Ow!

SUZE: Well I suppose it'll have to be Chinese Take-It-Away tonight, mmm?

JEZ: Can we play hide the Tofu dumplings like last time? Oh Tom congrats on your audition.

♂ TOM: Oh yes it's pretty amazing isn't it? Why don't we all sort of celebrate my good news? Why don't you come over for dinner tonight? I cook a fantastic spinach pie.

SUZE: You are looking at a committed vegetarian Tom, so thumbs up say I.

♂ TOM: I'd better just go and water down my spinach.

beryl comes down the stairs.

KITCHEN

tom comes in. linda is going through the post.

♀ LINDA: I've got one word to say to you.

♂ TOM: What?

♀ LINDA: Spinach pie.

♂ TOM: You know what your problem is don't you? You're bitter.

♀ LINDA: Oh am I?

♂ TOM: Yes, stuck in a job you don't enjoy. Answering the telephone. Twiddling around with your little switchboard. There's no joy in your life at all.

♀ LINDA: Listen mate, you don't know how important I am in the hurly burly world of media communications. One slip of these fingers and the whole entertainment output of Channel Five would literally disappear.

♂ TOM: Yes and wouldn't that be a shame.

♀ LINDA: And you've never made a spinach pie in your life.

♂ TOM: Winnie Mandela did it last night on Celebrity Ready Steady Cook.

♀ LINDA: The state of you. One audition in six months, blimey you'd think the Pope had come out.

♂ TOM: This could be it, Linda, this could be my big break you know. I could be up there on the TV screen reconstructing my socks off for the old Crimewatch UK and I don't know maybe a Hollywood producer's in town. You know, he's at the Ritz. It's late. He's ordered room service. Pastrami and dill pickle on rye. And he's flicking through the channels and he stops at a crime reconstruction and he thinks 'Who's this? He's bloody good!' And the next thing you know I've got my own winnebago and Cameron Diaz all over me like a rash.

♀ LINDA: Here.

♂ TOM: What?

♀ LINDA: Look at this.

♂ TOM: What?

♀ LINDA: Look, read it for me. Please read it for me, the writing's all joined up, go on read it.

♂ TOM: Linda, although I am already spoken for, know that the love in my heart for you is the size of a small principality.

♀ LINDA: Oh! What's principality mean?

♂ TOM: It's a country. It's a very small country. It's like Wales, it's very cruel.

♀ LINDA: I think that's really beautiful.

♂ TOM: No, someone's taking the piss. They haven't even bothered to sign it. No postmark.

♀ LINDA: It's hand delivered. You know who it's from don't you?

♂ TOM: Yeah some stingy bastard who couldn't be bothered to shell out for the cost of a stamp.

♀ LINDA: Jez! He's spoken for and when I went out there he'd got a tentpole, did you see it?

♂ TOM: It must be awful for you inciting erections wherever you go. I bet Trafalgar

Square was completely flat until you walked by.

LINDA: And why would he bother putting a stamp on it eh when he lives in the same house. It's Jez.

TOM: Give it to me. It doesn't look anything like Jez's handwriting.

LINDA: Well he's disguised it, ain't he, because he don't want Big Bird finding out. Oh the poor boy his heart must be breaking. He'll soon be cured tonight though won't he, eh? Eh?

TOM: I can't sit around all day talking about piss taking missals. I've got research to do. Now Linda, how do you talk like that?

LINDA: Like what?

TOM: Like a navvy in drag.

LINDA: I've got the diction of a Merchant Ivory Empress.

TOM: Look would you help me please Linda! Tomorrow I've got to be a convincing granny basher.

LINDA: And what would I know about that? Oh you're so racist. The slightest hint of a cockney accent don't mean to say I go around coshing old ladies. You condescending runt. Though there's always a first time.

beryl pops in.

BERYL: I'm just popping down Soho to do the phone boxes for Reeney so I need to know what time to be back.

LINDA: Why?

BERYL: Spinach and me go back a long way.

TOM: Out. Get her out of here!

BERYL: I used to be big pals with Popeye. He was one of my regulars.

LINDA: You're not invited.

BERYL: Well then this house meal isn't really a house meal at all then is it?

TOM: Um. No!

BERYL: Congratulations on your audition.

TOM: Thank you. Now leave. I must prepare. Being cockerney doesn't come easy to me.

LINDA: What does?

BERYL: Beryl hears there's a football match being shown down the pub today. Louts a plenty for the study thereof. To help you get into character like, you know.

TOM: Oh right, yeah, yeah. Thanks. Yes.

BERYL: Shall I see you about eight then?

TOM: Yeah whatever, whatever.

beryl exits linda is fuming.

LINDA: Tom! I don't want there to be another bird there!

TOM'S BEDROOM

tom dressed as a thug stands menacingly before his mirror. he takes his photo of simon shepherd and kisses it.

TOM: Simon Shepherd. Simon Shepherd. With your matinee idol looks and your smouldering bedside manner. Inspire me. (Thuggishly, to mirror) Listen darling you might be knocking eighty but you're gonna get a bunch of fives. All right?

BUS STOP

tom in character swaggers up to a bus stop where he glares at an old lady.

TOM: What you looking at?

OLD LADY: What?

TOM: You didn't fight no war for me, all right?

OLD LADY: I'm deaf.

TOM: Oh forget it then.

OLD LADY: There'll be one along in a minute.

TOM: Oh will there?

LINDA'S WORK

linda sits at the switchboard of a busy ad agency in soho.

LINDA: Hello Fast Track can I help you? Do you have an extension number for her please? Well no then I can't. Hello Fast

Track can I help you? Oh bring it all up love. No she's at lunch at the moment. Well your guess is as good as mine, yeah I mean she says she's on a diet but there was a distinct waft of chips when I brushed past here at elevenses. I know yeah she's a right fat cow isn't she? Bye. Hello Fast Track can I help — well if you can't say please don't bother to ring!

the office geek trevor passes her a parcel as an older woman mavis passes.

TREVOR: Can you organise a bike like that?
♀ LINDA: Yeah. Mavis? Catch!! Well she's the office bike.
TREVOR: I like bikes.
♀ LINDA: Great.
TREVOR: I like to get out there and build up a sweat. Do you wear deodorant?
♀ LINDA: What?
TREVOR: I don't. I reckon the body takes care of that sort of thing.
♀ LINDA: Trevor will you get out of my face?
TREVOR: It's nice to meet someone so like minded. My wife wears Body Shop Roll On. I haven't so much as touched her in three years.

PUB

tom in pub watching a football match on tv. a goal is scored and the pub erupts. tom gets knocked off his seat.
dream sequence.
bafta ceremony.
simon shepherd presenting an award.

SIMON: And the BAFTA for outstanding achievement in a crime reconstruction goes to . . . brilliant, Tom Farrell for the Crimewatch Granny Bashing.

as tom makes his way to the stage.

COMMENTATOR (VO): A very popular choice in the hall this. Tom Farrell,

whose portrayal of the wanted man in Crimewatch UK really plucked him from obscurity and turned him overnight into a household name.

simon shepherd slaps tom across the face fade back to:

PUB

FOOTY FAN: You all right mate?
♂ TOM: You all right mate?
FOOTY FAN: You taking the piss?
♂ TOM: Are you taking the piss?

the footy fan chins him

LINDA'S WORK

trevor slimes his way up to linda again. he points to her photo of liam gallagher.

TREVOR: Do you like Oasis?
♀ LINDA: Yeah because they wash, they're clean.
TREVOR: You can't fool me.
♀ LINDA: You're weird.
TREVOR: Do you know what I think's weird. Women shaving? Why do women shave? It's not the way nature intended is it, eh?
♀ LINDA: Leave me alone.
TREVOR: Anything interesting in the mail this morning?
♀ LINDA: Yeah a free offer on Bic razors. Now sod off.

SHARED HALLWAY

beryl is polishing the floor. linda comes in slipping.

♀ LINDA: It's like a bloody ice rink in here. What you polishing the floor for?
BERYL: I'm not one to eavesdrop but . . .

off. we hear a slap and sue scream.

BERYL: That's been happening every thirty seconds since four fifteen.

♀ LINDA: What?

the noise again.

BERYL: He's knocking her about.

♀ LINDA: Oh you've got to feel sorry for the bird, haven't you? I meant it ain't her fault she's not me.

JEZ: Hi Linda.

♀ LINDA: Oh watch big boy.

JEZ: Everything still on for tonight?

♀ LINDA: You betcha!

BERYL: Brute!

JEZ: (Slipping) Gosh, this is jolly good fun isn't it? It's better than Alton Towers.

♀ LINDA: Here I love a good ride.

JEZ: I need to go and get some wine for later.

♀ LINDA: Oh, wine makes me tipsy.

JEZ: Can't wait.

♀ LINDA: Oh Ciao baby.

LIVING ROOM

linda comes in tom is studying his face in a mirror.

♀ LINDA: All right you poof?

♂ TOM: Lindy, look at my profile and be honest with me, be honest with me. What does this profile say to you?

♀ LINDA: Retarded?

♂ TOM: It says four years at the R.S.C. It says Julius Caesar. It says Rupert Everett's young brother in cricket flannels in an Evelyn Waugh. It does not say East End villain on Crimewatch UK.

♀ LINDA: I take it your research didn't go too well then?

♂ TOM: It was about as successful as a comedy moment on EastEnders.

♀ LINDA: It's very difficult researching a role, isn't it?

♂ TOM: How would you know what it's like? The only time you've ever been on television was when you walked past the window on Richard and Judy. You're such a sad bitch.

♀ LINDA: I've been on stage. I was the Virgin Mary in the Young Offenders Nativity play.

♂ TOM: You played our Virgin Mother? You blasphemous bint.

♀ LINDA: I was a virgin. Well until the dress

rehearsal, anyway. My performance brought tears to that innkeeper's eyes. We never actually got to perform it for an audience because he ended up battering one of the three kings.

♂ TOM: Why can't something like that happen to me? You know all I want is for some nasty vile East End thug to come walking through that door so I can just absorb him. But since that's not going to happen I think I'll just retire.

♀ LINDA: We're still going to have our dinner tonight thought, ain't we?

♂ TOM: Oh no.

♀ LINDA: Oh Tom please. Please I've had my cat suit re-elasticated.

♂ TOM: No, dinner is off, we have nothing to celebrate.

♀ LINDA: Well what if I was to tell you I could get you a wife battering hooligan round here within the hour?

♂ TOM: I'd say shut up you lying slag.

♀ LINDA: Now don't get me wrong Tom, I'm a feminist. Right? I would never condone violence against women. But it has got to be said, Suze has got the sort of face you just want to slap.

♂ TOM: Are you trying to tell me that Jez is knocking her about? Has she told you this?

♀ LINDA: Beryl told me.

♂ TOM: Beryl once told me she had a thirteen year affair with Prince Philip. It doesn't necessarily mean it's true.

♀ LINDA: I heard screams.

♂ TOM: She could have just been reaching orgasm, you know what they're like.

♀ LINDA: And although thus far no one has laid a finger on me in a violent sort of way, touch wood, it has to be said I do attract bad'un's.

♂ TOM: Oh you don't still believe Jez sent you that card, do you?

♀ LINDA: Well I can't help it if he can't resist me come to bed eyes.

♂ TOM: You haven't got come to bed eyes.

♀ LINDA: I have.

♂ TOM: You have not. You've got shag me up a back alley after fifteen Babycham eyes. You only want him round here because you fancy him.

♀ LINDA: I feel sorry for the lad. Stuck in a loveless marriage, pining over his mega babe neighbour. I've got a big heart.

♂ TOM: Not half as big as your arse.

♀ LINDA: Well Jez obviously likes a bit of gristle on his bone. I mean have you seen the state of that Suze? She's anorexic. You watch at dinner. She'll shovel that food down her throat and then rush off to the bog with her fingers down her throat

♂ TOM: She'll do no such thing because they are not coming round.

♀ LINDA: Do you know you really disappoint me Tom. I really thought you were serious about your acting.

♂ TOM: I am.

♀ LINDA: Yet you're prepared to chuck away the chance of your big fat break.

♂ TOM: I just don't wish to believe that Jez is a wife batterer.

♀ LINDA: And what if he is? And you missed your chance?

♂ TOM: Alright, dinner's on. Dinner's on then.

♀ LINDA: What time are they coming?

♂ TOM: Eight o'clock. Eight o'clock.

♀ LINDA: Right I'm just going to go and make myself look beautiful.

♂ TOM: Okay, well hurry up you've only got two hours.

LIVING, ROOM LATER

linda looks a picture in her shiny green catsuit. beryl sits admiring it. tom fusses round getting everything just so.

BERYL: That's a very lovely outfit if I may say so Linda.

♀ LINDA: Thanks.

BERYL: I worked with a girl once who wore something similar. She met a very sticky end.

♀ LINDA: How many?

BERYL: Ended up as a traffic warden in Bromley By Bow.

LINDA
'Oh, were
you reaching
for my
knocker
there Jez?'

GIMME GIMME GIMME

LINDA: Great.

BERYL: Tried to stick a ticket on my shopping trolley once. I decked the stupid whore.

jez knocks.

LINDA: Oh come right through the door's on the latch.

JEZ: Hi peeps.

LINDA: Hi puddycat!

JEZ: Slight technical hitch. Suze can't make it. She's a little bit embarrassed by her appearance.

BERYL: That's it. I don't break bread with wife batterers so if you don't mind I'll be taking Maeve Binchy to bed. (Exits)

LINDA: Lesbian.

JEZ: Weird chick, huh?

LINDA: Now Jez. You stick your wine in my cooler. Here sniff up Jez, my oven's hot.

TOM: So Suze can't make it because she's a little embarrassed by her appearance. Really? Oh really? Why don't you tell me about it eh? Tell us how it started. Did you just flip or something? (Starts to take notes)

JEZ: Well actually it was a belated birthday present.

LINDA: Whatever happened to Milk Tray?

JEZ: She did ask for it.

LINDA: Yeah I'll bet.

TOM: You're just a melting pot of angst and emotions aren't you? Just sort of bubbling away under the surface. It's fascinating, because you're very calm aren't you Jez?

JEZ: Sorry.

TOM: Jez, Jez have you heard of the word psychopath?

JEZ: Is this some sort of word association game? Gosh I wish Suze was here, she loves free fall word play.

TOM: Yes, but I bet she'd find it a little difficult with a broken jaw hey? What do you think? Hey what do you think hey? Come on then. Put em up, do you want a fight then, do you want a fight?

JEZ: Hey, why would I want to hit dear sweet Tom?

TOM: Because you've just beaten up dear sweet Suze. That's a very butch thing to do isn't it, laugh yes, go ahead laugh, go on.

JEZ: Well I'd better go and get her then.

LINDA: Oh no, no, no, no. Don't do that.

JEZ: No, no I insist. Be back in two ticks.

LINDA: Oh bollocks! I just started to enjoy myself.

LIVING ROOM, FIVE MINUTES LATER

they have been joined by suze who has a red stripe across her top lip.

JEZ: Suze has been having some facial hair removed. And the electrolysis went a little bit wrong.

LINDA: A little bit?

SUZE: My beautician was pre-menstrual.

LINDA: Do you know? I am so lucky I haven't got the hideous embarrassment of a moustache. Do you know what Suze? I just remembered who you remind me of. David Seaman.

TOM: How dare you not be a wife batterer! How bloody dare you! I could sue you for loss of earnings!

JEZ: They thought I was trying to beat you up Kitty Lips.

LINDA: I never. He was just picking on you because you was black.

JEZ: So how did you two crazy cats meet?

TOM: In a nightclub now shut up.

SUZE: Oh how romantic.

JEZ: No darling they're not an item, remember?

LINDA: No I'm young free and single.

JEZ: And anyway, Tom's gay.

SUZE: Yes of course. Why do I always forget that? It's so obvious.

TOM: Shut up and eat. Shut up and eat. Shut up and eat.

SUZE: I met a gay person once. Well it was more of a lesbian. I'd gone to a convention of accountants at this hotel in Droitwich. Anyway I must have gone into the wrong bar because I ordered my egg nog and the next thing I know this woman has got her tongue down my throat. She was a bus conductress called Gwen. Do you know her?

TOM: No I don't know her, no.

JEZ: She had blonde hair.

TOM: No still don't know her.

SUZE: And a very, very long tongue.

TOM: Oh for goodness sake! Do you realise how offensive this is?

SUZE: I'm sorry.

LINDA: Just because Jez is black, do you expect him to know every single black person in the country?

LINDA: Don't be racist.

SUZE: Well he knew every black person at Eton.

JEZ: So you met at a club? Gosh that's very clubby isn't it?

LINDA: Mmm we were off our heads on E at the time.

SUZE: E?

TOM: Ecstasy, you bizarre horse.

SUZE: It's not the same as eggnog is it?

LINDA: It makes you think everybody's lovely.

SUZE: Oh well it is the same then.

LINDA: What?

JEZ: You've got . . .

LINDA: Jez?

JEZ: Sorry.

LINDA: Baby?

TOM: You've got a bit of spinach hanging out of your gob.

jez licks plate.

JEZ: Tom that pie was delicious. Really good, we'll have to get that recipe off you. We're always looking for fun things to do in the kitchen.

LINDA: It's great isn't it Tom? Studying heterosexual man in his natural environment.

TOM: Yes. Haven't had so much fun since I had my haemorrhoids lanced.

SUZE: Do you get that problem too?

TOM: No I don't Suze. Just a vague swipe at irony. But with you irony's rather like Concorde, isn't it? Goes way over the top of your head. Jez have you ever been to one of those um, footy ball things, matches?

SUZE: Oh Jez loves ball games.

LINDA: So do I.

TOM: So you could be quite sort of macho on the pitch then, on the pitch?

JEZ: Well I do like to get stuck in on a Sunday morning.

LINDA: That's my favourite time.

TOM: Well I tell you what we should do. We should all sing a footbally type song.

JEZ: Really?

TOM: Yes.

JEZ: How working class.

LINDA: Here I bet you've got a voice like hot honey dribbling down a gangplank.

TOM: Come on Jez, vamp it up.

SUZE: Oh let me, let me. I know a brilliant one.

TOM: No, no, no. I just need Jez to do this no.

SUZE: Oh please.

TOM: No, no you're no use to me at all. No.

SUZE: I'll scream.

SUZE: Who ate all the pies? Who ate all the pies? (Pointing to Linda) You fat bastard! You fat bastard! You ate all the pies! Come on!

TOM/SUZE/JEZ: Who ate all the pies? Who ate all the pies? You fat bastard! You fat bastard! You ate all the pies!

SUZE: Gosh it's so appropriate isn't it?

TOM: Come on Jez, give us a solo.

SUZE: You fat bastard! You fat bastard!

LINDA: Oh shut up you rake. Isn't it time you went to the bog? I want to dance. Ere, Jez? (Shows him card) I won't say a word!

JEZ: Let's have a look. Cripes what a garish piece of stationery.

LINDA: What?

SUZE: What does it say Love Trumpet?

SUZE
'Oh Jez loves
ball games'
LINDA
'So do I'

LINDA: As if you didn't already know!

JEZ: Dear Linda although I am already spoken for, know that the love in my heart for you is the size of a small principality.

SUZE: Someone's taking the piss.

JEZ: Big time.

LINDA: Give it back, and get out. Go on. Get out. And mind you don't slip on the slippery floor Suze, I'd hate for you to end up in traction.

SUZE: (Leaving) You fat bastard! You fat bastard!

LINDA: Get out!!

SUZE: Oh Linda you're such a good fun. You're full of surprises. Isn't it amazing how plain girls always have such super personalities.

LINDA: Piss off.

suze and jez go.

TOM: Well I think that I must live with the thickest most stupid person on the planet.

LINDA: He did send this to me.

TOM: You sad slapper!

LINDA: Well he couldn't say anything in front of Kiri Te Kanewa there could he? What's for pudding?

TOM: EastEnders.

LINDA: What?

TOM: Taped it. It's my last hope. I think I'll study one of the Mitchell brothers I think. Phil, yes. I think I'll study Phil, you know the alcoholic one with ginger fuzz round his lips. Ring any bells with you?

LINDA: Vile. I'm having a bath.

TOM: Rather pleased with the pie though. Did you see the way he licked his plate?

LINDA: At least someone's in for a good night. (Exits)

LINDA'S BEDROOM

linda is taking her make-up off. she hears someone calling her outside.

TREVOR (OOV): Linda! Linda!

she looks out of the window. trevor stands over the road,

playing with himself. she wretches.

KITCHEN NEXT MORNING

linda sipping a cup of tea. tom comes in brooding being phil mitchell from eastenders.

LINDA: I'm going to check the post.

TOM: Oi, watch it.

LINDA: What?

TOM: Will you shut it woman. I've just about had enough of your whinging voice all right?

LINDA: Tom?

TOM: Well you're having a laugh ain't you?

LINDA: (Becoming aroused) Oh Tom!

SHARED HALLWAY

they come out.

LINDA: Oh Tom you'll walk it.

TOM: Oh shut it you slag. (He shrieks) Oh Lindy I'm so excited you know!.

LINDA: Here, break a leg!

TOM: Yes, yes I will!

he skips to the front door slips on the floor and goes arse over tit.

LIVING ROOM

close-up of the answer machine.

NORMA (VO): Darling you didn't show. I've had a dreadful day. The musical was a nightmare. Su Pollard was sharp, the champagne was flat and now this. Well they're doing the reconstruction without you. They're using Jason Orange, ex Take That. I hope you're satisfied.

GARDEN

linda is pushing tom up the path in a wheelchair. beryl comes out. tom lunges out of the chair at her.

TOM: My big break?. Bloody bitch. I'll bloody kill you!

  GIMME GIMME GIMME

Episode Three
LEGS AND CO.

LIVING ROOM

Linda watching richard and judy, dialling a number on the phone. tom comes in in his wheelchair, his leg in plaster.

♂ TOM: It's a bit late to be phoning in sick isn't it? Still, I should be grateful you're not making me do it for once. Hello I'm sorry, Linda can't come in today because she's got twenty-four hour pancreatitis. Hello I'm afraid Linda can't come in today because her entire family have been wiped out in a tragic accident and she's got to stay at home and line the coffins.

♀ LINDA: Make me a cup of tea.

♂ TOM: Could we just have a little bit of disability awareness here please?

♀ LINDA: I've seen documentaries on disabled people. They climb mountains on redesigned skateboards. They do the Hokey Cokey in their wheelchairs. You mate, just can't be arsed.

♂ TOM: Have you got the painters in?

♀ LINDA: What?

♂ TOM: I mean are you late? Is that it? I mean has somebody actually slept with you?

♀ LINDA: I bet George Michael ain't this horrible to Ginger Spice.

♂ TOM: No, because he actually quite likes her.

♀ LINDA: He fancies her.

♂ TOM: He's gay.

♀ LINDA: There's no such thing as gay. It's just laziness. Listen mate it takes a long time to understand a woman's hidden treasures, all right?

♂ TOM: Yes, or find them under her rolls of fat. Engaged is it? See this is what happens when you don't go into work. The switchboard gets jammed.

♀ LINDA: I'm not phoning work. I'm phoning Richard and Judy. That Finnegan's like a second mother to me.

♂ TOM: I see. You're calling the agony line are you? What's today's enthralling subject I wonder. 'I'm incredible ugly and have no friends'?

♀ LINDA: It's redundancy.

♂ TOM: Redundancy. Why on earth would you bother... Linda have you been fired?

♀ LINDA: I want to talk to Judy.

♂ TOM: Oh bless you. Well you did bunk off quite a lot didn't you.

♀ LINDA: It had nothing to do with my work. They asked me to leave because I was too much of a distraction to the blokes in the office.

♂ TOM: What they actually said this to you did they?

♀ LINDA: No but every time I bent over that photocopier there was a mass exodus to the bogs. Now what does that tell you?

♂ TOM: Your visible panty line was making them vomit.

♀ LINDA: Get out.

♂ TOM: I will not get out. I'm expecting a visit.

♀ LINDA: Who from? Your imaginary friend?

♂ TOM: No actually, my um, my home help.

♀ LINDA: The shame. What's she going to do, wipe your arse and feed you soup?

♂ TOM: No she's going to help me bathe.

♀ LINDA: I could do that.

♂ TOM: You'll never see my penis, okay?

♀ LINDA: Not without a microscope, no.

♂ TOM: Actually you'd be doing me an enormous service if you did get out for the day, because the only reason I'm getting a home help is because I said I was alone here. Well I usually am.

♀ LINDA: Oh well pardon me for losing my job. I shan't be so gorgeous next time.

the doorbell rings.

♀ LINDA: That's probably someone from my work heartbroken because I've gone. 'Ere I bet I'm being stalked.

♂ TOM: No, no, no, no. That'll be Shirley.

♀ LINDA: Shirley?

♂ TOM: She's my home help. How do I look? Neglected, they sent me a letter you see. Oh by the way you just say you're a neighbour who's popped by to see if I'm okay. Oh no, no don't. That sounds dangerously like round the clock care. Just make something up. Just go and make something up.

♀ LINDA: I'll say I'm your wife.

♂ TOM: Don't you dare say you're my wife!

♀ LINDA: I'll say I divorced you because you turned out to be a poof with a home help fixation. Keep trying.

SHARED HALLWAY

linda opens the door to a motorcycle courier in leathers. he is holding a bouquet of purple flowers. she strokes one.

LINDA: Oh what lovely big purple heads.

LIVING ROOM

tom hears someone coming in

♂ TOM: In here Miss Home Help, a small bijou pad but mine own.

linda enters with the flowers.

♀ LINDA: (Singing) On the wings of love. (Speaking). 'Ere that would make a really good jingle for a panty liner advert. What do you think?

♂ TOM: Are those for me? Oh, a small get well gift from my agent. Oh I must give her a ring, pass on my sincerest platitudes. Shirley's a bit late isn't she?

♀ LINDA: They're not for you.

♂ TOM: (On phone) Hello? (To Linda) What?

♀ LINDA: I'm taking them in for bitch face downstairs.

♂ TOM: (On phone) Hello, do you handle Tom Farrell? Yes I think he's the new Simon Shepherd, goodbye. (Puts phone down) Oh put them down for goodness sake. The mauve is clashing hideously with your yellow teeth.

♀ LINDA: The courier what delivered them didn't think so.

♂ TOM: Oh what have you done now? Oh I dread to think. You've been out there about twenty minutes.

♀ LINDA: Really? There's no concept of time when you're in love.

♂ TOM: And what do you know about love?

♀ LINDA: It's in the dictionary between labia and lust.

♂ TOM: I thought I asked you not to say that word.

♀ LINDA: His name's Joe.

♂ TOM: Whose?

♀ LINDA: My new boyfriend.

♂ TOM: Linda when a man you don't know gives you flowers on your doorstep he is not acting on impulse, okay?

♀ LINDA: He asked me out.

♂ TOM: He's just doing his job. He did what?

♀ LINDA: And I said yes.

♂ TOM: Run that by me again?

♀ LINDA: Oh he's gorgeous Tom. Head to toe in black leather and an helmet so clean you could do your make up in it.

♂ TOM: No it can't be true.

♀ LINDA: He's picking me up tomorrow at two. Oh I expect I'll ride pillion.

she straddles the couch and bounces up and down.

♂ TOM: What are you doing? What are you doing?

♀ LINDA: I'm just practising. Oh it's a bumpy street.

♂ TOM: Just control yourself you filthy strumpet.

♀ LINDA: Here. (Picking petals) He loves me. He loves me lots. He wants to kiss me. He wants to kiss me lots. He wants to shaft me. He wants to shaft me lots.

♂ TOM: Where are you going?

♀ LINDA: Spend my redundancy money. I haven't got a thing to wear.

she leaves.

♂ TOM: Oh that's right abandon me. Yes go on, go ahead, yes abandon me go on. I'll probably break my other leg trying to answer the door. Probably lie there for days in a puddle of my own urine.

♀ LINDA: (Off) And get off on it!

SHARED HALLWAY

linda coming out as jez and suze arrive home.

JEZ: Oh hi Linda.

♀ LINDA: Oh some flowers came for you Suze.

SUZE: Oh super duper pooper scooper. It's our anniversary today Linds. I wonder who they're from.

linda reveals a few crappy stalks.

♂ TOM: I always say the size of my bouquet reflects the size of my love for Suze.

♀ LINDA: Oh well as long as they don't reflect the size of your knob. See you wouldn't want to be you.

as she leaves she passes shirley. a man on his way in.

♀ LINDA: Oh sorry love I'm spoken for!

LIVING ROOM

tom showing the terminally depressed shirley in.

♂ TOM: Do come through Shirley, do come through. Forgive me reliance on gender stereotyping, but with a name like Shirley I did think you were going to be a sort of woman type person.

SHIRLEY: Oh yeah that's very funny. Excuse me while I piss myself.

♂ TOM: I'm sorry.

SHIRLEY: Yeah well it's all right for you isn't it? You weren't cursed from birth with one of the most embarrassing names in Christendom.

♂ TOM: Well should I strip here or in the bathroom?

SHIRLEY: It weren't you who was bullied since you was that high. Or who had ten tons of shit kicked out of them at school. And why? Because you had a girl's name. So I changed schools and my name. Called myself Colin. Then some bastard from my old school changes too and tells everyone my real name's Shirley. What's the point eh, you tell me that. Everywhere I turn that bastard Todd Manson's there screaming Shirley! His name's Shirley.

♂ TOM: Where is he now?

SHIRLEY: Todd Manson may well be inside for GBH, but when my jim jams are on, he's in here. In my nightmares.

♂ TOM: It's a bit like um, it's a bit like Nightmare on Elm Street, isn't it?

SHIRLEY: You think I've got time to sit round watching videos?

♂ TOM: No I don't no.

SHIRLEY: If I'm not working I'm out jogging, building up my stamina. Trying to be something harder in case I bump into that Todd Manson again.

♂ TOM: Yes, Erm, I wonder what a home help actually does.

SHIRLEY: I don't find a cure for cancer. And I don't help infertile women have babies. All I ever wanted to be was a surgeon.

♂ TOM: Well it isn't too late, you could always go back to college.

SHIRLEY: No I've got a natural tremor.

♂ TOM: Oh my god.

SHIRLEY: It wouldn't be fair on the patients. (Breathes into a paper bag)

♂ TOM: Oh God what are you doing now?

SHIRLEY: Hyperventilating I'll be all right in a minute.

STREET

an old lady crossing the road. linda clucks past her. a car beeps at her to get out of the way.

♀ LINDA: Spoken for, sorry.

> # LINDA
> ## 'There's no such thing as gay. It's just laziness.'

she clucks across the road missing the car knocking over the old lady.

LIVING ROOM

tom and shirley.

SHIRLEY: So I thought I would never find happiness. Ever. Then I did.

♂ TOM: Oh that's fantastic. Listen I wonder if...

SHIRLEY: Seven and a half stone of it. In a woman called Brenda. There you are. That's Brenda. (Shows photo)

♂ TOM: What the one with the beard?

SHIRLEY: Done herself up as Father Christmas for the old folks in the home where she worked last Christmas Eve. Made me so happy seeing all those old men sitting on her knee, dribbling.

♂ TOM: Oh, oh Brenda's, she's very pretty.

SHIRLEY: Was. Topped herself Christmas Day.

♂ TOM: Oh for God's sake.

SHIRLEY: Have you ever tried to arrange a funeral over the Christmas period?

♂ TOM: No I haven't.

SHIRLEY: It ain't a bundle of laughs, I tell you. Can I have that picture back please, it's the only one I've got.

♂ TOM: What of Brenda?

SHIRLEY: No it's the only picture I've got.

♂ TOM: Look would you like to run my bath please?

SHIRLEY: I can't. I'm washing an obese nun's bedsores at twelve. She's a bit like you, a real talker. Tomorrow, run the bath before I get here. I'll see you later. If we live that long.

he goes.

LIVING ROOM, LATER

tom on the phone linda coming in with shopping.

♂ TOM: Oh yes hello I was wondering how I go about changing my home help.

♀ LINDA: Watcha lover.

♂ TOM: Oh hello. Well it says here you're an information line. Yes I do want some information. I want to know how I go about changing my home help. Look, oh for God's

sake. They're playing Patsy Cline down the phone to me now.

♀ LINDA: As a gay man you should demand Dana International.

♂ TOM: I know.

♀ LINDA: (Applying lip gloss) Mummy always said men love moist lips. (Tom groans) Oh you getting a bit frustrated? You know what you need? A date. Like me. I remember my first date. Billy from Borstal.

♂ TOM: You had boys at your borstal?

♀ LINDA: No he was the caretaker. He used to say I reminded him of Little Orphan Annie. Ah bless. He used to put me in this little red dress and had me running around with his old English sheepdog singing 'The Sun Will Come Out Tomorrow'. He got banged up shortly after.

♂ TOM: Is that the Health Centre or the Patsy Cline frigging fan club? Look I want to change my home help. My name is Tom Farrell, his is Shirley. Listen to me if I was being aggressive I'd come round there and slash your pedal pushers you bitch! (Hangs up)

♀ LINDA: I've told you before Tom. I'll give you a bath.

♂ TOM: You will never whip up a froth in my groinal area!

BEDROOM

linda sits at her dressing table seductively. she puts on a nipple pink crash helmet.

LIVING ROOM

shirley and tom.

SHIRLEY: I really thought you were my friend.

♂ TOM: Sorry?

SHIRLEY: I'm a laughing stock at work now.

You threatened my boss with violence.

♂ TOM: Oh please Shirley all I want is a bath.

SHIRLEY: (Exploding) Well all right then spazzy legs! Let's do what you want for a change, shall we? Have you run it?

♂ TOM: Yes I have.

SHIRLEY: I'd better go and check the temperature then hadn't I? Over there is it?

♂ TOM: Straight through there.

shirley exits. linda comes in in a pink leather jumpsuit and pink helmet.

♀ LINDA: Here, how do I look?

♂ TOM: Like a vibrator.

BATHROOM

shirley is trying to drown himself in the bath. linda comes in and checks her make-up in the mirror.

♀ LINDA: I shan't be two ticks. I've got my boyfriend coming round. Joe. He's a bit of a bruiser. I just thought I'd better warn you before you start getting any ideas. I'll probably bring him in, introduce him to Tom then we're

going to go out there and burn some serious rubber. And I don't mean tyres. Just practise taking this off. Oh Uma Thurman eat your heart out.

the doorbell rings. shirley comes up for air screaming. linda pushes him back in in her rush to get to the door.

♀ LINDA: Get out of my way weirdo.

LIVING ROOM

linda bringing joe in.

LINDA: Come right inside Joe. Oh wash my mouth out. Oh ain't you big. This is my flat mate Thomas. Our resident homo. Shall I get some glasses for the old bubbly? Anyone bought you bubbly lately Tom? No, I didn't think so.

JOE: Nice to meet you Tom.

♂ TOM: Yes delighted I'm sure.

♀ LINDA: Here get your hands off him. Blimey if it ain't nailed down. Here shall we pop into the boudoir for a drop of the old liquid?

JOE: Why not?

♀ LINDA: Indeedy!

they go. presently shirley comes in.

SHIRLEY: That seems to be warm enough. I'll just get the harness for you.

he heads out of the back door.

LINDA'S BEDROOM

linda and joe.

♀ LINDA: I'll just straighten this rug out.

she bends over so her arse is in his face.

♀ LINDA: I'm quite anal like that. You er... you like what you see?

JOE: It's big isn't it?

♀ LINDA: You like?

JOE: I was inside for a while.

♀ LINDA: Really?

JOE: They were tiny in there.

♀ LINDA: I'll just put a little bit of rhythm on, get us in the mood.

linda puts some pumping house on and shimmies for him.

JOE: It's quite hot in here, do you mind if I take my jumper off?

♀ LINDA: Oh you take off whatever you want darling. (Unzips her cleavage) I'm a free spirit. Grape juice? Bugger.

she whips the paper off his bottle.

BALCONY

tom looking up to shirley who is on the roof.

♂ TOM: Oh come on. What on earth are you doing?

SHIRLEY: What do you care?

♂ TOM: You can't jump. I need my bath. I'm in pain here.

SHIRLEY: My life's meaningless. That's pain. Nobody likes me, that's pain.

♂ TOM: Oh grow up. I like you.

SHIRLEY: If you like me so much why did you ask for another home help?

♂ TOM: Because... (Clutching at straws) I really fancy you.

SHIRLEY: What?

♂ TOM: I really fancy you and I was worried about being naked with you. That's why I asked for someone else.

SHIRLEY: But you're a boy. Oh my God you're a shirt lifter!

♂ TOM: I've never lifted a shirt in my life.

SHIRLEY: You were thinking lewd thoughts about me.

♂ TOM: No I wasn't.

SHIRLEY: What... you're not a shirt lifter?

♂ TOM: Look my sexuality is not really the issue here.

SHIRLEY: Well that's just typical ain't it? First of all I get a girl's name, then I bugger up my education. My girlfriend tops herself. I have recurring nightmares about Todd Manson and now my best mate decides to come out to me while I'm trying to commit suicide. Talk about inappropriate timing!

LINDA'S BEDROOM

joe and linda having a drink.

JOE: When I accepted the Christ child within me, I made a vow never to have sex before marriage.

♀ LINDA: Let's get married. (Clinking glasses) Up your bum and no babies!

JOE: Do you mind if we pray? Lord, thank you for this afternoon, for the precious time we spend together, for the grape juice. Anything you want to throw in Linda?

♀ LINDA: My knickers?

JOE: Linda remember who we're talking to.

♀ LINDA: Oh yeah and look after all the starving black babies in Africa.

JOE: Yeah. Yeah and Lord, shine your light on lovely sad Linda here and help her to see your glory in all things Amen.

♀ LINDA: Do you know? I think you've got healing hands.

she touches him up. tom pops his head round the door.

TOM: Oh my God. Linda, Linda you have to come quickly.

LINDA: Hold it right there and when I come back I'm going to tell you the story of Mary Magdalene.

SHARED HALLWAY

tom and linda running through.

LINDA: Tom, Tom my worst nightmare's through there.

TOM: Why?

LINDA: He respects me.

BALCONY

beryl pops her head out of her window and calls to shirley.

BERYL: Are you a window cleaner?

SHIRLEY: Leave me alone.

BERYL: How much do you charge?

SHIRLEY: I'm going to jump.

BERYL: Oh, sorry.

she goes back in. linda and tom come out.

LINDA: Now I used to be a Samaritan right, this will take a little bit of summonsing up in my counselling know-how but I'll give it a go.

TOM: Okay.

LINDA: Shirley you thick pillock! Get back in here and give him a bath.

TOM: Linda La Hughes!

LINDA: Oh sorry was I a bit too bleeding heart?

SHIRLEY: She frightens me Tom.

LINDA: I'll frighten you in a minute you inconsiderate wanker.

linda sees suze in the garden in a leather catsuit. jez is tied to a mattress in a blindfold.

LINDA: Suze! Suze! (To Tom) Go and get Holy Joe.

SUZE: What's happening peeps?

LINDA: This is Shirley.

BERYL: That's a woman's name.

SHIRLEY: Right, that's it.

LINDA: Can you break his fall?

SUZE: Right. (Squares up to catch him)

LINDA: No you prat with a mattress or something.

BERYL: I knew a woman called Brian once.

LINDA: He's trying to kill himself.

BERYL: I used to live in Croydon dear, happened there all the time.

SHIRLEY: What's she doing?

SUZE: Okay, oh hang on.

suze has dragged her mattress out. jez lies on it blindfolded in a leather thong.

JEZ: Where are we now pussy willow? It's pretty chilly. The utility room?

tom brings joe out.

TOM: Shirley, Shirley I have a Christian here who would speak with you. Will you turn round?

JEZ: (Taking blindfold off) Oh so this is where we are.

BERYL: Oh you've got nipples like tax discs Jez.

shirley sees joe and starts to panic.

LINDA: Joe's lovely Shirl, he's a sort of priest. Look on it as Last Rites. What's the matter Shirl?

SHIRLEY: It's Todd Manson.

TOM: No this is Joe.

LINDA: Yeah course it is.

SHIRLEY: It's a conspiracy.

joe climbs up to be with shirley.

JOE: Shirley I changed my name in prison. When I saw the light I took a biblical name, it's symbolic of my change of life. Joseph was like Jesus' step-dad.

SUZE: So who was his real dad?

SHIRLEY: Stay away from me. I'm not scared of you. I go jogging.

JOE: I've changed Shirley.

LINDA: Nice arse.

TOM: It's fabulous actually isn't it?

JOE: And I want to ask your forgiveness.

tom and linda squeeze joe's bum.

JOE: Do you mind this bottom belongs to Jesus.

♀ LINDA: Oh I'm bored now. Go on jump.

♂ TOM: Yeah jump!

BERYL: Yeah go on. I will if you will.

♂ TOM: Telly?

♀ LINDA: Yeah telly.

SHIRLEY: What are you doing Todd?

JOE: To show you how much I've changed. I want to jump instead of you. Go on, let me jump in your place.

BERYL: Oh I wanted to jump first, that's not fair. I live here.

JOE: You just stay where you are.

LIVING ROOM

tom watching from the window.

♂ TOM: Oh for goodness sake.

♀ LINDA: Look there's a bath full of water through there. Why don't you let me flannel you down?

♂ TOM: Shut up.

♀ LINDA: Oh look there's an horse called Shaven Haven. I shall be riding in the three o'clock on my shaven haven.

♂ TOM: Oh dear. Oh, oh, oh, oh. If he dies. I won't be held responsible will I? I mean I won't go to prison will I?

♀ LINDA: He ain't going to jump, it's just a cry for help.

off we hear a male scream.

BACK GARDEN

joe and shirley have both fallen onto the mattress. beryl pokes her head out.

BERYL: Oh do it again. I was watching the race. Do it again!

LIVING ROOM

tom on the phone, linda coming in with shopping bag.

♂ TOM: Yes well I think at this point it might be prudent to let you know I'm only one

phone call away from Esther Rantzen's office. How would you like to be exposed on national television hmm? No not on Hearts of Gold you blithering idiot. On That's Life. Did it? When did it finish? Oh God did they? What, a line up of everyone who'd been in it? Oh no I missed that. No. Of course I'll hold, yeah. Hey did you know that That's Life had finished?

♀ LINDA: Has it?

♂ TOM: Yes.

♀ LINDA: Oh that's a shame, I liked them barristers. Especially that Scottish one. She was a bit like an ugly version of me. Who's that?

♂ TOM: Oh it's some delightful woman from the local authority. Shirley's off sick apparently.

♀ LINDA: What are they sorting you out another home help?

♂ TOM: No, they're not. What? Oh God I'm on hold again. Well at least they're not playing Patsy Cline today. They're just playing the dialling tone. Oh they hung up. Oh what a bitch!

♀ LINDA: Phone back.

♂ TOM: Apparently because my plaster is coming off in two days I'm no longer a priority. What's that all about? What's in the bag?

♀ LINDA: My leathers. Taking them back for a refund. I sponged the crotch down with some TCP so they should be all right.

♂ TOM: When you go out would you please get me some grapes and a bottle of lucozade.

♀ LINDA: Have I got slave tattooed on my forehead?

♂ TOM: Just pop my whales on would you?

she puts on a cd of relaxing whale sounds then exits then returns.

♀ LINDA: Here Tom, you'll never guess what?

♂ TOM: What?

♀ LINDA: I've got a couple of people here to fetch and carry for you. Come in boys.

shirley and joe hobble in on crutches, their legs in plaster too.

SHIRLEY: Hiya mate.

JOE: Hi Tom.

♂ TOM: Oh carumba!

SHIRLEY: We thought we'd just pop round and say hi you and well we wanted to thank you both for bringing us two together again really.

JOE: We've got some brilliant news.

♂ TOM: Oh please tell me you've found another home help. Please tell me.

JOE: No Shirley's found God.

SHIRLEY: It was really careless of me to lose him in the first place.

JOE: And I just think that's something worth celebrating.

SHIRLEY: We've been praying for you both.

♀ LINDA: Oh you shouldn't have, really.

SHIRLEY: You see Tom I'm a bit worried about you being gay and that. And I want you to promise me that you'll stay inside until you convert. Because if you got run over by a bus or something, you'd burn in hell.

♂ TOM: Right I see. So I stay indoors for the rest of my life do I?

JOE: That's right.

♂ TOM: Okay.

JOE: And you've got to stop sleeping with men.

♀ LINDA: That shouldn't be too difficult, no one will have him.

JOE: The good Lord's quite clear on bottom explorers.

♂ TOM: I beg your pardon!

SHIRLEY: And we've been praying for you as well Linda. That you'll convert to the Lord, because then you could go out with Joe here. He only goes out with Christians don't you Joe.

JOE: It's funny but before I found God, I only went out with dolly birds. But I don't know, since I found the Lord I look deeper than that. I'm interested in the soul of a person. I'm interested in your soul Linda. I don't care how ugly you are.

♀ LINDA: Can I borrow one of your crutches?

♂ TOM: Please be my guest, there you go.

linda attacks joe with crutch tom attacks shirley with the other.

BATHROOM

tom in the bath in a bathing suit

made of flannels.

♂ TOM: Right I'm ready.

linda comes in wearing a blindfold.

TOM: Right. Forward, forward, forward, forward. Stop, stop, stop there. Loofah, soap, go, go.

she rubs his crotch.

♂ TOM: I don't think so actually.

♀ LINDA: You have to wash down there. It's the law.

♂ TOM: You do?

she rubs away to her heart's content a smile creeps across tom's face.

♂ TOM: Oh my God.

♀ LINDA: Oh Tom You're so fickle.

TOM
'And what do you know about love?'
LINDA
'It's in the dictionary between labia and lust.'

GIMME GIMME GIMME   37

Episode Four
DO THEY TAKE SUGAR?

LIVING ROOM

linda is fixing the hem on a party dress for beryl. tom is searching high and low for something.

♀ LINDA: Keep still.

BERYL: Oh this is really good of you. You see I used to be taller, but with age we shrink. Apparently Anne Robinson's three foot eight.

♂ TOM: Have you seen the 'News of the World' anywhere?

♀ LINDA: I thought you didn't read that anymore.

♂ TOM: No, I don't. But apparently there's a Simon Shepherd special offer on you see. If you collect fifteen special tokens you can send away for the entire series of Peak Practice for three ninety-nine, it's marvellous.

♀ LINDA: What a rip off.

BERYL: I shall be the belle of the ball in this. The Working Women's Reunion won't know what's hit 'em. There's going to be a talent contest.

♂ TOM: It's in the bloody bin!

BERYL: I shall do one of my old routines.

♀ LINDA: What, sleep with a G.I. for a pair of nylons?

BERYL: I haven't danced since the day Thatcher resigned.

♂ TOM: Why?

BERYL: Because I had an unfortunate incident with an apple pie in a well known fast food chain. I can't tell you the name for libel reasons, but he was old and he had a farm.

♀ LINDA: You shouldn't be reading that you know. That's right wing propaganda.

♂ TOM: Oh what joy! 'My twelve in a bed sex romp with Hartlepool FC' by Sugar Walls.

♀ LINDA: Slag.

♂ TOM: Oh I'm a huge fan of Sugar Walls.

BERYL: I curse the day that hot fruit dribbled down my thigh.

♂ TOM: We curse the day you were born.

BERYL: Otherwise I could have gone on a dancing version of that Stars In Their Eyes.

♀ LINDA: Oh I applied for that.

BERYL: Who as, Mama Cass?

♀ LINDA: No. That bird out of M People.

♂ TOM: Oh poor Sugar she's on her seventh divorce.

♀ LINDA: When I auditioned that Matthew Kelly couldn't get enough of me. He said we were soul mates. But of course when I blacked up they threw me out on my ear.

the phone rings.

♂ TOM: Excuse me, shall I get that? Shall I get that? Yes I'll get that. Why don't I get that, shall I?

BERYL: What's his problem?

♀ LINDA: He's gay.

♂ TOM: Linda it's for you.

♀ LINDA: Oh tell them I'll call them back. I'm three pins away from an even hem.

BERYL: I'll pop down later and show you my routine.

♀ LINDA: Well don't expect me to be free. Sunday's my day for waxing my legs. Mummy always said if you had legs like silk you could always get a man. Right that's even. Well who was it? Was it Liam? Is he leaving Patsy? Is he on his way over?

♂ TOM: Dream on hot pubes.

BERYL: How does Beryl look?

♂ TOM: Princess Margaret on smack.

BERYL: Is she?

beryl exits.

♀ LINDA: Oh that's nice isn't it? Not even a thank you. Well who was it?

♂ TOM: Sharon. On her way over. Who's Sharon?

♀ LINDA: It's my sister.

♂ TOM: Linda you don't have a sister, what are you talking about?

linda legs it out.

LINDAS BEDROOM

linda hyperventilating. tom comes in.

♂ TOM: Linda? What's the matter?

♀ LINDA: Gimme air! Gimme air! Gimme air! Gimme air.

he blows the hairdryer in her face.

♂ TOM: Hold on. Now look what is going on?

♀ LINDA: Sugar Wall's real name is Sharon La Hughes. She's my sister.

♂ TOM: Well she can't be, she's gorgeous.

♀ LINDA: She's a dog.

♂ TOM: She's a gay icon.

♀ LINDA: So am I!

♂ TOM: You're what we call a fag hag.

♀ LINDA: Just don't open the door.

♂ TOM: Oh but Sugar Walls is the thinking man's Mandy Smith for goodness sake. I mean you would have told me if you had a celebrity sister.

♀ LINDA: Listen mate there are two names in this world you just don't drop. Sugar Walls and Cheryl Baker. I mean I've known that girl since she was an egg and all she's ever been to me is trouble. I mean she's let me down more times than a lilo. I don't expect much from this life Tom, but I do expect loyalty. Is that too much to ask?

♂ TOM: Oh no of course not. Of course not. For the love of Twiggy we haven't hoovered. Linda I am trying to be sympathetic to you but we have a celebrity en route and dusty rugs. I knew we should have bought a hoover, but oh no says Linda. The carpet is nice and dark. It'll blend in. Well look.

he taps on the rug a cloud of dust erupts.

♂ TOM: Just pray she's not asthmatic. I don't want a celebrity murder on my hands okay? I don't want this to become the death place of Sugar Walls. There'll be coach parties. Chinese people with state of the art cameras. Sixty-nine Paradise Passage will forever be known as a tomb.

♀ LINDA: Death's too good for that bitch.

♂ TOM: What sort of a sister are you?

♀ LINDA: Spurned.

♂ TOM: Don't you dare be vulgar!

SHARED HALLWAY

tom rings suze's doorbell. she answers with a bowl of whipped cream.

SUZE: Hi Tommity Pi. Want some whipped cream?

♂ TOM: No I just need to borrow your hoover please quickly.

SUZE: Do you need the attachments? I know you're single.

♂ TOM: No I just want to borrow your hoover.

SUZE: Well it's got a number of settings for different floor types. Isn't that great?

jez appears semi-naked with cream on his nipples.

JEZ: Our favourite's deep shag.

♂ TOM: Well you'll never guess who we've got coming round to our flat.

SUZE: Oh can we guess?

♂ TOM: Well give me the hoover and I'll give you a guess. Give it to me.

JEZ: Suze loves guessing games.

♂ TOM: Does she? Does she? Right. Well it's a celebrity.

JEZ: Fern Britton.

SUZE: Pam Ayres.

♂ TOM: Dirty old slapper who's been on TV.

JEZ/SUZE: Ulrika Johnson?

♂ TOM: No, Sugar Walls, Sugar Walls is coming round to our flat. Can you believe it? She's Linda's sister. Isn't that amazing?

SUZE: Oh damn I wanted it to be Pam Ayres.

the front doorbell rings.

GIMME GIMME GIMME 39

TOM: Shit. Too late! (Throws the hoover back)

linda comes out.

♀ LINDA: Don't even think about it.

♂ TOM: Oh naff off.

he opens the door. sugar rushes in wearing sunglasses pointing outside.

SUGAR: Paparazzi search. Paparazzi search!!

♂ TOM: No there's no one. No one, no one.

SUGAR: Oh great. Which one is it?

♂ TOM: This way. This way. This way.

she heads in then clocks jez and suze gawping.

SUGAR: If you talk to the press, I'm not Sugar Walls.

SUZE: Are you Pam Ayres?

SUGAR: Yes, yes.

JEZ: Prove it.

SUGAR: My name is Pam Ayres and I be liking flares. Specially the sort that comes in pairs.

she goes in.

SUZE: Quick! Autograph book!

LIVING ROOM

linda, sugar and tom.

♀ LINDA: Sunday is leg waxing day. I don't see why I should have to change my plans for you.

SUGAR: Right Olive.

♀ LINDA: Don't call me that.

SUGAR: Look I had no where else to go. I'm on the run from the press and they wouldn't expect to find me in a shit hole like this.

♀ LINDA: You can only judge a shit hole by the turds that pass through it.

♂ TOM: Is your name Olive?

♀ LINDA: No! And you keep it schtum!

SUGAR: Have you ever seen On The Buses?

♂ TOM: Yes, yes I have actually. So Sugar. Is it a hideous nightmare being on the run form the press? I imagine it is.

SUGAR: Fact of life isn't it?

♂ TOM: Yes but they printed such terrible lies about you. I mean twelve in a bed sex romps with a well known football team?

SUGAR: Lies?

♂ TOM: Oh. Oh.

♀ LINDA: Where's my leg waxing cream?

SUGAR: My motto's the same as yours Linda. If it's got a pulse it's got a chance.

♀ LINDA: Excuse me, but I've got standards. The gentlemen callers at this house are barristers, financiers, rest'ranteurs, Ain't that right Tom?

♂ TOM: Well we had a pizza delivered once.

SUGAR: Fascinating. I'm going to crash.

♂ TOM: Oh, oh, oh. Please, please, please take my bed. It would be an honour.

SUGAR: I'm sure babes.

sugar goes.

♂ TOM: Oh. Sugar Walls called me babes. Did you hear that? Did you, did you, did you, did you? God she's so beautiful. She's so quick witted. She's so raw. You know there's a girl who's been to the brink, stared despair in the face and then dragged herself back by the straps of her own slingbacks. What are you doing? What are you doing?

she's trying to get a look at his legs.

♀ LINDA: Have you been using my Immac?

♂ TOM: Get off! (On phone) Degsy it's Tom. Guess what? Now before I tell you, you must promise not to divulge this information to a soul. Guess who we've got round our flat?

♀ LINDA: I've seen better legs on an oil rig!

linda goes.

♂ TOM: No guess again. No guess again. One more time.

LINDA'S BEDROOM

linda comes in to find sugar resting on the bed. she stomps around trying to wake her.

♀ LINDA: (Singing) Moving on up, moving on out. Moving on up, nothing can stop me. Yeah!

SUGAR: Is he gay? This room's a bit over the top.

LINDA: It's mine. Mummy'd turn in her grave if she knew I'd taken you in.

SUGAR: Poor cow would still be here today if she hadn't been so fat.

LINDA: She died of a broken heart because of you.

SUGAR: She electrocuted herself on her own Slendertone pads.

enter tom

TOM: Howdie Pam? Know who I am?

LINDA: Oh get out.

TOM: I just thought I'd give you a hand looking for your dilapidatory cream.

SUGAR: How did I break mum's heart?

LINDA: Hanging around with Shane Ritchie like you were the sixth Nolan. Getting your tits out for The Sun. Shagging all those pop stars. I mean do you really want me to go on?

TOM: Sugar. I'm an actor and I've often been likened to Robert Carlyle, particularly around the fringe and . . .

LINDA: Hurry up and find my cream.

SUGAR: Oi, don't be horrible to him. Tim's all right.

TOM: It's Tom. Tom, Tom actually. Sugar I've always wanted to know, what is it like representing the UK at the Eurovision Song Contest? I imagine its phenomenally exciting though. Is it, is it though is it?

SUGAR: It's all right.

TOM: Well I'm part of the Eurovision cognoscenti so I remember that night vividly you know, vividly. Yes first up were the Macedonian twins with a didgeri doo. Then that large lesbian yodelling for Siberia. Do you remember? Do you remember? 'Yodel for Peace' I think it was called. So haunting! And then oh the anticipation! 'Et maintenant, representant Le Royaume Uni. Miss Sugar Walls'. The orchestra striking up and then you leaping out of that enormous handbag.

LINDA: And then singing like Helen Keller with tonsillitis.

SUGAR: For your information Linda, 'Dee Doo Dum Dum' went platinum in Iceland.

LINDA: The Birdie Song went platinum in Iceland.

TOM: You know you're very popular on the gay scene.

LINDA: Yeah so's amyl nitrate mate and they both smell of old socks.

SUGAR: Did you know that I was down

to the last three to be Debbie McGee?

TOM: Really? Really?

SUGAR: I was gutted over that. She's got a lovely life with Paul.

LINDA: I've got a life. I've got a life. See that scar. You know where I got that scar? I got that scar when I was bottled in a fight in the Hooker and Firkin pub in Plaistow. That's what you call being a part of the real world mate. Something you don't know nothing about. It was one of the happiest nights of my life actually. The other girl lost two front teeth and her short term memory. The bitch. I do not look like Elizabeth the First.

SUGAR: You can be beautiful and be part of the real world you know.

LINDA: Don't you think I'm living proof of that?

SUGAR: Mum didn't half fill your head with some crap. I mean I think every little girl needs to be told they're pretty. But with some people it's more a case of 'Call social services they're taking the piss!'

LINDA: Why do you have to be so horrible about mummy all the time? That woman was like a rock to me when I was in Borstal. She wrote to me every week, sent me food parcels, little nail clippings.

SUGAR: Well I ran away before I was put away. You can't blame me for that.

LINDA: Do you know how I was born Tom?

SUGAR: Oh here we go.

LINDA: It came to pass that mummy went into labour in Smokers World in Romford Market. She gave birth to me on a crate of John Player Specials. In fact they called me John for the first two weeks because they didn't realise I was a girl.

SUGAR: You can't live in the past all the time.

LINDA: What do you expect? All I had down for today was waxing my bikini line and then the past comes along and slaps me round me practically perfect face.

TOM: Just ignore her. So what does the future hold for Miss Sugar Walls? Anything large up your pipeline?

SUGAR: Well actually I'm doing my own fitness video. Thrust for Life.

TOM: Are you fully cast?

SUGAR: No. Oh I'll be sniffing round for blokes in lycra who can do the crab.

TOM: Well I was pretty good at movement at drama school you know. I've got fantastic legs for restoration.

SUGAR: Well watch and learn.

sugar does the crab on the bed. the doorbell goes.

TOM: Could you get that for me please, Linda? This could be a whole new opening for me.

HALLWAY

linda lets jez and suze in.

JEZ: Hi Linda how's tricks?

LINDA: What do you want?

SUZE: We just wanted to borrow something.

LINDA: What?

JEZ: Well anything really.

SUZE: Yes so if we could just come in and browse.

JEZ: Something from the living room perhaps. Or maybe the kitchen.

SUZE: No darling not the kitchen.

tom comes in.

TOM: Linda, Linda, Linda. Would you come quickly please. Miss Sugar Walls is stuck in the crab.

LINDA: Oh why do I bother?

JEZ: Did you hear that? Sugar Walls and Pam Ayres in the same flat at the same time!

SUZE: Oh who shall we do first?

JEZ: Sugar. Save the best till last.

LINDA'S BEDROOM.

linda and tom helping sugar out of the crab.

LINDA: You'll never learn will you?

SUGAR: Oh watch my tits I only had them done last year.

TOM: And they're fantastic.

SUGAR: Oh thanks.

LINDA: You want to see them before mate. Two aspirin on an ironing board.

jez and suze enter.

JEZ: Hi cats.

♀LINDA: Get out.

SUGAR: Who are they?

SUZE: I'm Suze. Great pal of Lindy and Tom-tom's. Would you mind? If you could just sign it to Suze and Jez with a big showbiz kiss Sugar Walls.

♀LINDA: Oh that's typical isn't it? I mean one whiff of a celebrity and everyone's round like sheep. Baah! Baah!

SUGAR: Oh you don't have any bubbly do you?

♀LINDA: I don't drink.

JEZ: That's like saying Carol Vorderman doesn't do sums.

♂TOM: Well I'll go in search of Moet for Miss Walls.

♀LINDA: Baaah!

♂TOM: Beryl!

tom leaves.

SUZE: You've been such an added bonus. We only came round to see Pam Ayres.

JEZ: Is she in Tom's room?

♀LINDA: Yeah along with Boney M, Isla St. Clair and Manhattan Transfer.

jez and suze squeal and leave.

LINDA'S BEDROOM

linda and sugar.

♀LINDA: Why did you really come here? I mean you've never run away from the press before.

SUGAR: I've had a fall out with my best mate. I came here to get some space.

♀LINDA: What did you do?

SUGAR: Tried to shag her husband.

♀LINDA: It's only human.

SUGAR: Well it was Liam Gallagher.

linda slaps her across the face.

SUGAR: Oi what did you do that for?

♀LINDA: You do not know Liam Gallagher.

SUGAR: Patsy Kensit's my best mate. Well was.

♀LINDA: Done' lie!

SUGAR: Why would I lie?

♀LINDA: Prove it!

LIVING ROOM

linda on the phone sugar sitting close.

♀LINDA: Hello can I speak to Liam please? (Gasps) I love you. (Hangs up)

SUGAR: When I've made it up with Pats. I'll introduce you to him. He likes them rough.

♀LINDA: Would you really do that for me? I forgive you for everything you've ever done to me. You're the bestest sister in the whole wide world.

tom comes in with drinks.

♀LINDA: Who was that at the door?

♂TOM: It was just me. Just me, just practising you know. One never knows when I'll be called upon to you know answer the door convincingly as say a prison officer on She's Out.

♀LINDA: Oh well poor the bubbly big boy.

♂TOM: Yes, yes just coming. Just coming. Miss Walls.

♀LINDA: Here I've just spoken to Liam Gallagher. Sharon's going to introduce me to him.

♂TOM: Really?

SUGAR: Oh it's the least I can do.

♀LINDA: To sisters!

LINDA'S BEDROOM, NEXT MORNING

linda watches her sister sleeping. she prods her breasts fascinated. this wakes sugar.

♀LINDA: Morning babes. This is great isn't it? Just like old times. Here we could do lunch later. I've always wanted to do lunch.

SUGAR: Put the telly on and make us a cup of tea.

♀LINDA: Okay babes.

linda hops up and puts the telly on.

SUGAR: Lind, look at this.

♀LINDA: What babes?

ON TV

beryl is on 'this morning with maureen and brian'.

MAUREEN: So Beryl, you're actually Tom Farrell's landlady.

BERYL: That's right Maureen, Beryl is.

MAUREEN: And you had no idea that he was having an affair with Sugar Walls.

LINDA'S BEDROOM

SUGAR: Turn it off! I'm ruined.

♀ LINDA: Why?

SUGAR: They're saying that I've slept with someone who isn't famous.

♀ LINDA: I'll stick the kettle on!

LIVING ROOM

jez, suze and tom reading the morning's tabloid. tom is on the front of every single one.

JEZ: Listen to this. Champagne swilling Tom Farrell 34 refused to comment from the doorstep of his run down council flat in North London.

SUZE: Council? We've got to sue.

♂ TOM: I'm 29.

♀ LINDA: Tom what the bloody hell's going on?

♂ TOM: Well yesterday I accidentally answered the door to the paparazzi and they've got it into their stupid heads that you know me and Sugar are doing what you straight people do so well. And in your case so noisily.

♀ LINDA: Well how did they know she was here?

♂ TOM: Haven't got a clue.

SUZE: Well thank jiminy they haven't caught a whiff of the mysterious disappearance of Pam Ayres story.

JEZ: It's hardly headline grabbing stuff.

SUZE: Oh isn't it?

♀ LINDA: Oh shut up. This is you telling your mates this is. They've been on the phone to the press taking backhanders, you silly git.

JEZ: Oh Linda you get a mention here. A close friend revealed that Tom lives with his mother Linda.

♀ LINDA: Get them out of here, it's a pack of lies.

JEZ: Is your little sister up yet? She was so lovely yesterday.

SUZE: Oh we've bought 'Dee Do Dum Dum' for her to sign. And a copy of Lick, her one and only foray into novel writing. We love this book.

JEZ: It's given us a lot of inspiration.

♀ LINDA: Get them out.

JEZ: Now that's one thing your sister does very well.

the doorbell goes.

FRONT DOOR

linda answers it to norma and bruno struggling to get in past the paparazzi.

♀ LINDA: Oi what do you think you're doing dogbreath?

NORMA: I'm Tom's agent. I need to see my client. Come on Bruno.

JOURNALIST: Is it true they're going to elope?

♀ LINDA: No.

JOURNALIST 2: Are you Tom's mum?

♀ LINDA: What?

JOURNALIST 3: Are you Janet Street Porter?

♀ LINDA: Oh that's the nicest thing anyone's ever said to me.

LIVING ROOM

norma bounds over to jez.

NORMA: Tom, Tom. My favourite client. It may seem painful now, but heartface I've had Emmerdale on the phone.

♂ TOM: Excuse me, excuse me. Norma, Norma, go, go, go, go. I'm Tom.

NORMA: Quelle domage. That's Bruno he's your bodyguard. The agency will foot the bill. Where is she? Oh Sugar. I'm Norma Tom's agent. Do you two want to sell your story?

♀ LINDA: But it ain't true. Tom's gay.

NORMA: So's my husband.

♂ TOM: You said something about Emmerdale being on the phone?

NORMA: Sugar they're offering you 'Bawdy Slut in Barn.' Three lines, two reaction shots and a wooden leg, what do you say?

♂ TOM: What have they offered me?

NORMA: The wooden leg.

♂ TOM: Oh big fat hairy bollocks!

LIVING ROOM, LATER

tom going through some faxes. linda and sugar on the couch. bruno stands guard at the door.

♂ TOM: Oh my God how utterly and orgasmically thrilling. Sugar we have been invited to appear on Chit Chat At Tea Time! Isn't that exciting? Oh it's hosted by the lovely and adorable Lorraine 'Specs' Kelly. Do you know her? 'Hello I'm Lorraine Kelly and that's great'.

SUGAR: I can't do it. I've got cow milking practice for Emmerdale later.

♂ TOM: Well surely you can do them both?

♀ LINDA: Here we'll get you flown up to the Yorkshire Dales. Think of me as your P.A.

♂ TOM: Oh I've always dreamt of lying next to Lorraine Kelly on her chaise lounge and fingering her dainty bone china and licking the froth off of her cappuccino éclairs. Oh do it for me Sugar, say you will.

SUGAR: Oh all right then.

♀ LINDA: Oh see, you're not all bad are you? You know we're going to have such a great time together babes. You planned your summer holidays yet? I was thinking maybe Fuengirola, unless of course you fancy somewhere else.

SUGAR: Er . . .

♀ LINDA: Here Tom, how much does a P.A. get paid?

SUGAR: I'm just going to have a quick bath.

♀ LINDA: Is that part of my job description?

SUGAR: Oh bloody hell. (Exits)

♀ LINDA: Oh, see that? Artistic temperament. So you're going to pretend you're straight are you?

♂ TOM: For the lovely Lorraine, yes.

♀ LINDA: Hypocrite!

♂ TOM: Look who's talking.

♀ LINDA: I'm not a hypocrite.

♂ TOM: Then why are you being so nice to her then?

♀ LINDA: Because I'm the nice one mate. I mean why does everyone always expect me to be the bitch all the time? I mean all my life I've had it. 'Oh she's the pretty one. I bet she's a right bitch' Well sometimes it don't work out that way okay?

♂ TOM: Oh for goodness sake!

♀ LINDA: Where are you going?

♂ TOM: I'm going to buy a nice new blouse for Chit Chat At Tea Time. (Exits)

♀ LINDA: (To Bruno) And you can shut up an all.

LINDA'S BEDROOM

linda comes in and switches a tape of 'dee doo dee doo dum dum' on she lies on the bed and imagines:
dream sequence.

CINEMA

a limo pulling up. cheering crowds. sugar and linda getting out. dale winton arriving at the same time.

DALE WINTON: Linda, babe.

CINEMA TOILETS

dale and linda having dirty sex in a lock-up.

♀ LINDA: Oh but Dale, Dale I always thought you were gay.

DALE WINTON: No that's just an act to get me to the top. Don't tell anybody. It'll ruin my career.

♀ LINDA: Oh but Dale, don't you fancy Sugar?

DALE WINTON: Sugar? No she's just a filthy slut. You're the nice one.

HALLWAY

linda comes to the bathroom with her suitcase packed. she calls through.

♀ LINDA: Sugar. I'm ready when you are babes. Chit Chat At Tea Time, the Yorkshire Dales. So exciting isn't it? Oh I ain't half missed you babes. Have you missed me? Oh you all choked. Sugar? Sugar?

doorbell goes. linda answers it to jez and suze.

SUZE: Linda you will never believe what's happened.

♀ LINDA: What?

JEZ: Pam Ayres was in your flat the whole darned time.

♀ LINDA: Eh?

SUZE: We came out to get the post, what five minutes ago?

JEZ: Well if you're going to be pernickety about it, it was more like six.

SUZE: And we saw her come creeping out of here, scarf shades, bags like yesterday.

JEZ: Weird huh?

♀ LINDA: Well didn't she say anything?

JEZ & SUZE: My name is Pam Ayres. I cannot tell a lie. The time has come for me to say goodbye.

JEZ: Yes, yes I know. We felt the same way. Her poetry's really gone off.

LIVING ROOM

linda nurses a beer depressed tom comes in with a noisy shirt and bruno.

♂ TOM: Guess why I bought this? Look at it. See that bit there, it goes with my eyes. Can you see that? Come on, we should be ready, we should go soon.

♀ LINDA: She's gone.

♂ TOM: Oh, well where?

♀ LINDA: Don't know. Just gone. No P.A. job for me. No Chit Chat At Tea Time for you. Just gone.

♂ TOM: Well what did she say?

♀ LINDA: Oh she was all over me like eczema before she left. Told me how much she loved me, what an influence I'd been on her.

♂ TOM: Oh what a bitch.

♀ LINDA: She looked me straight in the eye and said, 'Never forget Linda, I love you.'

♂ TOM: Oh why do I bother?

he slumps in his chair. she picks up the phone.

♀ LINDA: Have you phoned out at all today?

♂ TOM: She always did have bad taste you know.

♀ LINDA: Have you?

♂ TOM: The only woman on Celebrity Ready Steady Cook to bring a pot noodle.

♀ LINDA: Tom!

♂ TOM: What?

♀ LINDA: Have you phoned out at all today?

♂ TOM: My agent hasn't stopped ringing but no I haven't phoned out, why?

♀ LINDA: Nothing.

♂ TOM: I am a silly old queen. I know which bus I'm on. It was silly to think I could pretend otherwise. Anyway I quite like my bus.

♀ LINDA: Night then. (Exits)

♂ TOM: I don't want to get on any other bus. Hang on it's only three o'clock.

LINDA'S BEDROOM

linda lying on her bed on the phone.

♀ LINDA: Hello, is that Liam? What you got on? Never mind who I am. What you got on? Oh really? Really? I got your number off Sugar Walls, that's right, that's right. Yeah. I'm one of those really gorgeous girls from Stringfellows. Yeah. Well I've got long blonde hair right down to my arse and I've got really huge melons. Oh really? Oh really?

she starts to rub her legs.

TOM'S BEDROOM

tom taking his shirt off. bruno watching.

♂ TOM: You're a conundrum. Standing there with your butchy bulk. Your great big manliness. Your huge tallness. Listen I'm just going to have a siesta so you'd just better go I think, all right?

BRUNO: Can't I jump in with you?

bruno jumps on top of tom.

LINDA'S BEDROOM

linda on phone having a post-coital cigarette.

♀ LINDA: That was great.

Episode Five
SATURDAY NIGHT DIVA

SITTING ROOM

*linda doing a face pack, smoking
and drinking wine. tom looking
in a mirror.*

♀ LINDA: (Sings) Saturday night ba-nah, ba-nah,
ba-nah, ba-nah. Pretty baby. It's Saturday
night, ba-nah, ba-nah, ba-nah, ba-nah.

♂ TOM: Do you think I look like Peter
Mandelson?

♀ LINDA: No.

♂ TOM: Oh thanks. Do you think Peter
Mandelson's gay?

♀ LINDA: No way Jose.

♂ TOM: Oh like you'd know.

♀ LINDA: What is it with you homosexuals?
Convinced that every other bloke on
the planet's an homosexual as well.
You're obsessed.

♂ TOM: How do you know Peter Mandelson's
straight?

♀ LINDA: The reason I know Peter Mandelson
is an heterosexual as opposed to an
homosexual is because I have first hand
experience of his wanton carnal appetite.

♂ TOM: Like when?

♀ LINDA: Like when I was down the South
Bank, the night Labour got in. Me and ten
million others singing 'Things Can Only Get
Better' Monsieur Le Mandelson squeezed
past me in the queue for the kebabs and I
can tell you now it was practically
penetration. Saturday night . . .

♂ TOM: Oh stop it, I know what flipping night
it is without you caterwauling that odious
piece of muzak at my head.

♀ LINDA: Ooh. You bit fat homo. Here have a
face pack. Do you want Hello Vera or See
Ya Cilla.

♂ TOM: (Flicking through 'Okay!') I'm just
admiring Thora Hird's box room actually.
Actually can I just take a little bit of time

out to admire Thora Hird full stop. She's a
lass from Lancashire with a heart of gold.
Half hip replacement, half hot pot. Aloe Vera
please. In fact I can't say I've ever met or
heard of another Thora. I mean what's that
all about? Maybe I'd get on in acting if I
had a unique name.

♀ LINDA: You know what you need mate.

♂ TOM: What?

♀ LINDA: Feng Shui. It's all in this magazine.
The reason why you can't get any acting work
is because your drawers are in the wrong
place. I reckon if you rearranged your room
you'd be in Silent Witness by Christmas.

♂ TOM: I've been in Silent Witness.

♀ LINDA: Yeah well maybe this time you won't
fall off the slab. You know there's a Feng
Shui exhibition on at Earls Court tomorrow.
Why don't you come with me?

♂ TOM: Oh no!

♀ LINDA: What?

♂ TOM: I suddenly feel terribly old.

♀ LINDA: Well carry on with your face pack, it
takes years off you.

♂ TOM: No but look at me Linda.

♀ LINDA: Oh do I have to?

♂ TOM: It's Saturday night and what am
I doing?

♀ LINDA: You're doing my head in mush.

♂ TOM: I'm sitting in, pigging out, drinking
wine, slapping mud on my face and planning
a Sunday run out to a craft fair.

♀ LINDA: It ain't a craft fair, it's Feng Shui.

♂ TOM: No, no, no, no, no. This is not going
to happen. I mean not so long ago I'd be
zipping up my party pants, doing a bucket
load of drugs and painting the town pink.
Now I'm knocking thirty and I've
transmogrified into Anne Widdicombe.

♀ LINDA: It's all right to stay in you know.
There's a Leonardo DiCaprio film on later
where he bares all.

♂ TOM: I couldn't give a monkeys if he sticks

a feather up his arse and sings YMCA. Linda it's Saturday night. Come on slap your war paint on and let's go clubbing like the old days.

⚢ LINDA: Oh I can't be arsed. Who are you ringing?

♂ TOM: Real friends. True friends. Loyal friends. (On phone) Hey Degsy, it's Tom. How's it going? Fancy meeting in town for a drink? Well I've found these new pills, called Tony Blairs, make you grin like a Cheshire cat. Oh come on they're wicked boy–! No? All right well when Leonardo calls. Anyway you've got to go now, bye. (Hang up)

⚢ LINDA: Who are you trying to kid? You know drugs don't agree with you. They just make you paranoid the next day. You say everyone in 'Hello' magazine is freaking you out.

♂ TOM: You don't get a comedown with Ecstasy.

⚢ LINDA: That's like saying you don't get reward points with Sainsburys. Anyway I thought we'd put a stop to all that.

♂ TOM: Oh God you foolish, foolish child. I was just trying to tempt Degsy out. I mean you take everything so literally don't you? I mean as if I'd do drugs. I mean as if. Well I don't intend to sit around all night watching some pube free adolescent getting his kit off. I'm going out.

⚢ LINDA: Well what about me?

♂ TOM: I asked you if you wanted to come and you said no. Which by the bloody by ruins my pulling chances quite frankly.

⚢ LINDA: Eh?

♂ TOM: The sight of you gyrating around in skin tight lycra's enough to turn any man queer.

⚢ LINDA: Oh get a life.

♂ TOM: That's exactly what I'm doing.

⚢ LINDA: You're going to miss Casualty.

♂ TOM: Oh my God. Oh my God. So? You think I'm glued to that stupid little box do you? You think I can't survive a week on this planet without my weekly fix of NHS drama? Huh? You really don't know me at all, do you Linda La Hughes?

⚢ LINDA: I'll tape it for you shall I?

♂ TOM: Yes please. (He Exits)

LINDA'S BEDROOM

linda at her dressing table. a taxi pulls up outside. she looks out and sees suze getting into the taxi and driving off. she has an idea.

KITCHEN

linda gets a pair of knickers and drops them out of the window.

JEZ'S FRONT DOOR

linda waiting.

JEZ: Who is it?

⚢ LINDA: The auburn Jerry Hall.

jez opens the door.

JEZ: Linda Hi, what can I do for you?

⚢ LINDA: I'm on an errand of a rather personal nature.

JEZ: Personal's my middle name. Fire away.

⚢ LINDA: Well I had some undies on my clothes maiden to dry, right next to my open window, when a slight gust sucked them off and dropped them on to your patio. Now I hate to share this with you Jez but my back opening's tight shut and I just can't loosen it. I was wondering would you retrieve said undergarments for me please.

JEZ: Is it a bra?

⚢ LINDA: Panties. I'd rather you didn't look at them, they're quite contemporary.

JEZ: Hang on two ticks. Are these they?

he comes back with a massive pair of granny pants.

⚢ LINDA: No you cheeky bastard!

BERYL: I'll have those, thank you.

they look round to see beryl upon them. she swipes the pants off them and retreats.

⚢ LINDA: Go and get mine.

jez disappears inside.

⚢ LINDA: Didn't hear you coming down the stairs.

BERYL: Well you wouldn't. Look at my feet.

beryl is wearing shoes made of mop heads.

BERYL: They bring the floor up lovely.

jez comes back with linda's pants.

JEZ: I don't think these are Suze's.

linda sniffs the crotch.

⚥ LINDA: No, that's my bounce. Suze not about?

JEZ: No, no, no she's out for the evening.

⚥ LINDA: Oh shame.

JEZ: Yes ever since she went on the game I hardly ever see her. (Laughs)

⚥ LINDA: You wouldn't happen to have a bottle opener would you?

JEZ: Of course babe, I'll just go and get it.

he goes back in. linda legs it into her flat.

LIVING ROOM

linda flies in grabs her bottle opener and chucks it in the bin. jez comes in with a bottle opener.

JEZ: I'm surprised you don't have a bottle opener

⚥ LINDA: Oh we do but Tom's taken it out with him.

JEZ: Oh what by accident?

⚥ LINDA: No he's taken a shine to it. You have to nail everything down when they come from a broken home.

she hands him a bottle of wine.

⚥ LINDA: Would you mind opening it for me please. I hurt my wrist in an encounter with a cross country runner this morning.

JEZ: Sure.

⚥ LINDA: Would you care to join me for a little drink?

JEZ: A quiet Saturday evening. Beautiful woman, I'd be a fool to say no.

⚥ LINDA: Then get that wrist action going baby, I want to hear my cork go pop!

THE EDGE BAR

tom cruising. he walks around with his rucksack on trying to look cool. he doesn't realise but his rucksack gets caught on a bar stool and he starts to drag it along with him. he removes the stool and stands in a doorway. he thinks a gorgeous hunk is eyeing him up. he gets excited and smiles back. the man mouths 'fuck off!' at him. tom panics and stumbles backwards through the doorway and down some stairs. at the bottom of the stairs he crashes into nino. nino is in his early 20s, gorgeous and italian. tom's drink has gone all over nino.

♂ TOM: Oh I'm sorry, really, I'm not drunk, not drunk I've just got rather a bad inner ear infection.

NINO: All my life I've longed to meet someone with an inner ear infection.

♂ TOM: Really?

NINO: Can I buy you a drink? (Licks the splash) Double brandy and coke, no ice.

♂ TOM: Well it waters it down you know.

LIVING ROOM

linda dancing to 'lady marmalade'.

⚥ LINDA: You know I love them All Saints. Well it's that fusion of black and white you can't beat it can you Jez? Well obviously you're married to Suze.

JEZ: Yes but it doesn't mean we sit around all day singing Ebony and Ivory.

⚥ LINDA: Really? Oh. You know who I love? Lionel Ritchie. Remember that (Sings) "Hello is it me you're looking for" Remember that? I thought the video for that was brilliant. That should have won an Oscar. That poor blind woman feeling his face and then making a model of it. That's talent that is.

JEZ: I just assumed she was an actress.

⚥ LINDA: Really? She was black, weren't she?

JEZ: I can't really remember, actually.

TOM
'Oh, big fat hairy bollocks.'

♀ LINDA: Jez, this is your heritage we're talking about here.

JEZ: Is it?

♀ LINDA: Here, Bob Marley he was great, weren't he? (Sings) 'No woman no cry'. What do you think he meant by that then eh?

JEZ: Gosh Linda you're so knowledgeable about black culture. Tell me what's your take on Idi Amin?

♀ LINDA: Oh I love him. He's like a second father to me. Well I'm a minority group myself ain't I? Red hair.

JEZ: Of course. That's in the history books. After the chapter on the slave trade.

♀ LINDA: You know I should have been black really. It was just a fluke of nature that I weren't.

JEZ: Yes and I'm sure having white parents didn't help either.

♀ LINDA: Irish parents! I mean that's practically black in this country isn't it? Here where's Suze tonight then?

JEZ: Oh she's at the woman's meeting.

♀ LINDA: Oh.

JEZ: I wish I was there too actually. Tonight they're dancing naked around a camp fire on Hackney Marshes.

♀ LINDA: Why go to Hackney when you've got heaven on a plate right here, eh? So how long have you been with thingy, you know.

JEZ: Suze? Three years.

♀ LINDA: Oh I bet you're gagging for a nibble on a different plate of muffins.

JEZ: No, no, no, not really. No she means the world to me.

linda is splattered now.

♀ LINDA: Oh? You're happily married then eh? No that's great. No really Jez that is great. You know but I really don't think I'm the settling down type you know, I really don't think I could be that boring.

JEZ: Do you think I'm boring? I don't find married life boring per se. I mean I have a good job, a lovely kitchen, weekend breaks. Fabulous orgasms. No the only thing I'm unhappy about is um, no, no. You don't want to hear this.

♀ LINDA: Oh no Jez. You can tell me if you've got a little problem. I'm a trained Samaritan. Oh yeah I mean I don't do it no more but when I did I was knock out. I mean I spoke to all sorts, black and white. Sometimes I didn't even ask them what colour they were.

JEZ: Why did you stop?

♀ LINDA: Well they don't bloody pay you do they love? I mean I'm not a charity am I? So what I'm saying to you is Jez, you know, if you've got a little problem, you know just tell me. If you want to offload. Divulge. Spill. Just let me know.

JEZ: No, no I'd rather not.

♀ LINDA: No go on just tell me one little thing about Suze you don't like, go on. No go on, does she stink?

JEZ: No.

♀ LINDA: I bet she does. I bet she's rank isn't she?

JEZ: No, no, no she smells lovely. Look the only thing we disagree about is well, I really want to get back to my Sunday League Football, but Suze says that Sundays are our time.

♀ LINDA: Oh what so it's all right for her to go cavorting around stark bollock naked with a load of lesbians on a Saturday night, but it ain't all right for you to have your football on a Sunday morning? Do you know what I'd do?

JEZ: What?

♀ LINDA: Ditch the bitch.

JEZ: We married for better or for worse.

♀ LINDA: Well have an affair then.

JEZ: Oh Linda you tickle me.

♀ LINDA: Do I?

JEZ: Yes.

linda sits astride him and tickles him.

♀ LINDA: Are you ticklish Jez? Are you? Are you ticklish? Are you ticklish? No go on let me see how ticklish you are. No come on Jez.

JEZ: No, no don't. No Linda!

he shoves her away forcefully.

♀ LINDA: All right, I was only tickling you.

JEZ: I'm going to the loo.

LINDA: Finish off what I started?

HOTEL FOYER

nino getting his keys from two diky receptionists. tom nodding his head a lot - he's off his tits.

NINO: Three fifteen please.

BEVERLY-JANE: Just three shakes of a monkey's tail sir.

NINO: Are you sure you didn't take no drugs?

TOM: No I just can't stop dancing. Could you turn the music up a bit please?

BEVERLY-JANE: I'm afraid that's my watch sir. Ticking.

TOM: It's fantastic, hold it up there.

BEVERLY-JANE: Oh Beverly-Ann could you get the keys for three one five please?

BEVERLY-ANN: Can do Beverly-Jane.

BEVERLY-JANE: Did you have a good evening sir?

TOM: I am twatted.

BEVERLY-JANE: Is that a Welsh name sir?

BEVERLY-ANN: Three one five sir.

NINO: Grazie.

BEVERLY-JANE: Off your face on pills sir?

TOM: No I'm just feeling very energetic. And this is not what you think, okay? We are brothers. And we're only sharing one room because it's cheaper than two.

NINO: Goodnight.

BEVERLY-ANN: Goodnight Sir.

BEVERLY-JANE: And happy shagging.

tom and nino go.

BEVERLY-ANN: Do you think he was on drugs Beverly-Jane?

BEVERLY-JANE: I don't know about him but I'm buzzing my nut off Beverly-Ann.

BEVERLY-ANN: Me too Beverly Jane.

LIVING ROOM

jez comes back from the toilet to find linda opening another bottle of wine.

JEZ: I thought you'd sprained your wrist?

LINDA: I have. I'm in agony. Go on you do it. And hurry up I'm dry.

JEZ: So what were we talking about?

LINDA: I don't know. I can't remember everything, can I? All right so I'm a little bit tipsy.

JEZ: Yes and the Titanic was a little bit wet.

LINDA: I had family on that boat!

JEZ: Actually I think, I think I should leave actually.

LINDA: Oh no I was only tickling you. You've got a one track mind. Well you can't get arrested for tickling you know. Well I suppose you can if there's a very big age gap.

JEZ: Are you sure you should have another?

LINDA: Oh what so I can't have a little drink in my own home now? I mean is there a law against that now as well eh? Lock me up and throw away the key I was smiling!

a knock at the door.

LINDA: Oh who's that? Every time I'm in with a chance there's a knock! Every one wants a piece of me! They're squeezing me Jez! They're squeezing me!!

suze enters.

SUZE: Linda is Jez here?

LINDA: Oh bloody hell it's Snow White with haemorrhoids. Well there's got to be some reason for that constant pained smile. Did I say you could come in?

SUZE: Er . . .

JEZ: We'll go, we'll go.

LINDA: No don't. I'm drunk I might do myself an injury. On your conscience be it. (Turns on Suze) And you?! I've heard all

about you!! Nicking all the black men so there's none left for the black women!!

SUZE: Why are you being so nasty?

♀ LINDA: Because I want to be. Why are you back so early? No black men for you to nick?

SUZE: It's a woman only group.

♀ LINDA: Lesbian!

SUZE: And it was a tad on the chilly side. So Wendy suggested we all go back to her place and do it round a three bar fire. Only when I saw she was council I just thought, home.

♀ LINDA: Home! Is that what you thought, home?!

SUZE: I'm not experiencing a totally tickety boo situation here pumpkin.

♀ LINDA: Yeah well he wouldn't be a pumpkin if you let him play his Sunday morning football. Have you got footballer's legs Jez? Let me see, go on let me see your legs.

SUZE: Look I'm being rebirthed in the morning and I can't afford too late a night.

♀ LINDA: Let me see your legs Jez, please let me see your legs.

SUZE: Ciao Linda.

linda throws herself at jez's legs as he leaves. she falls to the floor unconscious.

LIVING ROOM

linda making an alka seltzer. tom comes in merrily.

♂ TOM: Quick, quick, quick lovebites check, lovebite check! No, no? His name was Nino. Italian, on holiday. Flies back to Milano today. Posh hotel in Mayfair, had about oh what, about five minutes sleep.

♀ LINDA: Didn't take any drugs did you? I don't want you getting paranoid on me.

♂ TOM: Don't be so ridiculous. Of course I didn't do any drugs. Oh! Oh! What's that?

he backs away from the bread.

♂ TOM: What's that?

♀ LINDA: It's only a loaf.

♂ TOM: Well cover it up it's freaking me out.

she chucks a sheet over it. tom

shrieks again.

♂ TOM: Oh, what's that doing there?

♀ LINDA: It's the toaster.

♂ TOM: Well why is it staring at me! Why?

she throws a tea towel over the toaster.

♀ LINDA: You sure you didn't take any drugs?

the phone rings. tom hyperventilates.

♂ TOM: It's the police! They're going to do a drugs bust. They'll bang us up for life. Oh I'm a good girl I am!

nino's voice comes on answerphone

NINO: (VO) Tom It's Nino. I wanted to say goodbye. My taxi will be passing your house. I'll pop in say goodbye. Maybe you're not back yet, Ciao.

♂ TOM: God no he can't see me, what am I going to do?

♀ LINDA: Calm down, what's the matter? Was he a dog?

♂ TOM: Lindy I told him the smallest of porkies last night.

♀ LINDA: Like what?

♂ TOM: That I'm a top British actor in a soap opera called Up West.

♀ LINDA: Up West?

♂ TOM: Yes I play Dirk Beauregarde, the ladies man with a roving eye and a mobile sandwich business.

♀ LINDA: Why did you give him your address then you stupid prat?

♂ TOM: I fancied a postcard of Italy, I didn't think he'd shoot straight over. (Footsteps in the hall) Oh God that's him! No it's only Beryl.

beryl enters with a cake.

BERYL: Cooee. Beryl had a Scottish evening last night. Renee got out Brigadoon on video and made Dundee cake, only Beryl can't stand it, so she's giving it to you.

♀ LINDA: Did Beryl get pissed on Tennents Super and develop a life threatening crack habit? That's Scottish.

BERYL: No that's a misconception. Something up?

♀ LINDA: Tell her.

TOM: No you tell her. You tell her.
BERYL: Oh sock it to me quick.
LINDA: His dirty bit of trade's coming over and he thinks Tom is a big soap star because Tom here told him so.
BERYL: Is the trade backward?
LINDA: Italian.
TOM: So any advice?
BERYL: Go out. I would.
TOM: You ridiculous woman. Actually that's not a bad idea.
BERYL: Well you don't get far in prostitution without being inventive.
LINDA: Come to the Feng Shui exhibition with me.
TOM: It's very calming isn't it Feng Shui, it's very calming.
LINDA: Yes it is.
TOM: Right Linda grab your Pacamac!

the doorbell goes.

BERYL: Oh that'll be Renee come back for her bagpipes.

FRONT DOOR

beryl answers the door to nino.

BERYL: You're never Renee's grandson you're very tall for eighteen months.
NINO: Is Tom in?
BERYL: No, no allow me to introduce myself. Beryl Merrit, Tom's P.A. He was called away unexpectedly to film Call Your Bluff. (Seeing Tom and Linda come out) Miss Toksvig, my how you've grown!

LIVING ROOM

tom and nino.

TOM: Um look there's um, there's something I wanted to tell you. But you're not going to be overly impressed so er, so I won't.
NINO: I know you're not in Up West. I know it doesn't exist. I think you lie to me.
TOM: Yes I did. I'm a liar, I did I lied.
NINO: It's okay. I think it's funny.
TOM: You do? Oh thank God for that. Well I am known for my sense of humour in North London you know. Listen to this, listen to this. What do you call a man with a wooden head? Edward.

NINO: And what do you call a man with three wooden heads?
TOM: I don't know, I don't know.
NINO: Edward Woodward.
TOM: Even better. Super. You, know your knowledge of British character actors is bloody good.
NINO: Maybe I lied too.
TOM: Eh?
NINO: I say my name was Nino.
TOM: Yes.
NINO: It's Kevin.
TOM: Kevin? It's not very Italian.

nino starts talking with a mancunian accent.

NINO: And I'm from Manchester.
TOM: Oh dear. But you look so Italian.
NINO: Me dad's from Venice. He runs a fleet of ice cream vans in Whalley Range.
TOM: An idyllic childhood. How rare for the north.
NINO: I was having a laugh with myself doing the accent, pissed. I live with my fella in Liverpool. If I was Nino then Kevin wasn't being unfaithful.
TOM: Well you've very good at the accent.
NINO: Oh tar. I'm at the Paul McCartney School of Speech and Drama. Sorry.
TOM: No, no, no. Don't be, don't be. No, no. Um, listen um, would you mind terribly pretending to be Italian?
NINO: Would you mind terribly pretending to be on the box?

they head off for the bedroom.

BATHROOM, LATER

nino comes in in his undies to freshen up. linda follows him in she sits on the side of the bath fighting tears.

NINO: Hi.
LINDA: Hi.
NINO: I'll only be a sec. Are you all right?
LINDA: Maybe, maybe not. Maybe I'm the wife. Maybe I've always known that my husband was on the bi bus. But maybe I

LINDA

'I'm often mistaken for a ginger Uma Thurman.'

believed him when he said he was going to give it all up on account of little Liam.

NINO: What?

♀ LINDA: Our unborn love child. What sort of a future has Liam got eh?

NINO: I didn't realise.

♀ LINDA: Do us a favour. Do us all a favour. Do Liam a favour, leave.

NINO: I'm sorry. That's terrible. How could he?

♀ LINDA: Don't say nothing to him. I mean he may look like a mild mannered Jessie but underneath it all he's really handy with his fists.

nino exits fuming.

TOM'S BEDROOM

nino storms in and gets dressed. tom watches him like the cat that got the cream. just before nino leaves he comes over to the bed and whacks tom.

LIVING ROOM

linda placing a steak on tom's shiner. beryl is watching.

♂ TOM: Oh, oh that is nice.

♀ LINDA: Is it? Is it?

♂ TOM: Yes. Oh. Oh isn't it typical? The one man I meet who can cope with my very occasional, slight exaggerations turns out to be a lying compulsive violent man from Manchester. How can someone change like that? Going from so caring to so violent?

♀ LINDA: Well he was mentally unbalanced. I know I've never claimed to be Italian.

BERYL: Renee has. Trying to get a discount on a tiramisu.

the doorbell goes.

BERYL: Sister Beryl will respond.

♀ LINDA: Let this be a lesson to you. The homosexual underbelly is a very dangerous area to explore.

JEZ: Tom are you okay?

♀ LINDA: What do you want?

♂ TOM: Oh how heartwarming. Neighbours rallying round. Jez come closer for my sight is poor. I think I'm going to pull through but it's touch and go. Touch and go.

JEZ: What happened?

♀ LINDA: We never got to that Feng Shui exhibition, that's what happened.

BERYL: A word of advice. Never trust a bogus eye-tie.

JEZ: I came to see you really Linda.

♂ TOM: Oh well then.

♀ LINDA: Well you've seen me now get out.

♂ TOM: Oh could we keep the noise down please. I'm teetering on concussion.

BERYL: Quiet!

JEZ: I just want to say thanks.

♀ LINDA: Yeah any time.

JEZ: Not for being rude. Not for jumping on me, not for always mentioning the fact that I'm black. And not for being pissed as a fart.

♂ TOM: Well you've gone through most of her repertoire, what's left?

JEZ: For bringing up the football in front of Suze. We had a really good chat last night and well, these are my footballers legs.

jez steps out. he is wearing football shorts.

BERYL: Oh Jez.

JEZ: I played today. Scored an own goal and got sent off for tackling the referee but hey, at least I played. Suze and I are getting on better than ever now.

suze enters.

SUZE: You can say that again. Hi cats. Hey I like the steak Tom. You gays are streets ahead of us straights on the A to Z map of fashion.

♂ TOM: Oh naff off.

SUZE: Sorry I'm late Jezzie pie, my rebirthing overran. I had a really difficult labour and in the end they had to perform an emergency Caesarean. Still I'm here now and they even gave me some corn placenta so that's tea sorted. I'm so glad we're talking properly and it's all down to the lovely Linda.

JEZ: Ain't it the truth?

SUZE: Oh pussy willow I love you.

JEZ: Oh ditto dreamboat.

Episode Six
I DO, I DO, I DO, I DO, I DO

dream sequence.
the terry clinger show. a jerry
springer style show. linda is on
stage chewing gum angrily.

TERRY CLINGER: Hi I'm Terry Clinger
welcome to the show. Let's meet Linda.
Linda says she's fed up with her husband
Tom spending far too much time away from
home. She says he's having an affair with a
woman she's never even met. Linda says
enough is enough. Hi Linda.

♀ **LINDA:** Hi Terry.

TERRY CLINGER: So tell me about
this woman?

♀ **LINDA:** Well she's called Gloria and she's a
(Beep) slut.

TERRY CLINGER: How long have you and
Tom been married?

♀ **LINDA:** Five years.

TERRY: How old are you?

♀ **LINDA:** Eighteen.

TERRY: Linda, some people say Tom is gay.

♀ **LINDA:** (Beep)! If he was gay why does he
spend so much time round her place? He's
been round there every night this week.

TERRY: Are we ready to meet Tom?

AUDIENCE: Yeah.

TERRY: Bring him on.

tom comes on. he and linda fight
then stop.

♂ **TOM:** Hi Terry.

TERRY: Hi Tom welcome to the show. Okay
so, Tom, you're not gay?

♂ **TOM:** You know I is Linda.

♀ **LINDA:** Tell it to the hand, explain it to
the finger.

TERRY: And Linda says you've been spending
a lot of time with a woman called Gloria.

♂ **TOM:** Yes that's right Terry. I have. And I ain't
ashamed of that because she's my friend.

♀ **LINDA:** Oh what so you sleep with
your friends?

♂ **TOM:** I do not sleep with her you (Beep)!

TERRY: Now settle down. Settle down folks.
I know you're upset.

♀ **LINDA:** The only reason he goes with her is
because she takes it up the (Beep)!

♂ **TOM:** Don't go there!

♀ **LINDA:** Now I won't have no man parking
his car in my basement, you know what
I'm saying?

TERRY: Are we ready to meet Gloria?

LINDA'S BEDROOM

linda wakes from her dream
screaming.

♀ **LINDA:** Noooooooooooooooooooo!

KITCHEN

linda preparing a fantastic breakfast.

HALLWAY

linda carries the breakfast on
a tray to tom's room. she
calls through.

♀ **LINDA:** Thomas? I've made you a spot
of breakfast.

♂ **TOM:** Enter!

she goes to go in as he comes
out. they collide. the food
goes everywhere.

TOM: Oh you silly fat tart. Look is this for me though?

LINDA: Breakfast in bed for my favourite flat mate.

TOM: That would be a very good title for a show, wouldn't it? Breakfast in Bed. A sort of cookery come chat type pre 9am show for Channel Five. Must make a note of that. Get on to Kirsty Young.

LINDA: It's a fantastic idea.

TOM: You're in a very generous mood today.

LINDA: I'm always generous.

TOM: Just because you've slept with a Big Issue vendor Linda does not make you the Queen of Hearts, all right? Oh look there's a dog hair.

LINDA: No it's auburn. It's one of mine.

TOM: Precisely what I meant.

TOM'S BEDROOM

tom and linda sit in bed as he finishes his food.

TOM: Well Linda you've surpassed yourself. I didn't even know you could cook.

LINDA: Well Jerry Hall always said a good woman had to be a slut in the kitchen and a chef in the bedroom . . . She always did talk shit didn't she?

TOM: Hey Lindy look at us. Same bed. Do you know I could probably count on the fingers of my right hand the number of women I've been in bed with. I used to jump in with mother on cold winter mornings.

LINDA: Really?

TOM: And I very nearly ended up in bed with Stephanie Beacham once.

LINDA: Oh couldn't you go through with it?

TOM: Well no I didn't get the part you see, yeah. Cat on a Hot Tin Roof. I was up for Brick. Lovely theatre Westcliff-On-Sea. Robert Carlyle always gets my parts the bastard. The day he retires my career is going to soar.

LINDA: You'd have been brilliant as Hamish Macbeth.

TOM: Yes I know. 'Aye, there's a cold wet fog coming in o'er the Moors. Toto. I think we're stranded till tea time.'

LINDA: So poetic them Scotch ain't they?

TOM: Yes they are.

LINDA: This is nice isn't it?

TOM: What is?

LINDA: Us two. Sat here chatting. Chewing the cud.

TOM: Well it beats sticking pins in your eyes I suppose yes.

LINDA: I think it's really lovely.

she starts to cry.

TOM: Oh stop it. Stop it at once. You're getting snot all over my elk skin rug.

LINDA: Well aren't you even going to ask me why I'm upset?

TOM: No I'm not. Now get out of my bedroom you over emotional slutbag.

LINDA: I bet you're not this horrible to what's her name.

TOM: Who?

LINDA: Thingy. You're always round at her place nowadays.

TOM: You mean Gloria?

LINDA: Yeah Gloria.

TOM: What so I can't have friends now, can I, eh? I've got to eek out the rest of my days with some ginger fag hag with enough cellulite to cover Japan?

LINDA: You used to be lovely to me.

TOM: Well people change, okay?

LINDA: Yeah I bet Gloria'll change when you move in with her. I know that's what you're planning on doing. I feel it in my water.

TOM: I'm not going to move in with her.

LINDA: No?

TOM: No Lindy. You silly little kumquat. I'm going to marry her.

LINDA: Great. What?

TOM: I'm going to marry her. Look I was going to tell you, I was. Are you a tad upset? You are a bit aren't you? You're taking it very well though Lindy, very well. Very well.

linda starts to demolish the room in a rage.

TOM: Stop that. That was carved by the elbows of an ancient fingerless Macedonian tribe. (She smashes pictures) Not Simon Shepherd!

LIVING ROOM

linda sits smoking on the couch tom comes in.

TOM: Well my bedroom's doing a very nice little impression in there of Beirut, so thanks for that.

LINDA: Hypocrite.

TOM: If you just give me five minutes I can explain it to you.

LINDA: Are you, or are you not a big fat homosexual?

TOM: Well I wouldn't put it quite like that no.

LINDA: Well how would you put it then?

TOM: Um, I'm a gay man.

LINDA: I'm a gay man. I'm a gay man. So why are you marrying a woman then you wanker?

TOM: Gloria is a lesbian.

LINDA: Eugh! Turns my stomach.

TOM: Look we're not getting married because we're riddled with some sort of internalised homophobia for goodness sake.

LINDA: Don't bamboozle me with big long words.

TOM: Oh will you just shut up. Honestly this is just ridic. I mean you won't even let me explain. You want me to shut up? Do you want me to shut up? All right I will just zip up my mouth and shut up.

LINDA: Oh little queenie strop? You won't be able to do that when you're married. Gloria won't like that.

TOM: Gloria is American.

LINDA: Well so's Charles Manson mate, don't mean he's perfect.

TOM: She lives over here with her girlfriend.

LINDA: Eugh, what does she think about you two getting spliced?

TOM: Well if you must know she's going to be bridesmaid.

LINDA: You've joined one of them cults ain't you?

TOM: Oh don't be so stupid.

LINDA: Yeah well you can't brainwash me. I might have had more pricks than Ker Plunk but I'm not going to join no happy clappy bunch of zombies for no one.

TOM: What a stupid thing to say.

LINDA: You are. You're trying to brainwash me.

TOM: Oh for goodness sake. If I was joining a cult the last person I'd want in it would be you.

linda finds a book.

LINDA: What's this? The Gloria bible, Bible?

TOM: Right let me explain. And I will keep it to words of one syllable all right? So you can understand okay? Have you seen the movie Green Card?

LINDA: Yes.

TOM: Well I'm Andie McDowell and she is Gerard Depardieu.

LINDA: Well who am I?

TOM: I'm going to marry her so she can stay in the country and be with her girlfriend.

LINDA: Er, is Andie McDowell a lesbian? She looks like me!

TOM: For goodness sake! Look I need to keep this so we can prove to the authorities that we know each other intimately. I'll give you an example. Er, favourite colour?

LINDA
'Tell it to the hand, explain it to the finger.'

♀ LINDA: Nipple pink.

♂ TOM: No not you, Gloria.

♀ LINDA: Well how do I know? I've never even met the bitch!

♂ TOM: Oh. God. Just how stupid can one person be?

♀ LINDA: Well you've never met my cousin Velma. I wouldn't expect you to go on Mastermind answering questions about her.

♂ TOM: Look I am going to marry Gloria so that she can stay in this country and live with her beloved. Okay? End of story.

♀ LINDA: Some story, it's more confusing than Hansel and Gretal.

♂ TOM: Hansel and Gretal's not confusing!

♀ LINDA: Well when did you last stay in an house that you could eat?

♂ TOM: Oh!

♀ LINDA: It twists children's minds that does. So Tom are you still gay?

♂ TOM: Right look, given the choice between being stuck in a lift with Shirley Williams and Robbie Williams I think I'd plump for Robbie all right?

♀ LINDA: Answer the bloody question!

♂ TOM: Yes! I'm still gay.

♀ LINDA: When is this bloody wedding then?

♂ TOM: It's next Saturday.

♀ LINDA: What?

♂ TOM: Well I was going to tell you.

♀ LINDA: You are marrying some dykey bitch I've never even clapped eyes on next Saturday?

♂ TOM: Well you can clap eyes on her tomorrow. She's coming round for a dress fitting. Degsy, Degsy's doing the dress.

♀ LINDA: Degsy does dresses for drag queens.

♂ TOM: Yes but you haven't seen Gloria.

♀ LINDA: Oh my brain!

LINDA'S BEDROOM

linda unwell in bed. beryl taking her temperature. she looks taken aback at the result.

♀ LINDA: What?

BERYL: Well according to this you're clinically dead.

the doorbell goes.

♀ LINDA: Go and see what she looks like?

beryl looks out of the window.

♀ LINDA: Is she built like a brick shit house?!
BERYL: She looks like Geoff Capes in slingbacks. Come and have a butchers.

♀ LINDA: I'm too weak to walk.
BERYL: I used to be like that after a busy day at the Sauna.

laughter and merriment in the hall.

♀ LINDA: What are they so excited about? It's only a marriage of convenience.
BERYL: Beryl's wondering whether Linda's jealous.

♀ LINDA: Linda's wondering whether Beryl wants a slap.
BERYL: Pop through and see the young damsel, that might relieve your symptoms.

♀ LINDA: I would if I could, but I'm dying. I've got an horrible taste in my mouth. How do you explain that?
BERYL: This thermometer hasn't been washed since Renee's cat had mumps.

LIVING ROOM

gloria's brother vince is pacing around on his mobile.

VINCE: Yeah I'm going to be late. I'm up in Kentish Town with my sister, dress fitting for the big day. Yeah Bud I'll see you at six. Oh by the way did you get those polaroids of Cindy with the donkey? Yeah, yeah cool. Just don't let the animal rights guys seem them. Okay ciao Bud.

linda comes in and does a double take.

♀ LINDA: Bloody hell she is butch.
VINCE: Hi there you must be Linda. Great jugs.

♀ LINDA: You cheeky bitch.
VINCE: Vince Muncher I'm Gloria's brother.

♀ LINDA: Oh! I thought there was something a bit cocky about you.
VINCE: I'm based in the States. I make programmes for an adult

  GIMME GIMME GIMME

entertainment channel on the digital network. Here's my card.

♀ LINDA: Oh Fanny Fix Up. Oh.

VINCE: Yeah it's our most successful show. It's a bit like Blind Date, only we film the sex as well.

♀ LINDA: Oh are you looking for contestants?

VINCE: Do bears shit in the woods?

gloria comes in testing tom.

GLORIA: What's my favourite meal from the chip shop?

♂ TOM: Battered cod.

GLORIA: Chinese Takeaway?

♂ TOM: Hello Lindy, feeling better? Chicken Chow Mein.

GLORIA: Gloria. Hi. Italian.?

♀ LINDA: Second generation Irish.

♂ TOM: Spaghetti Carbonara?

GLORIA: Vongole! Vongole! Fish I eat. Meat I don't.

♀ LINDA: We heard.

GLORIA: Get me a coffee. (Snaps her fingers at Linda)

♀ LINDA: What?

GLORIA: Black no sugar. How would you like to be our bridesmaid?

♀ LINDA: How would you like a smack in the mouth?

GLORIA: Coffee!

♀ LINDA: Shut up!

VINCE: I have this thing about bridesmaids. So ripe for the plucking. Sat up there on top table, little bit of wedding cake dribbling down the chin. Gets me every freaking time.

♀ LINDA: I'll do it.

jez and suze enter with a book.

♂ TOM: Oh carrumba, who let the dick heads from downstairs in?

SUZE: Hi cats!

JEZ: Which scatterbrain left this on the path?

SUZE: The Tom Bible?

♀ LINDA: I'll have that.

♂ TOM: Don't you dare read that out.

♀ LINDA: Vince what does this say?

VINCE: Tom thinks the most sexiest person on TV is – Gaby Roslin?

♀ LINDA: Oh you liar!

♂ TOM: No I do, I think she's sexy.

♀ LINDA: The only time you stick your hands down your pants when you're watching telly is when Robson Green comes on.

BERYL: (Passing) Oh same here.

VINCE: Hey Tom, you left the most favourite sexual experience bit blank.

♂ TOM: Yes well I'm hardly going to impress the authorities am I, if I tell them my best sexual experience is rubbing against Ainsley Harriot's bottom on a nightflight to Munich am I?

SUZE: You could use our best sexual experience if you like. We don't mind.

♂ TOM: Thanks my dear. Pen, pen, pen. Okay come on best sexual experience spit it out.

SUZE: Well there was this time when we were on this accountancy course in Leatherhead.

JEZ: Do you know Leatherhead?

GLORIA: Is that something to do with S and M?

JEZ: No.

SUZE: Let me write it down, it's a little bit embarrassing.

♂ TOM: All right you do it, you do it.

VINCE: Tom's favourite hobby is football?

♀ LINDA: Wanting to sniff Michael Owen's jockstrap does not make you an ardent fan.

♂ TOM: Oh I'm often to be found on a Saturday afternoon feet up on the three piece, can in hand. Cheering Beckham on.

♀ LINDA: Yeah well most blokes say 'On me head Beckham!' not 'Give me head Beckham!'

JEZ: Is handcuffs hyphenated?

GLORIA: I didn't know you had so many room mates. (To Suze) Do you want to be bridesmaid too?

♀ LINDA: No she don't. Get out.

GLORIA: Oh get off the programme honey. Why are you so upset?

Is it because I'm using your flat for the trousseau fitting? Tough shit. I want to keep my outfit a surprise from India.

♀ LINDA: Oh we're getting global coverage Fab!

♂ TOM: Oh don't be so bloody stupid. You know full well India is her girlfriend.

GLORIA: (Flashing photo) That's India.

♀ LINDA: (Flashing her hand) That's eczema.

GLORIA: She'll be bridesmaid with you.

the doorbell rings.

GLORIA: Tinitus!! Is that stress?

♂ TOM: No that will be Degsy come to measure you up.

GLORIA: I think I'll take a valium.

♀ LINDA: Oh take the whole bottle love.

JEZ: (Finishes writing) Well that's as much as I can remember. I think in order to be really graphic we should pop down to Leatherhead and re-enact the whole thing.

SUZE: What now?

JEZ: You've still got the electrodes, haven't you?

SUZE: In my clutchbag. Ciao peeps! See you at the wedding!

JEZ: Bye cats!

vince follows them out.

♀ LINDA: Oi, Vince. Where you going?

VINCE: Leatherhead!

degsy comes in

DEGSY: No stand, stand. Are we over blessed bottom wise? I'm thinking bustle. I'm thinking mermaid fish scoop fantail chainmail. I'm thinking up here, down there, quieten down the noisy cleavage with some costume jewellery. Will the budget run to a hairpiece?

♂ TOM: This is Degsy.

DEGSY: Haute couture to the stars. Bonnie Langford, Lonnie Donnegan. Tanita Tikaram. I've stuck them all in maxi pants and made them huge.

♂ TOM: Degsy's also doubling as my best man.

GLORIA: Aha. Just one thing. I'm not wearing a dress. I'm wearing a suit.

degsy faints.

♂ TOM: Linda, Linda, smelling salts, quickly.

♀ LINDA: What?

♂ TOM: Smelling salts.

DEGSY: I'm fine. What did she say?

♀ LINDA: Don't worry Degs, I'll sort it. Glo'? A word of advice from your chief bridesmaid. Now we all know that you're a

refugee from the People's Republic of Lesbania, national costume:, checked shirt and clumpy boots. But it is law in this country that when you get married you have to wear a dress.

GLORIA: Look I have a very rare skin disorder. I cannot expose my legs to the light. It's very common in lesbians.

♂ TOM: Come on, come on think of India. You don't want her sitting home alone with a TV dinner for one because that's what will happen if this marriage is a failure.

GLORIA: Okay I'm going to shoot from the hip.

♀ LINDA: Eugh!

GLORIA: Degsy think subtle. I got great tits, it would be a shame to miss them. Stick Linda in a body bag and we're half way there. We go to the Registry Office, we come back here. I want lights, I want balloons. I want a woman only space in the kitchen. I want kd lang but I don't think I'll get her. And I know you guys are English but I'm saying no right now to karaoke.

TOM'S BEDROOM

the wedding day. tom in bed.
linda comes in with a cup of tea
and a cigarette for him.

♀ LINDA: Here you go, good old traditional English breakfast. Cup of tea and a fag.

♂ TOM: Still as hilarious as heart disease I see.

♀ LINDA: Did you sleep well?

♂ TOM: Uh uh, not a wink.

♀ LINDA: Should have taken a sleeping tablet.

♂ TOM: What after what happened last time? Four o'clock in the morning, rattling around in the medicine cabinet, took an E by mistake. Spent the entire night telling my posters how much I loved them.

♀ LINDA: What's this?

♂ TOM: Oh it's just some photographs of me and Degsy from when we were eighteen.

♀ LINDA: Oh you haven't changed a bit.

♂ TOM: Oh thanks.

♀ LINDA: Neither has Degsy. You often get that with mates don't you? The fit one and the ugly one. My best mate was a right bloodhound.

♂ TOM: Right. Thank you very much.

♀ LINDA: I don't know how you can fancy that Degsy you know. He's camper than a big van.

tom starts to get changed.

♂ TOM: I shall pretend I didn't hear that.

♀ LINDA: I've seen the looks you've given him.

tom gets embarrassed about
undressing in front of her.

♀ LINDA: I ain't going to look. Just because you fancy your best mate don't mean to say we all do. Not that you are my best mate.

♂ TOM: Yeah right. The only other person you speak to on a regular basis you say four words to: 'John Player special please!'

♀ LINDA: Well at least I get to speak when I go out of the house. At least I don't wander round Albert Square with a shopping bag. Extra! Extra!

♂ TOM: Oh go and get your bloody bridesmaid dress on.

♀ LINDA: Yeah I'd better make myself look beautiful for Vince. Did you seek the looks

he gave me? He's in porn. I was born to be on the top shelf.

♂ TOM: You?

♀ LINDA: I've got the body of a fourteen year old.

♂ TOM: Which one, Billy Bunter?

OUTSIDE THE REGISTRY OFFICE

tom and degsy get out of a taxi
and head up the steps. beryl takes a
photo.

♂ TOM: Beryl, Beryl, Beryl, I can't do this, I can't do this.
DEGSY: Be brave, be bold.
BERYL: Be butch.

another taxi and gloria india and
linda get out.

INDIA: Okay Linda?

♀ LINDA: Yeah I'm fine thanks India. Would you stop looking at my tits?
BERYL: All the best.

INSIDE THE REGISTRY OFFICE

everyone waiting. tom needs the
loo. he approaches the registrar.

♂ TOM: Do you have any pleasantly smelling lavatorial facilities close at hand? Just need to shake my lettuce.

the registrar points to the back of
the room. tom heads on out. the
wedding march strikes up and
gloria enters. tom retreats. linda
is convinced that india is trying it
on with her.

♀ LINDA: Get off me India!
BERYL: Oh she looks like a film star.

♀ LINDA: I'm often mistaken for a Ginger Uma Thurman.

there are 2 dogs
in the congregation,
dressed as bride
and groom.

BERYL: Where did the dogs come from?

♀ LINDA: (Nodding to Gloria and India) New York and Dalston.

♂ TOM: Ladies please. The sooner we get on with this the sooner I can go to the toilet.

REGISTRAR: If anyone here present knows any reason why these two people should not lawfully be joined together in wedded matrimony speak now or forever hold your peace.

♀ LINDA: Come on I'm baking.

♂ TOM: Come on.

REGISTRAR: I now pronounce you man and wife. You may kiss the bride.

GLORIA: I'd rather tongue the bridesmaid.

♀ LINDA: Oi, on your bike I'm not a dike!

LIVING ROOM

a party in full swing. suze and jez are dj-ing.

SUZE: This is MC Littlewoods sending out a special 78 to all you conjugal groovesters out there. This is my own personal remix of that horny haired pop minstral Prodigy and Edelweiss! Oh no it's not it's the Dooley's.

the dooleys comes on

♀ LINDA: You're right Vince, the camera loves me.

VINCE: I need to get a studio in London.

♀ LINDA: Oh I hope you've got all the right equipment.

VINCE: Just chop me off at the knees and call me tripod.

JEZ: Okay you crazy alleycats. It's time to chuck the bluebells. Wifey? Take it away!

GLORIA: Cut the wisecracks, big guy.

gloria prepares to throw her bouquet.

♀ LINDA: Watch how high I can bounce baby.

GLORIA: Okay I'm going to throw.

linda is desperate to catch it. so too is a drag queen tequila mockingbird.

♀ LINDA: Oh get out!

TEQUILA MOCKINGBIRD: Here's the number of my wig maker, you need it more than I do.

gloria throws the flowers. tequila and linda sramble around.

♀ LINDA: No, no it's my flat, it's my flat!

she swipes tequila's wig off and he runs out.

VINCE: You and I need to talk, I've got a proposition I want to make.

♀ LINDA: Oh I hope it's not risqué

TOM'S BEDROOM

tom finds degsy looking down

♂ TOM: You know if I was poor and working class I'd say penny for 'em.

DEGSY: Oh go back and enjoy the party.

♂ TOM: No, no, no, no. We can have our own little party right here. Degs do you remember this? (Dances for him) Walk up to the phone box, walk up to the phone box. Pick up the receiver. Pick up the receiver, Take the baby for a walk ... No? What's the matter. Degs. Desuree. Desdimona.

DEGSY: What?

♂ TOM: Listen you know what you should do? You should get married like me. It's bloody fantastic.

DEGSY: Tom I've got a confession to make.

♂ TOM: It was you who stole my spandex boob tube in 1982! Oh it's all right Degsy I forgive you.

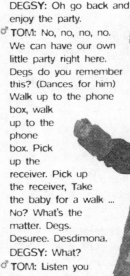

DEGSY: No I'm being serious.

TOM: Well who did bloody steal it then?

DEGSY: Tom!

TOM: What, what, what, what?

DEGSY: In the past few months, I've found myself growing very fond of someone.

TOM: Right, yeah.

DEGSY: Someone quite close to me.

TOM: Your mother?

DEGSY: Recently this fondness has developed into a physical attraction.

TOM: So it is your mother then?

DEGSY: Oh Tom please.

TOM: No sorry, no sorry, sorry.

DEGSY: I'm just afraid this will affect our friendship.

TOM: Well knock me down with a pretty big feather Degs. I mean who would have thought it? But it's all right you know. Tell me. Is this person you are thinking of sort of pretty devilishly fit?

DEGSY: Oh yes.

TOM: Oh yes and pretty devilishly horny too?

DEGSY: Oh God yes.

TOM: And pretty devilishly me! Eh Degs? Well that's allright! Why would it affect our relationship? Even if we ended up living together.

DEGSY: What?

TOM: Oh I like living with Linda, she's harmless enough I suppose. But then they said Chernobyl was harmless didn't they? No don't say any more, don't say any more. I must go back to the party, see you later.

linda runs in

LINDA: Guess what? Guess what? Guess what Vince wants me to do, guess! Guess! Go on, guess!

TOM: No I'd rather flick flack down Oxford Street in a string vest and plimsolls, come on let's get back to the party.

LINDA: No. Degsy. I might need your advice.

DEGSY: Oh ditch the perm love, it's not working.

LINDA: No on fashion tips.

TOM: Got a spare decade have you?

LINDA: Fashion for a big day. Come in you gorgeous hunk of manhood!

vince comes in.

LINDA: Now do to me in here what you did out there.

vince kneels.

TOM: No, no, no, no we're sensitive homosexuals, no.

LINDA: Now open your mouth.

TOM: No, no.

LINDA: Say it.

VINCE: Work for me Linda.

LINDA: Vince is doing a programme over here called Poor White Trash, Get It On.

VINCE: I'd love you to front it for me Linda, you're the epitome of sleaze and vulgarity. What's your answer?

LINDA: Well I shall keep that to myself for the time being as part of my feminine mystique. But I have to say in order for us to work well together as a team, we may have to sleep together.

VINCE: Really?

LINDA: Regularly.

VINCE: I'll give it my best goddam shot!

TOM: I've got very good news too. Come on, champagne, champagne!

HALLWAY

tom and linda skip down the hall.

LINDA: Oh ain't it great Tom? a career and a shag all rolled into one!

TOM: And Lindy, I also bring good tidings. My unrequited love for Degsy has been requited.

LINDA: Speak English!

TOM: He loves me!

they run off and party.

VINCE: How do I tell her I'm impotent?

DEGSY: How do I tell him I've gone straight?

JEZ
'Do you know Leatherhead?'
GLORIA
'Is it something to do with S & M?'

**AS INTERVIEWED BY PAT MAJAXI,
THE WELL KNOWN FEMINIST JOURNALIST**

FULL NAME:

Linda Lolita Lulu La Hughes, though when I was born I was called John coz I was born on a crate of John Player Specials down Smokers World on Romford Market. They only realised I was a girl when I was about eight. They entered me in a fancy dress competition up Butlins. I went as a flasher. I opened the front of me raincoat and Daddy turned to Mummy and went, 'Bloody hell, Doll, where's his winkle?' Oh, how we laughed!

AGE:

I is only about 28 or something. If I look older it's coz I had to look after Mummy a lot. She died of a broken heart the day my sister Sugar ran off with Shane Ritchie. I think she shoulda saved herself for his brother, Guy. Mummy took a lot of looking after coz she was the size of a house. But she had a heart the size of a block of flats.

EDUCATION:

Yeah, I've heard of that. It's great.

WELL, SCHOOLING THEN...

I was expelled from the Convent of Our Lady By The Zebra Crossing in East Ham for importuning a priest, whatever that means. I don't remember. I was out of my head on a forerunner to Pritt Stick at the time. I then attended the Eva Braun Borstal for Young Fallen Women in Bromley-by-Bow, where there were a lot of lezzers with smelly bras. I once did half a jigsaw of a cat licking a wine glass.

ROLE MODELS:

Obviously Princess Lady Diana of Hearts and me were very similar. I heard she could never keep a pickled egg down – I'm exactly the same. Beyoncé Knowles from Destiny's Child is like a coffee-coloured me. I identify a lot with black people

on account of the racism I attract on account of my red hair. I too is a minority group. Like puffs. Oh and Selina Dion, another singer. She is a lesson to all you ugly birds out there – it is possible to make it, but you will have to make do with an ugly git boyfriend what looks like your dad. I love ugly people. I like showing them that pretty girls can have a personality as well.

PIN UPS:

I used to like Liam Gallagher 'til he had all them kids. I'm sorry, but it would do my head in if I was performing a sexual act upon him and he had the baby alarm strapped to his belt. I then went onto Robbie Williams. But someone said he don't drink no more, and I can only get aroused if he smells of Brut 33 on his nipples and Woodpecker cider on his breath. I recently went onto Danny from Popstars. I think Elton John has got a cheek saying Danny looks like Shrek. Has he looked in the mirror lately? If I had a bad syrup and silly specs, I don't think I could show my face in public.

FAVOURITE TV PROGRAMME:

Through The Keyhole. If I was a lot older it would be hard to pass on David Frost. Whenever he looks into the camera I feel slightly abused, and I like that. The guests on this are always really, really intelligent – Lorraine Chase, Mark Curry. It can get a bit heavy though. It's like Newsnight in the afternoon.

FAVOURITE PERFUME:

A special fragrance called Poppers, that all those gayboys use in the clubs. They put it up their noses. I dab it behind me ears.

SERIES

We were fortunate enough to have series two commissioned by Jane Root, the new controller of BBC2, while we were filming series one. But we talked a lot about the first series, to see how we could make a second one better. The producers all felt that the show worked best when it was Linda and Tom on their own, with only minor interruptions from the supporting characters. Audience research seemed to point to this too, though when we came to film the second series audiences at the studio felt a bit cheated if Jez, Suze and Beryl weren't in the episode.

Another thing people seemed to like was the slapstick. Linda punching Tom every episode, that sort of thing. It was in this series that I started to play up Linda's stupidity even more. Kathy became tougher about not saying lines that were too clever for her. All in all, I think this made for a stronger second stab.

MILLENNIUM

An exercise in refining the characters of Linda and Tom. Getting a lot of their back story and letting them play around together. This episode felt like the show was finally hitting its stride. Another appearance by Sir Simon, and a fleeting glimpse of Melinda Messenger – who's no trouble! My friends Steven and George were very excited that they got a mention in this, though they were quite unimpressed that I described them as 'heroin addicts'. George said he really wanted to tell his mum, but thought that she might believe it was true. He went on to say, 'If only you'd said I was a coke addict, that would have made it so much easier.'

My favourite joke about the difference between a straight man and a bisexual man (six cans of lager) is in this episode. The old ones are always the best!

TWO

TEACHER'S PET

Miss Walls returns. And what do you know? Patsy Palmer in the flesh! My boyfriend's niece Laura was an extra in the theatre scene, and reported back that the other extras were insanely jealous that the camera seemed to be favouring her as they piled out of the show. They thought this constituted favouritism. It did.

How ironic that Elaine Lordan asks Tom what it's like in *EastEnders*. I like to think it helped her get the part of Lynne 'Brown Baps?' Slater.

STIFF

The inspiration for this episode was a review that *Time Out* had given the show. They said that Gimme was 'the best sitcom Joe Orton never wrote'. So I wondered what we could do that was suitably Ortonesque and I came up with the dead body in the coffin. This was the episode that provoked the most mirth in the rehearsal room. Kathy and James found it very hard to keep a straight face when Chris Simon was around. Many thanks to Rosalind Knight for so fearlessly stepping into that coffin.

PRISON VISITOR

Kathy suggested the storyline for this. Somehow I think she really enjoyed frolicking with Phil Daniels – as did James! I was chuffed to bits when, the day after this aired for the first time, I overheard a group of people in a motorway café discussing the bit where Linda sits on the rubber ring, and they were laughing so much they could hardly get their words out. Of course, when I told my partner to listen in they had changed the conversation and were talking about grouting. He still insists I made it up.

When the cat trainer was leaving with the cat at the end of the recording, she informed us all that 'He really enjoyed this job. He's had a great time on it.' That cat is a STAR!

SERIES TWO

DIRTY THIRTY

My abiding memory of this episode is that James Dreyfus was never happy with it. I don't think I've ever rewritten something so much in my whole life.

I was chuffed here to be working with Anna Keaveney (Sheila), whom I had idolised as a teenager when she played battleaxe Marie Jackson in Brookside. Marie Jackson was such a hardfaced cow that the biggest insult at our school was to say 'Yer ma's Marie!'

GLAD TO BE GAY?

James can't have been that keen on this one either – I overheard him in the bar after filming it saying 'Well that was the most abominable piece of crap I've ever been in in my entire life!' Oh, how we laughed!

The marvellous Moya Brady appeared in this as Linda's lezzie love interest. It was really just an excuse for a load of vile jokes about lesbians – rather like a lot of the series. But it was great that the biggest lesbophobe in the world ended up sleeping with a woman. Twice!

SOFA MAN

James liked this one, because he had an opportunity to do some clever ranting. I made an appearance as 'man on sofa' and did a Scottish accent. In fact the people in my flats all started looking at me sympathetically after this aired. They assumed I was a talentless actor who didn't get much work. They'd be right.

When Tom says, 'You're so far back in the closet you're in fucking Narnia!', my Mum said, 'You've used that before.' And indeed I have.

GIMME GIMME GIMME

Episode One
MILLENNIUM

dream sequence.

TRENDY LOFT PARTY

linda walking through a party having a great time. she bumps into melinda messenger.

MELINDA MESSENGER: Linda, hi.
♀ LINDA: Oh hi Mel.
MELINDA: I wish I could look as good as you in a frock like that.
♀ LINDA: Well wish on babe. See ya. Wouldn't want to be ya.

LINDA'S BEDROOM

linda lies sadly on the bed.

dream sequence.

PARLIAMENT HILL

tom sits looking out over the view of london with simon shepherd.

SIMON: It's beautiful isn't it?
♂ TOM: Oh yes, yes it is.
SIMON: I'm so sorry Tom.
♂ TOM: Why?
SIMON: I know we had the Peak Practice Reunion to go to but ever since our eyes met across the set of a crowded GP's surgery, you play dysentery brilliantly by the way. I just knew that I wanted to see the Millennium in here. With you.
♂ TOM: I know. Yeah, I know.

simon takes tom's hand.

TOM'S BEDROOM

tom holding his teddy bear's hand.

LIVING ROOM

linda helps herself to punch then pulls down the christmas tree.

♂ TOM: (Singing) Should old acquaintance be forgot. (Humming) Hey Lindy. (Pointing to her red top and orange hair) Red, orange, red orange. Love the look, love the look babe. (chucks a green hat on her) There we are. Traffic lights.
♀ LINDA: Oh shut up.
♂ TOM: Oh no! What's happened to poor Timothy tree?
♀ LINDA: Oh leave it. It'll have to come down soon anyway. It's bad luck otherwise.
♂ TOM: You don't believe in all that superstitious claptrap do you? God you're frighteningly working class.
♀ LINDA: It's true. My nana left her tree up for too long once, and the very next day she spontaneously human combusted.
♂ TOM: No you're lying.
♀ LINDA: It's true. All that was left of her was her little Chuff. Wandering around the lounge it was all lost and dribbling.
♂ TOM: Oh, oh, oh, oh. Stop it. Stop it.
♀ LINDA: No Chuff. It was her Jack Russell. Pass me a chocolate star fish off the tree.
♂ TOM: Excuse me, what's the magic word?
♀ LINDA: Twat.
♂ TOM: Thank you. Yes I did rather well with the tree this year didn't I? One used to get so excited in days of yore, when Mama would first dress the yuletide-esque branches. A tangerine here, a candle-ette there. The first glimpse of angel round my baubles.
♀ LINDA: We used to have a Tiny Tears Doll on the top of ours. All done up like an angel it was. Till mummy decided to get one of them ones that wet themselves.

She got drenched and the whole estate got short circuited.

TOM: Bet that made you popular.

LINDA: We were the victims of an hate campaign. Dog crap through the letterbox. Bricks through the window. It was even worse when they found out it was our fault. What's in this?

TOM: Well it's vodka, gin, brandy, lemonade and just a splash of coconut milk. Isn't it phenom? One should always have a welcoming tankard just in case any first footers pop by. What time are you going out to your party? You should be getting ready, have you seen the time?

LINDA: No Tameka phoned. She blew me out.

TOM: What over the phone? She must have a very long tongue.

LINDA: Do you know I think they must have got a puppy for Christmas. Because I could hear her fella shouting in the background I'm not having that dog back in my house, then she says 'Party's off.'

TOM: You're such a sad bitch. Hang on, hang on, hang on. Does that mean you're not going out? Why are you wearing more make-up than Scritty Politti?

LINDA: A lady should always look her best Thomas. Mummy used to wear so much mascara she had to throw her head back to get her eyes open.

TOM: I was really looking forward to having the flat all to myself tonight. Ring her back!

LINDA: No! It ain't my fault you ain't got no mates.

TOM: I've got a couple of pals coming down from my days at Wolverhampton Rep actually.

LINDA: Who?

TOM: Steven and George. We did a three handed Julius Caesar together.

LINDA: I don't want to know about your sexual conquests.

TOM: Oh shut up. Anyway they rang this afternoon, they said they were coming down. They were so chilled, they were like 'Hey Tom we're coming down. Hey Tom we're coming down bwoy!'

LINDA: Tom: they're smack heads, they're always coming down.

TOM: Well anyway, anyway I issued a smatter of invites. Tom Farrell at home. Green lettering, yellow background. Little tip I picked up from Princess Di's smiling butler. And now you're going to be here, damn you!

LINDA: Well I don't know why you're bothering. The Millennium's a bit like Steps. Over rated.

TOM: Excuse me but Steps are Abba for the nineties. Oh we can't say that anymore can we? What do we say now, what do we say? The zeros?

LINDA: Eh?

TOM: Well you know we had the eighties, we had the nineties and now we've got the zeros. Maybe it's the naughties.

LINDA: Here I've got a naughty nightie. Mummy gave it to me as a puberty present. Here.

TOM: What?

LINDA: I've done a seventy minus one in it.

TOM: Yeah welcome to the naughties. Yeah I like that, I like that.

LINDA: It didn't half chaff my neck though. You see the fella thought he was turning me on, whereas in fact he was strangling me. Bless him.

TOM: Linda if you insist on staying in tonight and ruining my Lesbian and Gay Pick and Mingle, may I make one tiny request please? Can we have a little bit less of the La Hughes family history please. To kill some time until my friends arrive, what's on television?

LINDA: I don't know I'm not psychic.

TOM: Well you're the one with the telly pages, not me.

LINDA: I'm only looking at the pictures, give me a break.

TOM: Well could you hazard a guess from the pictorial profferings please?

LINDA: Maureen from Driving School's on Question Time.

TOM: Oh don't be so ridic. That's absolutely ridic.

LINDA: No look there's a picture. It's that geezer from Question Time, three MPs and Maureen from Driving School.

TOM: It'll be Ann Widdicombe you ridiculous mule. What else is on? What else is on?

♀ LINDA: Fern Briton with an 'aggis. Here what do you have to do to be a television presenter?

♂ TOM: Well you've got to be attractive.

♀ LINDA: Right.

♂ TOM: You've got to sleep with loads of producers.

♀ LINDA: Really?

♂ TOM: Read autocue.

♀ LINDA: Ah no see I'm dyslexic.

♂ TOM: Thick.

♀ LINDA: Dyslexic.

♂ TOM: You are too working class to be dyslexic.

♀ LINDA: Owning class mate, me dad owns his own council house.

♂ TOM: Yeah, cut your veins open you'd have blue blood pumping away there wouldn't you?

♀ LINDA: Everyone knows blood's red. And you call me thick?

♂ TOM: Blue blood you daft trollop. As in the Royal Family.

♀ LINDA: Oh I hope they're not on tonight. Moaning northern ponces.

♂ TOM: Sorry?

♀ LINDA: You know that docusoap. You know the one where they all sit around talking about television and smoking. I mean how many people do you know who actually do that eh?

♂ TOM: What else is on?

♀ LINDA: Who Wants To Be A Millionaire. Oh what a rip off. Phone a friend? Phone a friend? What if you haven't got any friends?

♂ TOM: What are you getting so worked up about, you've never tried to go on it.

♀ LINDA: And the questions they ask, they're so bloody hard.

♂ TOM: No it's not it's all things like arrange these days in the order they come in, Monday, Thursday, Wednesday, Tuesday.

♀ LINDA: Yeah well we haven't all got a degree in date arranging have we?

♂ TOM: Get away from my punch. That's my punch, that's for my guests.

♀ LINDA: Don't be so selfish it's only a little drink. I'm glad I'm not selfish.

♂ TOM: Me selfish? Selfish? Selfish? Who did

the Christmas tree eh? Who dressed it mmm, mmm? Who made the Christmas dinner? Who made the Christmas punch? It didn't all just magically happen over night you know, the little Christmas fairy didn't jump down and do it.

♀ LINDA: Yes you did.

♂ TOM: Yeah that's right yeah. When in doubt resort to homophobia.

♀ LINDA: I ain't phobic about homos. I just can't stand the sight of them. Now get out of my way. I'm going to phone daddy. I'm going to leave him a message on his answer machine. (On phone) Hi daddy, it's Lindy Daddy. Happy New Year. Thank you for my computer. Love you lots. Linda.

She goes to sit down again and rearranges her pants.

♀ LINDA: Oh I've got something in my eye.

♂ TOM: You know sometimes you make me physically sick.

♀ LINDA: Funny enough daddy used to say that. He used to tie me to the roof rack of his car drive seventy miles an hour round the Isle of Dogs and say 'Linda La Hughes you make me physically sick' Bless him.

♂ TOM: And you wonder why he never answers the telephone?

♀ LINDA: How can he? He is in an iron lung.

♂ TOM: Yeah right.

♀ LINDA: Yeah right. You've seen the picture.

♂ TOM: I'm supposed to believe that that's an iron lung am I? (Gets photo)

♀ LINDA: Well what else would it be?

♂ TOM: It's a sideboard. How many iron lungs have you seen with a couple of drawers in them and a carriage clock on top?

♀ LINDA: Well Daddy's got a special one. He has. Why would he lie to me.

♂ TOM: So you won't go round and bore the liver out of him.

LINDA: Daddy loves me. (Exits)

LINDA'S BEDROOM

linda playing on a child's computer game.

COMPUTER: Press the letter K. Try again. Press the letter W. Try again. Press the letter L. This is the letter L, L.

TOM: Oh it's your new laptop. Oh. (Singing) Twinkle, twinkle little star, how I wonder what you are. High above....(Speaking) Oh right. I think my friends are still stuck in traffic or something.

LINDA: Yeah right.

TOM: What's happened to your posters of Liam?

LINDA: We're history. I could never bring up another bird's child. Me Aunty Dot did that. Only for six weeks then she had to give it back. I mean I said to her at the trial, you should have asked permission.

TOM: Do you want to play a game? Charades perhaps?

LINDA: What like Give Us A Clue?

TOM: Yes, just like Give Us A Clue, yes. I'll be Lionel Blair, you can be Liza Goddard.

LINDA: No I want to be Liza Tarbuck. Look at my hair.

TOM: Alright you're going to be Liza Tarbuck. What are you doing? What are you doing?

LINDA: I'm assembling my team.

TOM: Oh right.

LINDA: (Assembling dolls) That's Carol Jackson from EastEnders.

TOM: Welcome Carol.

LINDA: And that's Cerys from Catatonia. (Singing) It's all over the front page, you give me road rage.

TOM: Yes I get the picture, I get the picture.

LINDA: Carol you dirty bitch!

TOM: What are you doing now?

LINDA: Carol fancies you.

TOM: Oh shut up.

LINDA: I'm not asking him that.

TOM: What, what's she asking? What?

LINDA: Carol wants to know what colour are your undies?

TOM: Well they're sort of red, no, no, no when we're ready ladies please.

LINDA: Call me Liza.

TOM: Alright when we're ready Liza. It's a song okay? And it's two words and I'm going to do the second word. Okay? (Points to her)

LINDA: 'Pretty Woman.' My go.

TOM: No, no. Second word, right? (Does 'sounds like')

LINDA: Oh it's that deaf bird that plays the drums. Oh what's her name? Oh this is so hard.

TOM: No, no, no, no. Sounds like?

LINDA: No I don't know what she sounds like, I've never heard her.

TOM: Sounds like this. (Pulls her hair)

LINDA: Oi, watch it.

TOM: Well what is that?

LINDA: Perfect. 'Perfect Day.' (Singing) It's just a perfect day.

TOM: No, no, it's a curl.

LINDA: Curl.

TOM: It's a curl.

LINDA: Curly wurly.

TOM: It rhymes with curl.

LINDA: Curl, burl, big burl, big burls of fire.

TOM: It's girl. Girl you stupid bitch.

LINDA: Carol says she can see your thing.

TOM: Oh for goodness sake. All right so the second word is.

LINDA: Go on then.

TOM: The second word is girl.

LINDA: Girl Girl? I've never heard of it.

LINDA

'A lady should always look her best Thomas. Mummy used to wear so much mascara she had to throw her head back to get her eyes open.'

TOM: I haven't done the first word yet.

LINDA: You're just trying to confuse me.

TOM: First word, first word is. (Points to her bedspread)

LINDA: Eiderdown, Eiderdown Girl. I win, my go.

TOM: When have you ever heard of a song called Eiderdown Girl?

LINDA: Eiderdown Girl always living in an eiderdown world?

TOM: Sit down. Sit down. Look. (Runs his hands up his jeans)

LINDA: Stop turning yourself on.

TOM: What are my clothes made of?

LINDA: Something cheap?

TOM: Material!

LINDA: Denim!

TOM: No, no that's it. It's the Madonna song 'Material Girl'.

LINDA: Oh she is looking so rough isn't she? Well come on then.

TOM: I've just done it. It's the Madonna song, 'Material Girl.'

LINDA: Bloody hell you went round the houses a bit didn't you? Now it's my go.

TOM: It is such an effort to ever do anything with you, ever, ever.

LINDA: Right who's in your team?

TOM: I don't know, um this is Simon Shepherd and this is Michael Owen.

LINDA: No that's Robbie Williams.

TOM: All right it's Robbie Williams, get on with it.

LINDA: Right now Robbie might get this one.

TOM: Okay.

LINDA: Okay? It's a song.

TOM: Right.

LINDA: It's got, it's got one word. Here we go. (Sings) Millennium.

LIVING ROOM

linda and tom drinking more punch

LINDA: We should have taken in a show. I love a good play.

TOM: You? The last play you went to see was the Chippendales, which incidentally is not a play.

LINDA: It was in a theatre, it had an interval. I had ice cream.

TOM: Theatre should be exciting.

LINDA: I was stuck to my seat. It took three usherettes to prise me off.

TOM: I should go to the theatre more often you know. It's your fault I never go to the theatre. Always showing me up! Jumping onto the stage during Annie.

LINDA: I was born to play that part. (Singing) The sun will come out tomorrow.

TOM: Yes and when we went to see Cats, what did you shout to the lovely Elaine Paige? 'Show me your pussy. I'll show you mine.' And when we went to see Jesus Christ Superstar you ran around in the interval telling all the children. 'He dies in the end.'

LINDA: Oh stop shouting at me.

TOM: I'll shout at who I bloody well like.

LINDA: Sssh. I feel queasy I think that milk in my cup of tea this morning must have been off.

TOM: Just imagine, imagine, imagine all the families gathering together at this moment, all cracking open a bottle of port and ruminating.

LINDA: Oh don't be disgusting.

TOM: Will the Millennium bug really happen? Will computer systems crash all over the world? Imagine how we would have fared a thousand years ago. You'd probably have rickets.

LINDA: My auntie Shirl had them. Very bow legged she was. She couldn't stop a bull in an alleyway. She played cricket for East Ham Ladies you know. Here she put the ricket into cricket.

TOM: I'd have probably have been on first name terms with Oscar Wilde.

♀ LINDA: Do you know what, she used to sit me on her knee and I'd drop straight through to the floor. The amount of times I cracked my head open. Oh we didn't half laugh Tom.

♂ TOM: Actually it's highly probable I would have been going out with Oscar Wilde.

♀ LINDA: Who?

dream sequence

oscar wilde sits writing. tom comes in.

♂ TOM: I'm back dear Oscar. How's the er, how's the play coming along?
OSCAR: So, so Tommy. Not totally bonkers about the title though.

♂ TOM: Oh what's it called at the moment?
OSCAR: The Importance of Being A Snakeskin Handbag.

cut to linda dressed as lady bracknell.

♀ LADY LINDA BRACKNELL: A handbag?
OSCAR: Have you met old Lady Brackers?

♂ TOM: What the hell are you doing here? This is supposed to be my dream sequence.

♀ LADY LINDA BRACKNELL: Oh kindly piss off you old poof.

♂ TOM: Oscie, don't you think clutchbag would be more aujour d'hui? Most people have one. In Paris it's become quite de rigeur for even men to carry one. No clutchbag it ought to be.
OSCAR: Thomas you are so earnest. If only everyone in life was as earnest as you.

♂ TOM: Well why not call it that?
OSCAR: The Importance of Being An Earnest Clutchbag. It's genius. You are quite, quite the thing.

♀ LADY LINDA BRACKNELL: It'll never work.

LINDA'S BEDROOM

linda putting her coat on. tom comes in.

♂ TOM: Where are you going?
♀ LINDA: Church. Come on, a thing came through the door. Midnight communion, there'll be free wine.

♂ TOM: No, no, no I don't want to be religious. I mean what the hell has the year 2000 got to do with Jesus Christ?

♀ LINDA: Well Christmas is his birthday isn't it? He was born in a stable to save the world from sin. Yes there was cattle and a donkey and cake and everyone had a lovely time. Except Mary because she was knackered. I'll see you next century.

♂ TOM: No, no, no, no, no please don't leave me rattling around in this big house. I'm scared Lindy, I'm really scared. The bogey man will get me, the bogey man will get me. Please don't go. Please.

♀ LINDA: All right.
♂ TOM: Oh thanks.
♀ LINDA: Okay.
♂ TOM: Thanks.
♀ LINDA: I'll stay, it's probably freezing outside anyway.
♂ TOM: Yes it is.
♀ LINDA: I'd get nipples like chapel hat pegs.
♂ TOM: Here, here. Come and lie down with me on the bed here.
♀ LINDA: Eh?
♂ TOM: Come and lie down with me here. Here come and have some punch with me.
♀ LINDA: Yeah?
♂ TOM: Yeah come on, come on. Cheers.
♀ LINDA: Oh this is nice isn't it?
♂ TOM: Yeah it's great, yeah. I'm splattered.
♀ LINDA: Oh it's good for you though Tom, getting pissed. It's not so good when you piss the bed but it is good. Here I wish you weren't an homo.
♂ TOM: Do you?
♀ LINDA: Yeah.
♂ TOM: Do you want to know something?
♀ LINDA: What?
♂ TOM: I wish you were a bloke.
♀ LINDA: No. What's it like having a knob?

♂ TOM: It's great.

♀ LINDA: Yeah?

♂ TOM: Yeah.

♀ LINDA: Bet it gives you something to look at when you're bored don't it?

♂ TOM: It's bloody fantastic actually. Yeah.

♀ LINDA: It's quite nice having a patty though.

♂ TOM: A patty?

tom and linda on bed.

♀ LINDA: That's what mummy used to call it. I'd get up for school in the morning, right, she'd go 'You cleaned your teeth?' I'd go 'Yeah!', I hadn't. She'd go 'You washed behind your ears?' I'd go 'Yeah'. She'd go 'You washed your patty?' I used to laugh my head off when Patty Boulaye came on the telly.

♂ TOM: My mummy used to call mine my tail.

♀ LINDA: Oh that's a bit confusing isn't it? No wonder you get pleasure round the back. So how old were you when you had your first fumble?

♂ TOM: Er I don't recall.

♀ LINDA: Oh come on, everyone remembers their first time. Well except me I was off my head on vodka and glue. I only knew I'd done it because my brownie uniform was on back to front and I couldn't find my pants.

♂ TOM: How old were you?

♀ LINDA: Seventeen.

♂ TOM: What on earth were you still doing in the Brownies?

♀ LINDA: They kept putting me back a year didn't they? I think it was because there were quite a lot of dogs in our group and they wanted to keep me there to up the pretty stakes, do you know what I'm saying?

♂ TOM: That'll be it yes. Oh, oh, oh, I do remember my first kiss though.

♀ LINDA: Yeah?

♂ TOM: Yeah, yeah. It was in the school pantomime and I was playing the dame and I had this beautiful long blond wig and on the opening night there was a power cut and in the black out... Kevin Stamford grabbed me and snogged the face off me.

♀ LINDA: I've had my best sex in the dark. Well blokes prefer it that way don't they?

♂ TOM: All week I kept giving him embarrassed little smiles and he'd turn away. And then one lunch break he came and sat next to me and told me how during the school pantomime in the blackout he'd grabbed **Tracy Duggan** from Mr Taylor's class and snogged the face off her. He thought I was **Tracy**.

♀ LINDA: No?.

♂ TOM: Do you want to know the worst part?

♀ LINDA: Go on.

♂ TOM: He said she was a crap snog.

♀ LINDA: Oh dear. Here I had my first kiss when I was eight. Sampson his name was. I'd gone up the back field with my mate Patsy Clap and there was this horse there called Sampson. No, no Tom, Tom it was an accident. I yawned he licked.

tom runs out in horror slamming the door behind him. on the door there is a poster of a horse.

TOM
'You are too working class to be dyslexic!'

LIVING ROOM

tom helping himself to more punch. linda comes in.

♀ LINDA: So this bloke you snogged was he bi what's it. you know, bisexual?

♂ TOM: No.

♀ LINDA: Was he gay?

♂ TOM: No he was straight.

♀ LINDA: Well what's the difference between a bisexual man and a straight man?

♂ TOM: In my experience? About six cans of lager.

tom starts to cry.

♀ LINDA: Oi, oi, oi, oi, oi, oi. Don't you Gwynth Paltrow it with me mate.

♂ TOM: I'm just sick of it Linda.

♀ LINDA: What?

♂ TOM: Well everything, look at me.

GIMME GIMME GIMME 75

♀ LINDA: Which bit?

♂ TOM: Am I always destined to be the crap snog who gets a bloke by mistake hmm? I'm nearly thirty you know, I should be out there, I should be out there enjoying myself, not stuck in here with a horse kisser. Most people I know make bowls and punch and first footers drop by and drink it. They don't just polish it off themselves. All my friends are living together. They all have joint bank accounts, they all have rows, they kiss they make up. I can't even do that can I? No, because they'll always say 'Tom Farrell you're a crap snog.'

♀ LINDA: Oh will you shut up going on about being a crap kisser.

♂ TOM: Yeah well it's true isn't it?

linda grabs tom & kisses him passionately, afterwards.

♂ TOM: How was it then?

♀ LINDA: Crap. It's even worse than Samson.

♂ TOM: Shut up.

♀ LINDA: Oh you'd probably do it better with a bloke. I mean I did feel a slight bit of resistance but I always get that, that's just blokes isn't it?

♂ TOM: I really wanted tonight to be special, you know? I really thought that suddenly everything would slip into place. But it hasn't has it? No, no, no. Because tonight's like any other night. Another shitty night in an endless row of crappy shitty little nights.

♀ LINDA: They do say people kill themselves more at New Year.

♂ TOM: That's really cheered me up, thank you very much.

♀ LINDA: Well they used to say the world was round.

♂ TOM: Maybe I should shut the front door mmm? Looks a bit desperate doesn't it?

he hears people in the house behind partying.

♂ TOM: Oh stop enjoying yourselves!!

he falls into a chair. they both sit there miserable.

♀ LINDA: Here.

♂ TOM: What?

♀ LINDA: (Singing) The sun will come out tomorrow. Bet your bottom dollar that tomorrow there'll be sun. Just thinking about tomorrow. Clears away the cobwebs and the sorrow, till there's none.

♂ TOM: (Singing) When I'm stuck with a day that's grey and lonely I just stick out my chin and grin and say, oh …

they both pass out. some first footers can be heard off, singing.

FIRST FOOTERS: (Singing) Tomorrow, tomorrow, so you've…

cores of first footers enter singing.

FIRST FOOTERS: got to hang on till tomorrow. Come what may. Tomorrow, tomorrow I love you tomorrow, you're always a day away.

tom and linda are dead to the world.

LINDA
'What's the difference between a bisexual man and a straight man?'
TOM
'In my experience? About six cans of lager.'

Episode Two

TEACHERS PET

LIVING ROOM

Linda reading a magazine. tom comes in dressed as sushi.

♂ TOM: Oh huge great dangly scrotum sacks.

♀ LINDA: What?

♂ TOM: Well I've done it again haven't I, look.

♀ LINDA: What?

♂ TOM: Isn't it obvious?

♀ LINDA: No you'll have to tell me.

♂ TOM: I was so desperate to get home from that bloody place I came back without getting changed again.

♀ LINDA: Daddy used to wander about in some outrageous outfits. He was a teddy bear in the fifties.

♂ TOM: Yes I think you mean Teddy boy.

♀ LINDA: No teddy bear. Big red ribbon round his neck, fluffy brown all in one. Called himself Cuddles. Mind you that was shortly before he was sectioned.

♂ TOM: I wondered why people were staring at me on the tube. I thought they recognised me from EastEnders.

♀ LINDA: Tom you ain't been in EastEnders for six years. And even then all you did was buy a kagool from Bianca's Casuals.

♂ TOM: Yes and the bitch short changed me. I was very good in EastEnders though, wasn't I?

♀ LINDA: Well I missed you didn't I Tom? On account of the fact that I blinked.

♂ TOM: Oh we've got it on video somewhere.

♀ LINDA: Oh no, not again!

♂ TOM: Oh well can you blame me mmm? When I left drama school I had huge things planned for me. Not traipsing round Tesco's in a pair of gussetedly challenged tights promoting raw fish. I'm fed up with it, absolutely fed up with it.

♀ LINDA: (Looking at magazine)
Since when has my hair been brown? Oh no it's Catherine Zeta Jones. I thought I was looking in a mirror.

♂ TOM: I know what I'm going to do, I'm going to become a teacher. Yes I shall become a teacher of thespians.

♀ LINDA: It turns my stomach.

♂ TOM: Sssh, it's an excellent idea. Every day I shall hold acting classes in this very through lounge. Voice work, movement, dialect. Bit of mime, all will be mastered by tomorrow's Emma Thompsons, the day after that Robert Carlyles and the day after that Letitia Deans.

♀ LINDA: I ain't having her in here, she gets on my tits.

♂ TOM: Yes I must away to find my calligraphy biro. Methinks I'll advertise with a small sign in the newsagents window. Yes anon, fair titian temptress the muse awaits.

♀ LINDA: Oi Gobshite, I am not having my gorgeous flat turned into no bloody poxy fame school. I don't want to get up in the morning and find fifteen anorexics chucking up in my loo.

♂ TOM: Actors don't do that. They mill around with perfect posture uttering inspirational nuggets like "Do you know? This is the only job where you actually get paid for doing something you love!"

♀ LINDA: Well that's bollocks. What about prostitutes? No Tom I won't allow it.

♂ TOM: Oh come on I'll give you a cut of the profits.

♀ LINDA: Well what are you waiting for then? Oh my God! Look, look it's Sugar, do you remember my sister from the last series? Look, look.

TOM: Oh what's she doing? Getting her tits out for Mencap again?

LINDA: No it's one of them At Home With The Stars things. Oh look at her lavatory pelmet. Oh and look, look at her windows. She ain't got no nets up. So common!.

TOM: Here let me see that, let me see that. 'Former Eurovision chart topper and page three icon Sugar Walls invites us to share her beauty tips and her joy at making her West End stage debut in Toothache'. What the bloody hell's Toothache?

LINDA: Is it when this hurts? (Touches head)

TOM: Remove this odious rag before me before I vomit all over my sushi. (Exits)

LINDA: Tosser!

FRONT DOOR

tom comes out and finds sugar about to ring the doorbell.

TOM: Sugar!
SUGAR: Where is she?
TOM: If you mean your sister, she's inside.
SUGAR: Oh what for this time?
TOM: No she's in the house.
SUGAR: Oh.

tom lets her in, then follows her in himself.

LIVING ROOM

sugar and linda having tea. tom sneering at them from his chair.

TOM: You, what's Toothache?
LINDA: Here do you remember this cosey Sugar? Mummy made it. She could bang out fifty a day when she was in the nick.
TOM: Come on, come on, what is Toothache?
SUGAR: Well ain't you heard of it Tom?
TOM: No.
SUGAR: It's the new Ben Elton play.
LINDA: Sugar, Sugar? Oh I'm a poet and I don't know. It.
SUGAR: Anyway Ben Elton, can you believe it?
LINDA: I know isn't it great? Is he famous?

SUGAR: Oh Linda, you really make me laugh.
LINDA: That's because I'm naturally funny. Do you know sometimes I walk down the street and people just burst out laughing. Here Marilyn Monroe was the same. Only she was a bit bigger round the hip. Fat cow.
SUGAR: I mean I ain't read all the script but it is great. He's bringing it out as a play, a film, a book, a drama series, a sitcom and a dance routine, all at the same time. So the exposure is going to be immense.
LINDA: Do you know I always thought it would be me that would end up on the boards. I can still get my leg around my neck with a bottle of tequila inside me.
SUGAR: So can I.
TOM: So can I. I can get both legs up if it's a really big bottle. So anyway how did an ex page three bimbo get mixed up in this creme brule-ish mess of a wannabe theatrical nightmare?
SUGAR: Well I met the director up the Groucho Club and he got all political on me.
LINDA: (Like a football chant) Boring! Boring!
SUGAR: Said he could see I was a feminist because I was the only bird who left my pants on in 'Loaded'.
LINDA: Oh do you remember them photographs Uncle Ernie took of me in my nappy? Clicking away for hours he was.
TOM: So Mrs Equity talk me through your character.
SUGAR: Oh I play Vilma a hick from the sticks who roams the countryside with her lesbian lover. I mean I don't know whose playing her yet but Denise Van Outen's been fingered.
LINDA: Nice.
SUGAR: I've got to do three lesbian sex scenes. It's Ben's most political show to date.
LINDA: You know what though Sugar, Mummy would have been so proud of you. Your name up in lights. It's a shame you can't ring dead people isn't it? But I suppose the only problem is though Sugar you can't act.
SUGAR: I was in the school nativity play. Played the Archangel Gabriel.

LINDA: Yeah but you kept getting your line wrong. You named the baby Judith.

SUGAR: Well I can't remember everything.

TOM: You're so unprofessional.

LINDA: Here I've had a thought. (Winks at Tom)

TOM: What are you doing?

LINDA: You want Toothache to be a big success don't you? (Winks again)

SUGAR: Well of course.

TOM: Why are you winking at me like?

LINDA: You don't want to be a show up do you Shugs? (Winks once more)

SUGAR: No.

TOM: Stop it! Stop that!

LINDA: Well do you know what I'd get if I were you?

SUGAR: Surgery?

LINDA: No a drama coach. Now do you see why I was winking?

TOM: Oh yes, yes. So Sugar did you know that I was a fully experienced drama teacher.

LINDA: Yeah and I bet you'd be willing to pay.

SUGAR: Of course. I'm loaded.

TOM: When can you start?

LINDA: Start now Sugar, go on start now, start now!

SUGAR: Oh sod it why not? I was only having my bikini line tinted later. I can phone and cancel.

LIVING ROOM,
TEN MINUTES LATER

tom taking his first acting class. sugar starts taking her trousers off.

TOM: All right let's start with a little warm

up shall we? Hands and legs are shaking. Come on then, hey, hey, hey, hey, hey what are you doing? What are you doing?

SUGAR: Well the director always makes us get naked for the warm up.

TOM: No thank you. No, no panties on please. And Linda you're not included.

LINDA: Oh why can't I take mine off?

TOM: No in the class, in the class, you're not included. Right we are going to start by pretending to be a set of bagpipes.

LIVNG ROOM, LATER

tom and sugar are doing lip exercises in the corner. jez and suze sit at the table with linda. on the table sits a big doll.

JEZ: So you see we're trying for a baby.

LINDA: What one that looks like that?

SUZE: Not quite, you see ours will probably be mixed race.

JEZ: Actually it's a pretty safe bet really.

LINDA: Really?

SUZE: And to test our appropriateness for parenthood we're caring for Petula here for a week.

JEZ: You see the thing is we have an appointment with our bank manager this afternoon and if we really did have a baby we'd have to arrange child care facilities.

SUZE: We phoned round all the local nurseries and none of them are prepared to take a life-size doll.

TOM: Oh that's astonishing.

JEZ: Isn't it? So we wondered whether you would mind, minding her? A bit of a pun there.

LINDA: I love a bit of punnilingus on a Wednesday afternoon.

TOM: I'm afraid that's quite impossible, I'm leading a drama workshop and I shall be tied up pretty much all day.

LINDA: Yes and I'm observing.

SUZE: Well we will of course pay the going baby-sitting rate.

LINDA: I'll do it.

SUZE: Right now she'll need to take some air at some point, but her nappy shouldn't

LINDA

'I always thought it would be me that would end up on the boards. I can still get my leg around my neck with a bottle of tequila inside me.'

need changing until we get back. So happy baby-sitting.

♀ LINDA: Oi, oi, oi. Cash up front, that's how they do it nowadays and it's a tenner an hour. Wop it on the table.

LIVING ROOM, LATER

tom and sugar have scripts. linda is watching eating crisps.

♂ TOM: Okay hush up class, hush up. Now this is taken from a light romantic comedy I wrote. Um, that is set in an abortion clinic. So from my piece 'Forget me not Foetus' I'd like you to read Agamemnon's speech. Now Agamemnon is a seventeen-year-old smack addict from small town Scotland, all right?

SUGAR: (Reads) Och aye da noo sweet Jimminy.

♀ LINDA: Oh that's brilliant. No that is, you sound just like Lulu.

♂ TOM: Just be quiet.

SUGAR: A million tales of woe have I tae tell you.

♀ LINDA: Oh it's so sad.

SUGAR: Och aye da no sweet Jimminy, and she takes the razor blade and slowly slashes her wrists.

♂ TOM: No, no, no, no. Those are the stage directions. Don't read the stage directions.

♀ LINDA: She can read them if she wants. She can read whatever she likes.

♂ TOM: Look who's directing this scene, me or you? Me, so shut up. Okay Sugar my lovely, what say we try getting it on it's feet.

SUGAR: Which means?

♂ TOM: Just stand up, get up. All right, now

remember you've just slashed your wrists so there's blood seeping all over the place.

SUGAR: Cor you've got to remember a lot of things at the same time in acting haven't you?

♂ TOM: Yes you do. Right, so from the top. And action.

SUGAR: Me arrrrms, me arrrms. Me arrrrms is seeping bloodiness all over. If they find me a here it'll be up to the gallows for me hen.

♂ TOM: Stop, stop. What are you doing? What are you doing down there?

linda is patting the floor.

♀ LINDA: I'm the cleaner. I'm mopping up all the blood.

♂ TOM: Sit down. Now Sugar, that was very good, but I want you to give me a little bit more pain alright? So think of something that has caused you great pain in your life, hold on to it then try the speech again, okay take a moment to yourself, take a moment.

sugar thinks then places her hand on linda's head.

♂ TOM: Not quite what I meant, never mind, never mind. Okay right so, you're at the top of the bill on the London Palladium right, so play it to the back row! Action!!

SUGAR: Me arrrrrrrrms! Me arrrrrrrrms!

♀ LINDA: Oh she's like a young Nanette Newman.

SUGAR: Linda.

♀ LINDA: We washed this many dishes in ordinary liquid (Yells) but this much in fairy liquid!

SUGAR: Will you get her out of here please, she's doing my head in.

♀ LINDA: I can't even be nice to my own sister, blimey!

SUGAR: Oh she was like this as a kid, she never knew when to shut up. We had to stick her in a kennel from the age of eight just so we could get some bloody sleep.

♀ LINDA: You make me sound abnormal.

♂ TOM: Look are we going to do some acting or not?

♀ LINDA: It was lovely my kennel, I had a **TV** in there.

SUGAR: Maybe this wasn't such a great idea Tom.

♂ TOM: No, no, no this is a fantastic idea. Linda! Get out.

♀ LINDA: Oh I'm going. This is boring anyway. I'm going to go and see some of my mates. Here I've got loads of mates these days.

♂ TOM: And take Petula with you.

♀ LINDA: Piss off. What do you think I am a mug?

♂ TOM: If you don't take care of it, and if you kill their dolly they'll never be able to have children.

♀ LINDA: Good.

SUGAR: Oh go on Lind you'll be great with that dolly, one day you're going to be a brilliant mother.

♀ LINDA: All right then.

STREET

linda pushing petula along in a pram.

♀ LINDA: Come on sweetheart. Little baby girl. Going for walkies.

a mother with toddlers pass. they laugh at linda.

♀ LINDA: I'm only looking after it. Jesus.

GARDEN WALL

linda sits on a garden wall, smoking a cigarette, the doll in her arms. a social worker approaches.

SOCIAL WORKER: Hi I'm a social worker. What's your name?

♀ LINDA: Linda.

SOCIAL WORKER: Is this your friend?

♀ LINDA: No it's a doll.

SOCIAL WORKER: I can get you into a halfway house by nightfall.

♀ LINDA: Piss off.

linda storms off down the street.

SOCIAL WORKER: Bloody care in the community!

STREET

linda pushes the pram. the doll is under her jacket and she whacks it. two horrified posh women pass.

♀ LINDA: Bitch. Showing me up like that.

CONCERNED WOMAN: What do you think you're doing? I'm going to report you to the NSPCC.

♀ LINDA: Oh shut up, it ain't alive. Now don't explode. Linda loves you. You little bitch.

LIVING ROOM

sugar sits with books tied to her head. tom looks at her oddly.

♂ TOM: How are we going to solve this little conundrum I wonder? Can you fit three fingers inside you?

she places three fingers in her mouth.

♂ TOM: Yes you can, ease them out gently, that's good. Now try the sentence once more.

SUGAR: Tom tell me about your time on EastEnders. Is that right?

♂ TOM: Yeah it's very good, very good, very good.

SUGAR: Is it hard work doing a soap?

♂ TOM: And the miners think they've got it bad. At least they're underground, I was out in that market in all weathers.

SUGAR: Who were the majority of your scenes with?

linda enters.

♀ LINDA: He was only in one. Ha, ha I've got sweets!

♂ TOM: My scene was with Dame Patsy Palmer. Yes she was very impressed with me, very impressed. She looked me right in the eye and she said, 'Tom I'll never forget your genius as long as I live. Next to you I am but nothing.'

SUGAR: That's amazing.

♀ LINDA: Oh listen to you speaking all posh. The only plum that's been in your mouth was Shane Ritchie's.

♂ TOM: Anyway Sugar would you like to come to the theatre with me tonight just to see how the professionals do it?

SUGAR: Blinding guv'nor.

♂ TOM: I hear Macbeth is in town. Shall I book some tickets?

SUGAR: I'll get my credit card.

♀ LINDA: Great I'll get my face on.

linda hurries out.

LIVING ROOM, LATER

linda talking to petula drunk.

♀ LINDA: See they wanted me to go with them alright, but when they phoned the theatre there was only two seats left. So I mean what can you do? Oh but it ain't half great having her back in my life though. Yeah, oh little top up baby? Go on get that down your mush. You're drunk.

suze shouts through from the hall.

SUZE: (OOV) Linda we want Petula back!

♀ LINDA: No you can't have her, she's asleep.

JEZ: (OOV) Linda please!

♀ LINDA: No you can have her back in the morning. She's my mate.

THEATRE BAR

tom and sugar coming out in the interval.

SUGAR: Oh I love that Lady thingamebob. Oh she's got a heart of gold.

♂ TOM: It's Macbeth.

SUGAR: Oh yeah.

♂ TOM: This is another very important lesson that you have to learn. It's very bad luck to say Macbeth in the theatre.

SUGAR: Well they're all saying it on stage. Oi anyway I'm going to shake my lettuce. Shout us up a bacardi.

tom goes to the bar. he can't believe his eyes. here is none other than patsy palmer.

♂ TOM: Miss Palmer? Miss Palmer?

PATSY: What?

♂ TOM: It's me, it's Tom. Tom Farrell. Do you remember? I was playing the third market stall browser on the left. I was in combats, you remember me now?

PATSY: No.

♂ TOM: 'Way hay lass. That's a classy kagool!' That was my line. 'Way hay lass, that's a...' (Fingers her top)

PATSY: Get off me.

♂ TOM: You're very good you know. You're very very good. Where did you learn to cry like that? And shout! Because you could shout for Walford you know. Oi Rickaeee! Oi, Rickaee!! Rickaeeeeee!!!!!!

she decks him.

PATSY: Piss off!

sugar returns from the toilet.

PATSY: Sugar!

SUGAR: Oh hi Pats. Oh I didn't expect to see you here. How's your piles?

PATSY: Oh don't. Why don't you come and sit in my box? We've got a spare seat!

SUGAR: Oh brilliant. Tom I'm going to sit with Patsy I'll see you tomorrow.

PATSY: What do you think of the show?

SUGAR: Oh I think it's hilarious.

they walk off, leaving tom in agony on the ground.

LIVING ROOM

linda with doll. linda reading a story to petula. tom comes in from the theatre and gets a glass of water.

♀ LINDA: And she rams this porridge all down her filthy neck, right. And then the three bears come back. And the mummy goes, 'Oi what do you think you're doing? Get out of my house or I'll have the old bill on you.' And Goldilocks is like, 'Do I look scared?'

♂ TOM: No, don't, don't pollute that young child's mind with your oral dirt.

♀ LINDA: Where's Sugar?

♂ TOM: She'll be back for classes in the morning. I think. No more stories. Night then.

♀ LINDA: Night. Oh I wanted her to come back here. Oh never mind pet, she'll be back in the morning. Yes. So once upon a time there was this filthy bitch called Snow White. And she was shagging these seven dwarves, I know it's rotten isn't it?

LIVING ROOM, THE NEXT MORNING

linda comes in to find tom reading the papers.

♀ LINDA: Morning

♂ TOM: Oh good morning.

♀ LINDA: Where's Sugar?

♂ TOM: She'll be here soon. Look, look. I'm all over the papers. Look! (Reads) Sugar Walls and her acting coach Tom Farrell stepped out in style last night when they attended a performance of Macbeth in London's glitzy West End. See? I couldn't have asked for better publicity for my drama school.

♀ LINDA: Oh she scrubs up well our Sugar, doesn't she? Oh my God who's that gorgeous creature? Oh my God it's me. I'm in the papers. What does it say? What does it say? We can revel.

♂ TOM: Reveal.

♀ LINDA: Reveal that this is Sugar Walls's beautiful sister. Ain't it the truth!!

♂ TOM: No it doesn't say beautiful.

♀ LINDA: No?

♂ TOM: No it says backward.

♀ LINDA: What?

♂ TOM: We can reveal that this is Sugar Walls's backward sister. While Sugar lives the high life and earns thousands through personal appearances and showbiz marvellousness, disowned, penniless Linda

TOM

'If we are quick I can stop at the garage and grease up my slacks.'

lives off state benefits in Kentish Town with only a dolly as her best friend.

♀ LINDA: I knew I shouldn't have hung around with that.

the doorbell rings linda turns on the doll.

♀ LINDA: You little cow. You wait, wait till Sugar gets here, she'll tell them I'm not backward. The bastards. They're picking on me Tom because I'm unique. You see this face mate, it's a curse. That'll be her, that'll be Sugar. You wait she'll tell them what I'm really like.

SHARED HALLWAY

linda comes out. suze and jez are there with a tabloid.

SUZE: How do you explain this?

JEZ: Dragging our daughter through the gutter press.

SUZE: What have you done with her?

♀ LINDA: That slut of a daughter is more trouble than she's worth. Now open the door it'll be Sugar.

SUZE: If you've laid a finger on her.

♀ LINDA: It's a doll. Sugar!

SUZE: Right I'm calling the police. This is kidnap.

FRONT DOOR

sugar addressing the press on the doorstep. linda listening in the hallway.

SUGAR: How many more times do you need telling? I'm here for my acting class. That ugly pig person in the papers is not my sister. I don't have a sister and if any of you had bothered to read my biography, Top Shelf, you'd know that I'm an only child orphan.

she enters and sees linda.

♀ LINDA: My bedroom, five seconds.

LINDA'S BEDROOM

linda and sugar come in.

♀ LINDA: Do you remember when we were little when we used to play Charlie's Angels? Me you and Tracy Boyle? Do you remember Tracy Boyle? She lived above the chippy only had the one arm.

SUGAR: Of course I do, she always stank of vinegar.

♀ LINDA: Oh you do remember her? But you don't remember me, your own flesh and blood.

SUGAR: Actually I'm wrong, it was you who stank of vinegar.

♀ LINDA: You just can't help yourself can you?

SUGAR: What?

♀ LINDA: You've always been jealous of me. Well I am sorry I have got the body of an angel. I am sorry I am this popular. I am sorry I'm doing all right for myself. Fate smiled down on me and made me perfect and I'm sorry.

SUGAR: Linda I don't know what you see when you look in the mirror. But it ain't what the rest of the world sees. Now I'm late for my acting class.

♀ LINDA: It's cancelled.

SUGAR: Right well I'll just go shall I?

♀ LINDA: I think it's wise. And just remember I might be five years younger than you.

SUGAR: Older.

♀ LINDA: But you will never escape from me. Do you know why? We're the double of each other. Folk have always said it, we could swap heads.

sugar leaves. linda has a moment of doubt. she looks at herself in the mirror.

♀ LINDA: I'm fine.

LIVING ROOM LATER

tom and linda.

♂ TOM: So it's back to sushi promotion. Oh brilliant. This is all your fault Linda La Hughes.

♀ LINDA: Don't have a go at me. I'm the monkey not the organ donor.

♂ TOM: The inconsiderate little floozy. Why didn't she at least pay me. What a bitch!

♀ LINDA: I know. I wouldn't piss on her if she was on fire. I'd get my bellows out and I'd stoke her up good and proper. Burn bitch burn!

♂ TOM: Burn, fork her, fork her!

♀ LINDA: Stick a match up her arse and light it!

the phone rings.

♂ TOM: Pick that up.

♀ LINDA: You pick it up.

♂ TOM: I'm in distress.

♀ LINDA: I'm in this dress!

♂ TOM: Oh what's the point.

norma leaves a message.

NORMA: (VO) Hi Tom, Norma here.

♂ TOM: Oh great it's my agent. Bugger off!

NORMA'S OFFICE

norma on the phone to tom.

NORMA: Good news darling, you've been offered a job. It's to play the part of Gus the petrol pump attendant in Ben Elton's new piece, Toothache. It's West End, it's five grand a week and you don't even need to audition. Call the office for more details, Ciao darling.

LIVING ROOM

tom and linda shellshocked.

♂ TOM: Sugar must have put in a good word for me. Oh good old Sugar Lump. Oh I've always loved that girl.

♀ LINDA: She's great. She's like a sister to me.

♂ TOM: Insisting that I take the part of Gus. Gus the petrol pump attendant.

♀ LINDA: I can just picture you on stage with your nozzle in your hand, for all the world to see. Oh and I bet you'll look gorgeous in a greasy pair of overalls.

♂ TOM: I've got some somewhere, shall I put them on now? Oh I can't believe it's finally happening, I'm going to be a star.

♀ LINDA: Don't my mascara will run. Who's a clever boy then? Come here.

they hug.

♂ TOM: I am Lindy. Oh I want to go and put on some overalls right now. Oh what am I talking about? In a week's time I'll be on five thousand pounds and I can buy all the overalls I want. Oh precious child. You'll be a kept woman, what do you say to that?

♀ LINDA: Mine's a Tia Maria and coke!

♂ TOM: If we're quick I can stop at the garage and I can grease up my slacks.

they hurry out. the phone rings again.

NORMA'S OFFICE

norma on the phone.

NORMA: Hello Tom, Norma here, listen darling ignore that last message, I've really ballsed things up. It wasn't you they wanted after all. You see I thought they said Tom Farrell but in fact it was Tom Marrow the stand up comic who's really big in fresh produce. Well I thought it was strange that they wanted you. Ciao darling.

LIVING ROOM

petula rattles then explodes.

Episode Three
STIFF

SHARED HALLWAY

tom coming in followed by linda. their front door is wide open.

♂ TOM: Oh get a move on for goodness sake you galumphing great gibbon. I don't hold this door open as a hobby you know.

♀ LINDA: All right, hold your horses, what's the hurry?

♂ TOM: There were two nuns in a phone box out on the street.

♀ LINDA: I know. Lezbos.

♂ TOM: Oh shut up you stupid horse. You know very well that nuns in the street means bad luck. Now give me the keys.

he sees the open door.

♂ TOM: Oh my God, Lindy look, look, look! We've been burgled. Oh my God I'm having a panic attack!

♀ LINDA: Calm down, I probably forgot to lock the door on my way out. Now come on my fish pie's thawing.

jez comes down the stairs.

♂ TOM: Jez, Jez, Jez!

JEZ: Hi neighbs.

♂ TOM: Have you heard any strange sounds coming from our flat?

JEZ: Well I did hear a certain amount of humping around. Just thought you two had finally got it together. Mind you I've been taking Viagra so it is possible that I'm hallucinating. Oh my God I am, the blouse it's freaking me out.

♀ LINDA: (Sings) Freak out! Le freak, c'est chic!

LIVING ROOM

linda comes in and finds a coffin in the middle of the room.

♂ TOM: (Off) The bedrooms are okay, how's the lounge diner?

♀ LINDA: It's fine apart from the dirty great big coffin in the middle of the room. I wonder who left that there.

tom comes in.

♂ TOM: What? My God. It's those nuns. Every time I see nuns this happens. God it's those nuns, it's those nuns, it's those nuns, it's those nuns!

♀ LINDA: It's only a coffin.

♂ TOM: God, you're very eerily at ease around death aren't you Lindy? What's that all about? Oh I know it's because you saw your mother isn't it? Yeah, right, right.

♀ LINDA: It was very distressing actually. She wanted to be buried to Elvis, you know the music. Only the funeral director got it wrong, buried her as Elvis. Put her in his Las Vegas gear you know, big quiff, the shades. Even got the pout.

♂ TOM: Well we're going to have to look aren't we? We're going to have to look. Right okay. I don't think that I can, I don't think that I can, I don't think that I...

♀ LINDA: Calm down Tom, now you'll be all right with me, hold my hand.

♂ TOM: Okay. Oh what are you going to do with it?

♀ LINDA: Look Tom when you die it's just like slipping into another room.

♂ TOM: Is it?

♀ LINDA: Yes, another room, where you are dead. Now come on.

♂ TOM: Oh God I just remembered something.

♀ LINDA: What?

♂ TOM: We forgot to buy Pringles. Oh, oh look it's a woman, look at the shoes. I wonder who it is? I wonder who it is?

♀ LINDA: Eddie Izzard?

  GIMME GIMME GIMME

TOM: If Eddie Izzard was dead which I very much doubt, what would he be doing laid out in our living room?

LINDA: Well he's quite surreal.

TOM: Move the hanky off her face.

LINDA: Here. I shall call upon my spirit guide Madame Cholet to aid me in this revelation. I will let her hands guide my hands. Oh. (She pulls off the cloth) Well bugger me in Burnley it's Beryl our landlady.

TOM: I wondered why there were cobwebs on her catflap.

LINDA: Here, she looks great don't she?

TOM: Yeah.

LINDA: That make up's fab.

TOM: Very good. They're experts. Done years on television, retirement comes and they all go and do corpses. You're probably looking at the handiwork of the chief make up designer on A Passage to India.

LINDA: Here I wonder how she, I wonder how she, went.

TOM: Well far be it for me to cast aspersions but she did have a lot of sexual partners. She's been down that clap clinic that often she's got a strain of gonorrhoea named after her. Maybe it was clap that took her.

LINDA: No the clap's really painful. She looks dead happy.

TOM: Well I've seen her happier.

LINDA: Here when Lady Di died they had a book of condolence down the Happy Shopper.

TOM: No I don't think it would be appropriate. She used to shoplift there. Probably got a packet of giblets tucked down her blouse as we speak.

LINDA: Here let's say something nice about her.

TOM: Shall we? Oh that's uncharacteristically lovely of you. Pray do.

LINDA: Up in heaven a star is shining down on earth my heart is whining. Save a place at Jesus' table I'll be with you when I'm able.

TOM: Where did that come from? I feel quite nauseous now.

LINDA: Mummy's wreath. A jar of Valium made out of midnight roses, I had somebody write that on the card.

TOM: Do you know I could murder a brandy now.

LINDA: Wet the baby's head? Good idea.

TOM: God I feel so numb. People say that don't they? They say 'I've just heard that so and so's died and I just went completely numb.' Must hold on to this feeling. Never know when I might be called upon to use it in say an episode of Midsummer Murders or something. I'm a geography teacher in specs and we're on a camping trip and one of my students has just slipped down a crevice and I get a visit from Bergerac and he says 'It's bad news I'm afraid. Demi's dead.' And I say, 'Oh I feel so numb.' Good isn't it?

LINDA: Yeah it's great. Shock's a funny thing you know. When mummy died, daddy was found in a skip with a pair of her pants on his face singing 'I Who Have Nothing'. He brought shame to the family.

TOM: What I want to know is why?

LINDA: Well he was tone deaf.

TOM: No, no, no why?

LINDA: Well I don't know. Here.

TOM: What?

LINDA: I'm going to touch her.

TOM: Are you? Are you? Okay that's very brave of you, courage mon petit courage. Go on go ahead. You're very fearless you're an inspiration.

as she puts her hand into the coffin, the doorbell rings. linda gasps.

LINDA: She's alarmed!

TOM: That's the doorbell you stupid great oaf. Maybe it's someone who can throw some light on this situation. Go and see who it is, go on.

linda exits. tom works up the courage to touch the corpse. he puts his hand into the coffin, then quickly grabs it back.

♂ TOM: Oh, oh God I'm sorry I meant to touch your hand. I'm sorry. You know that I'm gay though anyway don't you? You can't forget that just because you're dead. I'm gay all right. I'm gay? Okay?

bob hobbs funeral director has come in and overheard this.

BOB HOBBS: Save your breath man, it's too late to come out to her now.

♀ LINDA: Thomas this is the funeral director.

♂ TOM: Oh hello.

BOB: Bob Hobbs. Sorry we have to meet under such circumstances. It's far nicer to meet in holiday destinations or public houses don't you agree?

♀ LINDA: Discos?

BOB: I prefer Pringles.

♂ TOM: We forgot to buy any. Oh I'm sorry we're all a little bit shellshocked now. Do have a seat.

BOB: Yeah the death of a loved one can be quite traumatic apparently. Grown men weep, Dwarves collapse.

♀ LINDA: I'm sorry if we seem a little distracted Mr Hobbs, we had no idea that she'd died.

BOB: I'm surprised the coffin wasn't a give away. Anyway I was just passing I thought I'd pop by and see everything was in order with, damn what was her name?

TOM/LINDA: Beryl.

BOB: I've had a lot on my mind lately.

♀ LINDA: Would a drop of brandy help?

BOB: It's far too late for that.

♂ TOM: So when's the funeral? I mean I'm assuming there is going to be a funeral. I mean we can't just have this knocking about like some embarrassing old heirloom. It'll be Aunty Leonie's lava lamp all over again.

BOB: You mean you don't know when the funeral is?

♂ TOM: No.

BOB: I can't tell you how encouraging it is to meet people as forgetful as myself.

♂ TOM: No, no, no not forgetful, we just don't know why she's here.

BOB: Oh, oh I see, I've left all the paperwork in the Volkswagon Camper. I use it as a...

♀ LINDA: Hearse?

BOB: Do I? That's outrageous. No, no runaround, yeah use it as a runaround. Yeah we toyed with the idea of downsizing the hearses but the camper van was seen as a little tacky. The wife's got a couple of stickers up in the back window boasting of certain beauty spots we've visited over the years. I mean who wants to be reminding of the Gaping Gill when you're burying your mother? Or the log flumes at Alton Towers.

♂ TOM: But why have you laid her out, why downstairs?

BOB: We always lay the body out downstairs. The punters seem to like it. I mean who wants a stiff in the bedroom?

♂ TOM: I mean how did you get in? I mean we didn't let you in, we've been out all day we come back to this, it's all rather bizarre isn't it? It's like some crazy TV show set up.

BOB: That's because it is, Smile, you're on Candid Camera!

♀ LINDA: No! No!

tom runs round the room looking for the hidden camera.

♂ TOM: I knew there was something fishy about this.

♀ LINDA: Oh no I hope I didn't swear! Oh Mr Hobbs my mouth when I get going I come out with all sorts.

♂ TOM: Is this the camera, is this camera? Is this the camera? Oh Beryl it's all right come on you can get up now! We know it's a trick, come on.

BOB: Actually that was a joke. You should have seen the look on your faces. Oh I've always wanted to say that.

♀LINDA: What you mean we ain't going to be on the telly? Oh well I'm glad actually, no I am glad. I mean they do say the **TV** puts six pounds on you and I'm practically anorexic.

♂TOM: So who did bloody let you in then?

BOB: Oh maybe someone gave us a key. That would explain this. I wondered what that was. (Reveals key)

♂TOM: Maybe somebody gave you a key and you can't remember who that was. Fantastic. Well who else are we supposed to tell about this?

BOB: Well it's traditional to tell family and friends. I mean you could tell a complete stranger but they don't often give a...

♀LINDA: Shit?

BOB: ...donation. Anyway see you at the funeral.

♂TOM: Right okay. (Bob Hobbs heads into the garden), No that way, that way.

BOB: What?

♂TOM: That way. Well what are we going to do with this?

LIVING ROOM

we flick through tom and linda's use for the coffin. one minute it's a coffee table, the next a step machine for a step class. then linda is in it and tom is sawing her in half. then linda is ironing on it. suddenly it's a piano. tom is playing it and linda is singing 'roll out the barrel!' then we finish on it as a coffee table. tom and linda have their feet up on it. it's covered in ashtrays and empty tea cups. they are watching television and drinking brandy.

TOM: I love this programme. This is televisual brilliance at it's best. You can keep your 'Our Friends in the North' you can keep your 'I Claudius' Linda. You cannot beat a good 'Through the Keyhole'. Something wrong? You've very quiet.

LINDA: It was telling Jez and Suze earlier, it brought it all back to me. Beryl's dead Tom. It always happens to me. Every time I get close to somebody they end up in one of these.

TOM: Wincey Willis? Wincey Willis who the bloody hell is Wincey Willis?

LINDA: It's like Wendy Strokes in Borstal. I said to her, I said, you're my new best friend. I'm going to be by your side for the rest of your life. Twenty minutes later, hung herself.

suze and jez come in to pay their respects.

TOM: Oi, oi do you know who Wincey Willis is?

SUZE: Oh I told you he'd say something inappropriate. Where is she?

TOM: She's over there, blubbering her little eyes out.

JEZ: Have you no respect for the dead?

TOM: Oh oh yeah sorry. Yeah I'm really unhappy actually, teetering on the brink of gloominess over here.

SUZE: I only saw her two weeks ago. She was going for a loaf, she was so full of life Linda, life.

LINDA: Don't look at me, I didn't kill her. I've got witnesses and this time they're good ones.

JEZ: I saw her last week when I was out buying my Viagra. She told me she was going on a long journey.

LINDA Here, maybe she topped herself.

SUZE: Oh and what would you two care! You hated her.

TOM: Excuse me but we were always having her down here doing things for us.

SUZE: I'd never ask an old lady to be a draft excluder.

LINDA: It was windy!

SUZE: She loved you two so much and all you ever did was treat her like shit.

TOM: That's libellous. Get me some more brandy.

JEZ: We certainly wouldn't use her as a coffee table.

TOM: It's an occasional table actually. Occasionally it's a table and occasionally it's a coffin, okay?

LINDA: Yeah and anyway you two were hardly her number one fans.

SUZE: Yeah well at the end of the day she was a second rate has been hooker. I'm sorry I'm in shock. I mean Beryl was our landlady.

JEZ: Exactly which makes us...

TOM/LINDA: Tenants.

JEZ/SUZE: Homeless.

LINDA: Well the selfish little bitch. (Kicks the coffin)

TOM: How dare she commit suicide and leave us destitute! How dare she!!

JEZ: We don't know that for sure.

SUZE: Yes she would have left a note surely?

JEZ: Do you have keys to her flat?

TOM: Keys? Have I got keys? Do I look like a keys'ey type of person?

JEZ: But there might be a clue up there.

SUZE: Well someone will have to break in. I can't I'm middle class. I used to have ponies. I had to be surgically removed from one of them. Linda you'll have to do it.

TOM: Come on.

BERYL'S FLAT

linda breaks the lock and she and tom run in. he heads straight for her drinks cabinet.

TOM: Well I wonder who lives in a house like this. David it's over to you. Oh it's fantastic, whiskey! You know this is very good for shock you know, which is good because I didn't realise quite how shocked I was. What are you doing, what are you looking for?

♀ LINDA: Well I don't know. A suicide note? A will, anything. Oh that's gorgeous. (Nicks a feather boa)

♂ TOM: Linda are you stealing things? That's out of ord, that's really out of ord.

♀ LINDA: Oh shut up. It's traditional to nick things out of dead people's houses.

♂ TOM: Is it? You know I've often pictured my own funeral celebrations. A crisp autumnal morning, the hallowed dome of Saint Pauls, a reading by Sir Simon Shepherd.

♀ LINDA: I don't think you should have any more of that, you're pissed. Here look at this. (Nicks a whip) Dirty bitch.

♂ TOM: Pissed? I'm not pissed. I don't even know the meaning of the word pissed. Well pardon me if I'm just a little bit emotional.

he passes out, he is so drunk.

LIVING ROOM

suze and jez peering into the coffin. linda drags the comatose tom in.

SUZE: Cripes and stripes they're dropping like flies.

♀ LINDA: Oh shut up you tart. He's pissed.

JEZ: (Getting turned on) She looks great.

SUZE: That Viagra's really taking effect isn't it Jez?

♂ TOM: Oh I'm a good girl I am.

SUZE: Shall I pop downstairs and slip into something see through?

JEZ: Please.

SUZE: Catcha Beryl. (Exits)

♀ LINDA: So you feeling a little frisky Jez?

JEZ: It's this Viagra I'm on, I'm being drawn to the strangest things.

♀ LINDA: Jez? Oh Jez. Have you ever seen that film Basic Instinct? (Crosses her legs)

JEZ: No.

♀ LINDA: What about, There's Something About Mary? (Crosses them again)

JEZ: No I'd better go, order a wreath or something.

♀ LINDA: Here what about your Viagra whatsit?

JEZ: It seems to be wearing off.

he hurries out.

LINDA'S BEDROOM

tom and linda.

♂ TOM: I don't want to be homeless Lindy.

♀ LINDA: Neither do I.

♂ TOM: Then listen to my plan. What say we pretend that Beryl's body was never here at all, that she's just disappeared that she's never died mmm? Then we could keep this flat all to ourselves.

♀ LINDA: That's a dreadful idea Tom. Goes completely against my Catholic teachings. Mind you the garden is big enough for a make shift grave.

♂ TOM: And that funeral director has got the memory capacity of a goldfish. When he comes back we could all be like Stepford Wives and just go, 'What dead body Mr Hobbs? What dead body Mr Hobbs? What dead body Mr Hobbs?'

♀ LINDA: Oh no, no, no because somebody organised the body being here didn't they? We're going to have to face it Tom we're out on our ear. What am I saying,? She probably left a will. I mean maybe this whole house is ours.

♂ TOM: Wake up and smell the coffee Linda. You scary witch.

STREET

pedro, a gorgeous spanish man clambers out of a taxi with a straw donkey and a sombrero.

FRONT DOOR

pedro rings the doorbell linda answers in her dressing gown.

♀ LINDA: All right I heard you the first time.

Oh! My nipples! They've got a mind of their own.

PEDRO: I look for Beryl. I can't believe she has gone.

♀ LINDA: Oh wait there a second.

SHARED HALLWAY

linda has got dressed up and is hurrying back to the door. tom fights with her.

♂ TOM: Yes but who is he?

♀ LINDA: I don't know but whoever he is, he's bloody gorgeous.

♂ TOM: Really?

AT THE DOORWAY

♀ LINDA: Would you like to slip in?

PEDRO: Muchas Gracias.

♂ TOM: We were just making everything just, just so.

PEDRO: You are good people, you are good people.

♀ LINDA: You're not so bad yourself baby.

♂ TOM: Um I'm Tom by the way.

PEDRO: Hello Tom by the way. Pedro Hermano Fernandes De San Pastillo.

♀ LINDA: Oh that's a bit of a mouthful isn't it? Just the way I like it. You come with me Pedro, cor ain't you taut.

LIVING ROOM

tom and linda drag pedro in.

PEDRO: Where is she? Where is my Beryl?

♂ TOM: You want to see Beryl? (He whips the lid of the coffin off) Yeah you want to see Beryl. Here she is!

PEDRO: How can this be? How can this be? Oh mi carina, oh mi carina. How does this happen? Tell me Lindy, tell me Tom by the way. How does this happen?

♀ LINDA: I don't know, her heart stopped beating didn't it? I don't know.

PEDRO: I leave her not fifty days ago at the airport. Lovely Beryl, lovely Beryl I planned to spend the rest of my life with her and now you tell me she is dead. How did she die?

♀ LINDA: Oh ain't he gorgeous?

♂ TOM: Mmm. Got a backside you could get

lost in.

PEDRO: You are Beryl's sister?

♀ LINDA: No you cheeky bastard.

PEDRO: You're too ugly, you're too ugly.

♀ LINDA: No your English very bad. The word is beautiful, it's beautiful.

PEDRO: You are the son?

♂ TOM: The sun the moon and the stars baby. So how do you know her?

PEDRO: I see Beryl in my bar. I give her oily olives and spicy saveloy. I know how to make the ladies happy.

♀ LINDA: I'm licking my lips.

PEDRO: She has my name tattooed on most intimate part, I show you.

♂ TOM: No, no it's not necessary. Really not necessary.

PEDRO: I have her name tattooed on very long part of my body. I show you?

♀ LINDA: It would be cruel to stop him wouldn't it?

PEDRO: You want to see Tom by the way?

♂ TOM: Oh yes, yes, yes. How long is this part of your body?

PEDRO: You can see it from here.

♀ LINDA: No get it out.

pedro pulls his top off to reveal a beryl tattoo.

PEDRO: My chest is long no? I must see my name on her pretty gavina.

♀ LINDA: Her what?

PEDRO: Her gavina, her lovely pretty gavina.

he reaches into the coffin linda and tom wretch.

LINDA'S BEDROOM

linda on her bed. tom comes in.

♀ LINDA: Did you phone the funeral director?

♂ TOM: Yes it's not very promising. Got a very stupid answerphone message. Lots of giggling in the background. Someone shouting out 'His head's on back to front.'

♀ LINDA: And how's my potential new boyfriend?

♂ TOM: Oh you sad slapper. You see the thing you have to learn about hot blooded Europeans Linda is that they don't mind a little bit of man on man contact.

♀ LINDA: You wish. Every time he looked at you his sombrero flopped.

♂ TOM: Anyway I can speak Spanish, listen to me. Diagame, donde est medico homosexual?

♀ LINDA: What does that mean?

♂ TOM: Excuse me where is the nearest Gay Men's Health Centre?

pedro comes in downcast.
he sits on the dressing table stool
and weeps.

♂ TOM: Chico chico mi latino. Living La Vida Loca por favor.

PEDRO: It has gone.

♀ LINDA: What has baby?

PEDRO: My name on her intimacy.

♂ TOM: Oh, oh, diagame donde est medico homosexual?

PEDRO: I know what she has done Lindy. She has had the lasers. She has had the lasers.

♂ TOM: Shall I rub you Pedro? Yeah I'll rub you shall I, yeah. Listen Pedro, sorry to bugger you, er sorry to bother you. But when did Beryl go to Spain?

PEDRO: I'm so lonely. I'm so tired from my flight.

♀ LINDA: Well come and lie down next to me. Come to Linda. Snuggle your head in my bosom I'm very maternal.

PEDRO: Tom by the way, you come on bed too.

♀ LINDA: No there's not enough room.

♂ TOM: Yes there is.

PEDRO: This remind me of when I am little boy.

♂ TOM: *(Singing)* Little boy blue come blow my horn.

PEDRO: I sleep in bed with my brothers and sisters. Each night is cold in mountains. We have to do this to keep warm and then we play, raining.

he tickles them with his fingers
like rain.

♂ TOM: Oh this reminds me of an exercise we used to do at Drama School called 'We're all in a tent' so come on. We're all in the tent and it's windy so blow.

♀ LINDA: Yes and there's a goat outside who's escaped from the zoo and he's all licky.

PEDRO: No comprendo, no comprendo. I don't understand. We was at airport only fifty days ago and now she's dead. Stone dead, no, no, no it's not days is minutes.

♂ TOM: Sorry?

PEDRO: Fifty minutes ago we was at the airport and now she dead. I feel her presence near me. Maybe it's her ghost. Yes her ghost.

beryl enters very much alive.

she has a gun.

BERYL: So there you are. That's the last time I carry a gun through customs. So where have you stuck that bitch twin sister of mine?

LIVING ROOM

beryl peering into the coffin.

BERYL: Are they lovebites?

♂ TOM: No, no bruises. We dropped her earlier. Oh Beryl, Beryl, it's so good to see you again it's such a relief.

♀ LINDA: Yeah we thought we were homeless.

♂ TOM: No we didn't no, we thought she was dead.

♀LINDA: Oh yeah.

BERYL: I thought I'd died and gone to heaven when I met him. Nice isn't he?

♂TOM: He's alright in a sort of wailing kind of way. So where have you been then?

BERYL: Holiday. When I found out what she'd left me in her will I cashed in a couple of fake giros and flew to Fuengirola dear. I lost him at Heathrow on the way back.

♂TOM: So you're a twin.

BERYL: I've got a boa like that Linda.

♀LINDA: Have you? Oh what a coincidence.

BERYL: I've got that jigsaw too.

♂TOM: Oh that's spooky.

BERYL: Pedro, bedtime.

beryl and pedro exit.

♂TOM: Oh that's right go on leave us then. We don't mind having a corpse cluttering up our through lounge!

tom smells something odd. so does linda. they sniff into the coffin unsure where it's coming from, then linda smells her armpits.

♀LINDA: No it's me.

he nods.

STREET

the funeral procession leaving the house. beryl behind the coffin. suze taps jez.

SUZE: Oh Jez look.

JEZ: What?

SUZE: Beryl's come to her own funeral. Oh sweet.

BERYL'S FLAT

linda and tom break in again to return the things they stole. pedro calls through from the bedroom.

PEDRO: Beryl Eres tu?

♀LINDA: It's Pedro, he couldn't have gone to the service!

♂TOM: Quick let's get out of here.

linda peers into the bedroom.

♀LINDA: No, he's all tied up on the bed with a mask on.

tom looks.

♂TOM: Blimey. He's very much in proportion isn't he?

♀LINDA: Not half.

♂TOM: Look we should go.

♀LINDA: Er no I've got to put this back in it's rightful place, you go I'll follow.

tom exits.

PEDRO: Beryl, Beryl is that you?

♀LINDA: Yes dear it's me. Who's been a naughty boy then eh?

she takes her whip and goes in. we hear a crack of the whip and then pedro cry out.

PEDRO: Madre de Dios!

LINDA

**'Oh come on, everyone remembers their first time...
I was off my head on vodka and glue. I only knew I'd done it
because my brownie uniform was on back to front and I
couldn't find my pants.'**

Episode Four
PRISON VISITOR

LIVING ROOM

linda on couch, tom comes in.

♂ TOM: I'm back. Hi Linds.

♀ LINDA: Hi. How did your audition go?

♂ TOM: Really well. Slight hiccup though I was doing the monologue from Peter Pan and I couldn't remember what Tinkerbell's name was.

♀ LINDA: It's Tinkerbell.

♂ TOM: Mmm. The first line is Tinkerbell, Tinkerbell, Tinkerbell, Tinkerbell, so I just ended up miming it. I don't think they noticed.

♀ LINDA: Tom does the bowl need bleaching again? What's that smell?

♂ TOM: Close your eyes. Close your eyes. Look.

he brings in a cat.

♀ LINDA: Urgh, what's that?

♂ TOM: It's a little puss puss.

♀ LINDA: Oh no wonder the flat's so rank.

♂ TOM: Oh look at its eyes Lindy, look.

♀ LINDA: No, the only place for cat's eyes is in the middle of the road. Bin it.

♂ TOM: You're so cattist.

♀ LINDA: It'll crap everywhere Tom. Kate Winslett could come in here and crap on the sofa and I'd still tell her to get out.

♂ TOM: Damoose Damoose is staying.

♀ LINDA: The what?

♂ TOM: Damoose. That's what I'm calling her.

♀ LINDA: No I always said if I had a pet I'd call it Elaine.

♂ TOM: Well you can call it Elaine and I'm calling it Damoose. I spoke to my agent earlier on today. She said there was a part

going on Coronation Street. The Battersby's are getting a cat. Auditions are next week.

♀ LINDA: Oh Tom you'd be brilliant.

♂ TOM: Yes I know. No not me, for the cat. This cat could earn us five grand a week. It could earn us a small fortune. Hey, do you want to stroke it?

♀ LINDA: No.

♂ TOM: Come on Lindy, come on. Demoose. This is Lindy okay, hold out your hand. The one without the warts.

♀ LINDA: Piss off. Designer clothes and claws don't go together. Bin it.

♂ TOM: I pity you and your attitude to pets Linda. Pets have made this nation. Pets have made us what we are today. Pets win prizes.

♀ LINDA: Tom I ain't a pussy person. When people look at me they don't think cat, they think dog. Now come on I need you to write me a letter. Come on, I'll dictate you scribble.

♂ TOM: No I won't.

♀ LINDA: Write it or I'll batter the cat.

♂ TOM: All right come on get on with it, who's it to?

♀ LINDA: It's to this gorgeous hunk out of the paper.

♂ TOM: Right, okay.

♀ LINDA: Dear Freddie. My name is Linda La Hughes. I have got gorgeous red hair and a figure like Rachel Welch in Journey to the Centre of My Earth.

♂ TOM: And a face like Jabba the Hut.

♀ LINDA: Write what I say or I'll sit on the cat. I was so sad when I read your interview and how you said that you never get no visitors and that you were so lonely in there. So, if you want me to come then honey I am all yours. All my love Lindy. Kiss, kiss, love heart, kiss.

♂ TOM: Kiss, kiss, love heart, kiss. Oh that's quite sweet, is he in hospital?

♀ LINDA: No. You haven't done my envelope yet, here you are.

♂ TOM: Oh right, okay, go on.

♀ LINDA: Windrush.

♂ TOM: Windrush.

♀ LINDA: Nine two nine two.

♂ TOM: Nine two nine two.

♀ LINDA: Wormwood Scrubs.

♂ TOM: Wentworth Scrubs. Oh, oh I've just about heard it all now. Are you trying to tell me that you're so desperate you'd trawl through Her Majesty's prison system to find yourself a life partner?

♀ LINDA: You're just jealous because you never thought of it first. Oh they're all up to your tricks in there you know. But when they get on the outside it's bye bye bottom, hello breasts.

♂ TOM: Do you even know what he's in for?

♀ LINDA: I don't know he didn't say. Do you want to see his picture Tom? He's gorgeous.

♂ TOM: No I want no part of this subversive scheme, it's time to feed Fluffy bums.

♀ LINDA: Yeah well at least I lay my affections on human beings. You weirdo.

♂ TOM: It's quite normal to develop feelings for fluffy animals. Look at Richard Gere.

♀ LINDA: Yeah Cindy Crawford was a right dog. I'm going to go and post my letter. See you.

LIVING ROOM

tom is looking out of the window. linda comes in with the mail.

♀ LINDA: What's that there that's so fascinating? Is Michael Owen doing naked star jumps?

♂ TOM: Don't you have any sense of occasion you homophobic harlot? I've just let Damoose out for the very first time.

♀ LINDA: I remember when I was let out for the very first time. I was six months old. Daddy tied me to the back of Aunty Sue's Alsatian and sent me down the shops. A little sign in my hand, forty B&H.

♂ TOM: Oh look she's nibbling on an herbaceous border. Oh, oh look now she's washing herself. Oh lickety, lick, lick, lick, lick.

♀ LINDA: Blimey if I could do that I'd never go out. Tom? Does that say Wormwood Scrubs? Read it to me please, read it to me, read it to me.

♂ TOM: This is a visiting order for next Friday.

♀ LINDA: Yes! I'm going to be a prison visitor. I'm going to be a prison visitor.

♂ TOM: Shut up, shut up. Freddie Windrush? Is this the same Freddie Windrush as in Freddie the Stick Windrush?

♀ LINDA: The Stick? That must mean he's nice and lanky.

♂ TOM: When I played Reggie Kray's chiropodist in Dead Men Don't Wear Mauve. I had to read up all about East End serial killers and if I'm not very much mistaken Mr Windrush is in for a series of brutal batterings.

♀ LINDA: Oh, oh no. Did he get life?

♂ TOM: I think Linda that he did.

♀ LINDA: Oh no that's dreadful. Still there's always conjugal visits.

♂ TOM: But Linda he's a monster.

♀ LINDA: But he's my monster.

♂ TOM: But Linda he killed people.

♀ LINDA: Oh it was probably an accident.

♂ TOM: Linda a small child wetting itself is an accident. A pensioner falling off a stair lift is an accident. Murdering people to death is an entirely different league.

♀ LINDA: You've always got to put a dampener on things haven't you? Every time I meet a bloke it's 'Oh his clothes are vile, oh his breath stinks.'

♂ TOM: Oh he's a serial killer.

♀ LINDA: I've got to get some cleavage blusher. Where's the giro?

ABOVE
One must always tickle one's knob when greeting guests.

LEFT
Linda is often known to let one drop whilst on the dance floor.

ABOVE
The clothes say vibrator. The face says 'Come in.'

RIGHT
Just you watch. Three vodkas later it'll be tongues at dawn.

ABOVE
A moving study of parenthood. Though the words 'Hayley from Coronation Street' spring to mind.

LEFT
Tom with Sir Simon Shepherd. Matinee idol. Icon. Doctor.

ABOVE
The naked hunk uses the old 'red glass to cover your arousal' technique.

RIGHT
Says Linda 'I don't know who this old dog is but she a) tried it on with me, and b) smelt of cheese.'

LEFT
Hamper by Harrods.
Headware by Ida's
Ironmongers on Kentish
Town Road.

BELOW
Wetting the baby's head.
Tom and Linda feign misery
when they think that
Beryl's sucked her
last lollipop.

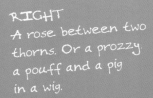

ABOVE
Tom says 'Come stroke my boy-pussy it's twitchin'!'

BELOW
Linda says 'If a lady lies like this when a man is doing sex to her she can eat a bag of crisps at the same time.'

Jez and Suze pop over to watch 'Will and Grace'.

♂ TOM: We need that money for food.

♀ LINDA: Tom, I've got a date on Friday, you think I'm going to eat?

PRISON

all the prisoners run for it when they see linda coming in freddie can't as he is handcuffed to his table.

FREDDIE: Cor you're a big piece ain't you?

♀ LINDA: Thanks. Here I brought you some grapes.

FREDDIE: I ain't in hospital.

♀ LINDA: That's a shame, I look fab in a nurses uniform.

FREDDIE: I used to have a uniform, straight jacket. They said I was psycho. How can I be a film?

♀ LINDA: That's funny because my nickname at school was Rosemary's Baby. It was stupid because my Mummy's called Queenie. Oh look you've got a tattoo. What does that say?

FREDDIE: Mummy.

♀ LINDA: Oh were you close to your old girl as well?

FREDDIE: No it's short for mummification.

linda eats his grapes.

♀ LINDA: Bless. Oh I've got a bit of juice dribbling down my chin. Oh you've got a filthy mind ain't you?

FREDDIE: Can I ask you something?

♀ LINDA: Yes they are real.

FREDDIE: When I get out of here will you look after me?

♀ LINDA: But Freddie you're not getting out, you're in your for life.

FREDDIE: But say I did, would you keep the bed warm for me?

♀ LINDA: I don't know. I'm quite shy and retiring. I was going to be a nun. Loved the rosaries, the church, the habit. It's just the rug munching I couldn't get into.

FREDDIE: I ain't had a woman in five whole years.

♀ LINDA: Then Freddie yes, I will keep the bed warm for you. So what do you get up to in here then Freds?

FREDDIE: I'm on an access course in anatomy. Specialised subject the scar. I study photographs in the prison library.

♀ LINDA: Oh, oh that reminds me. I brought some snaps. C'est moi. They're laminated so they're wipe clean.

FREDDIE: Nice gash.

♀ LINDA: That's where I had my appendix out. It's like a little smile isn't it?

FREDDIE: It's the same shape as the Trevi Fountain. It's beautiful baby.

♀ LINDA: Oh, oh.

LINDA'S BEDROOM

linda gets ready for bed listening to 'together we are beautiful' by fern kinney. she gets into bed as she does, freddie comes clattering through the window.

♀ LINDA: Freddie!

FREDDIE: I told you I'd come baby.

♀ LINDA: Promises, promises.

FREDDIE: Show me your gash, now.

he leaps on top of her.

♀ LINDA: Oh Mr Windrush!

LIVING ROOM, NEXT DAY

freddie's stroking the cat. linda walks in agony.

FREDDIE: I used to have a cat but it was bad.

♀ LINDA: That's Tom's pride and joy.

FREDDIE: Tom?

♀ LINDA: The fella I live with.

FREDDIE: What? I thought you were my bitch and all along you're some Tom's bitch. It's not bent Tom Parsnip from Stepney Green is it? I'll have him.

♀ LINDA: No it's bent Tom Farrell from Kentish Town.

FREDDIE: The freaky fraudster with the frightening fringe?

♀ LINDA: No it's not that sort of bent. I'll give you a clue it rhymes with fomosexual.

FREDDIE: If he grasses me up then he'll have to die.

♀ LINDA: Don't say that.

LINDA

'Tom I ain't a pussy person. When people look at me they don't think cat, they think dog.'

FREDDIE: Sorry babe. Habit of a lifetime.

♀ LINDA: I know we'll have to pretend you're someone else. Oh and we mustn't let him go anywhere near the television you're probably all over the news.

FREDDIE: Let's run away babes.

♀ LINDA: Oh yes Fred, where to?

FREDDIE I've got mates in Benidorm.

♀ LINDA: Oh I love Italy.

FREDDIE: No Spain babe.

♀ LINDA: Oh yeah, that Benidorm.

FREDDIE: I've ordered false passports. Go on get some sun on your pasty skin.

tom enters.

♂ TOM: Morning.

FREDDIE: Got any snout?

♀ LINDA: Tom this is um, Fritz my long lost German cousin.

FREDDIE: All right?

♂ TOM: But he's got a cockney accent.

FREDDIE: I can have one if I want one you nonce!!

♂ TOM: Yeah all right all right.

♀ LINDA: Tom you should be impressed I mean even you can't do a cockney accent and you're English.

♂ TOM: Yes I can, yes I can. Listen, listen. Apples and pears, strike a light.

tom recognises freddie. but isn't sure why. then the penny drops.

♂ TOM: You're an actor aren't you?

FREDDIE: Yeah.

♂ TOM: Yes I knew it. I've seen you somewhere haven't I? I've seen you on the television. Do you want to see my show reel? What we do in England is that we record everything we've ever done on television and then we just play it to people. Come on it'll only take five minutes, have a look.

♀ LINDA: No Tom, the television's broke.
♂ TOM: Is it?

freddie kicks it.

FREDDIE: It is now.
♀ LINDA: Fritz's in a bit of a bad mood this morning aren't you Fritzy?
♂ TOM: Have you had a row with your agent or something? Oh mine's crap. I call her every day and she says to me 'I would get you work but no one will employ you.' I mean what's that all about?

linda hands freddie a bacon buttie. he caresses her.

FREDDIE: Cheers darling.
♂ TOM: Very tactile your distant relatives.
♀ LINDA: Well Germans are very misunderstood Tom. You want to meet Fritzy's mum Helga. She'd sit on your face as soon as look at you.
♂ TOM: So Fritz what brings you to England? An audition or something? Any parts in it for me?
FREDDIE: What is this? Twenty bloody questions?!!
♂ TOM: Oh you're so like me. Keep it a secret so the competition doesn't get a look in. Very wise, very wise.
FREDDIE: Sorry Tom I didn't mean to shout at you. I'm on an anger management course in the nick – of time.
♂ TOM: I was a supporting artist on Oliver Twist, do you know it?

freddie does some elaborate hand signals to the cat who goes and gets him the sauce bottle.

♀ LINDA: No, no, no. Fritz no stop it, stop it, stop it Fritz.
FREDDIE: Cheers mate.
♂ TOM: How did you do that?
FREDDIE: Me and cats have an unspoken language. We can communicate it's easy.
♂ TOM: But, but that's fantastic. How did you learn to do that?
FREDDIE: It's a secret.
♂ TOM: Will you teach me?
♀ LINDA: Right, I'm going to go and pack.

♂ TOM: Pack? Pack? Where are you going?
♀ LINDA: Nowhere. Pack it's German for put the bins out.

she exits.

♂ TOM: So, Fritz you can teach a cat to do almost anything?
FREDDIE: Within reason, I do have morals you know.
♂ TOM: This is fantastic, you couldn't have come at a better time. It's so exciting! (Hugs Freddie) Oh God I'm sorry, I'm sorry! My show biz emotions just ran away with me there.
FREDDIE: It's all right Tom boy. I quite liked it.

their eyes meet dangerously.

LINDA'S BEDROOM

linda dressed as a spanish lady, playing maracas. tom comes in.

♂ TOM: What on earth are you wearing?
♀ LINDA: What these old rags? I always knock about the house in these.
♂ TOM: Oh. God I wish my agent would ring. She's going to be so pleased with Damoose. Fritz has got her doing all sorts out there. First time I've ever seen a cat doing the can can. Fingers crossed the cat is heading for soap superstardom.

freddie enters.

♂ TOM: My liege what news from court? I'd have been fantastic in Pride and Prejudice.
FREDDIE: The passports are at the Left Luggage at Heathrow babe.
♂ TOM: That's very good. Now where's that from? Let me guess, let me guess.

I'm thinking cockney villains. I'm thinking Helen Mirren in batwing sleeves. Long Good Friday?

FREDDIE: Eh?

the phone goes off.

♂ TOM: That will be my agent, won't be long.

he exits.

♀ LINDA: Come here you. Don't mention the passports in front of the poof.

FREDDIE: They didn't have a photo of you so I told them to use one of Su Pollard and paint it auburn.

♀ LINDA: Oh.

FREDDIE: All we need now is hard cash.

♀ LINDA: How much are we talking?

FREDDIE: Well first up I thought we'd need twenty quid. Then I realised I was making my calculations based on 1963 prices, don't ask me why. So taking into account inflation and the fact that neither of us will be wearing hot pants...

♀ LINDA: You speak for yourself.

FREDDIE: The amount we really need is three and a half grand.

♀ LINDA: Oh bugger. Hang on we get five grand if the cat gets the part in Corrie. Get out there and get training it.

LIVING ROOM

the cat is doing cartwheels behind the couch. tom is on the phone to norma as he speaks, freddie enters.

♂ TOM: Well let's put it this way Norma, the cat is heading for the top. Well if you didn't call to speak about the cat, what did you want? An audition for me? A life guard? Yes of course I'm butch enough. Damoose get away from the wallpaper with those naked flames. It's not topless is it? Oh no can do, no unless they stick me in a vest. No I've got a scar from neck to navel following a mistaken tracheotomy. (Freddie's eyes light up) Well I only went in to get my nails filed. Yes I am suing. Yes for plastic surgery. No not for my face, for the scar. So the answer's no, so call me back when you've

got an audition time for Damoose. Oh and I'd better ask um, how was your mother's thingy, your mother's funeral? Yes, oh dear. Yeah. Well time's a great healer. Goodbye.

tom sees freddie looking at him.

FREDDIE: You're in good shape Tom. It's only right a boy should look after himself. Do much sport?

♂ TOM: Well a little bit of croquet if I'm in the country.

FREDDIE: I recently shared a small room with a country lad and we grew what can only be described as tomatoes. He'll be gutted I'm here, I never said goodbye.

♂ TOM: Do you want to phone him?

FREDDIE: He's deaf in one ear. I don't know which one I'd get.

♂ TOM: Why are you telling me all this?

FREDDIE: I think we understand each other. Sometimes a man's got to do what a man's got to do. Ain't that right Tommy baby?

♂ TOM: Possibly.

FREDDIE: Come to daddy.

they kiss.

♂ TOM: Fritz. Fritz I always said I'd never do this with another actor. Oh actors are so self obsessed aren't they? Always talking about themselves non bloody stop. You don't think I'm like that? Do you Fritzy? Eh, what do you think? It's just that I think I've got a pretty good handle on myself, what do you say hey? Self obsessed, me, me, me?

FREDDIE: Don't speak.

♂ TOM: You know a lot of directors say that to me.

LIVING ROOM LATER

linda comes in singing. tom approaches her seriously.

♀ LINDA: (Singing) I'm off to sunny Spain. Y viva España.

♂ TOM: Please be seated.

♀ LINDA: Oh.

♂ TOM: There's something I have to tell you. Here, here, here take my hand, take my hand.

♀ LINDA: Oh.

♂ TOM: We've known each other for quite a

long time now haven't we? Been through a lot together thee and me.

LINDA: Yes Tom.

TOM: And every relationship changes. And I think from now on we're going to be closer, quite a bit closer.

LINDA: Mummy told me there'd be days like these.

TOM: Hush, please don't say a word. We're going to be, oh I can hardly bring myself to say it. Family.

LINDA: Oh Tom, if only you'd told me yesterday we could have had some sort of future together, but Tom I'm already spoken for.

TOM: No I haven't fallen for you, you fool. I've fallen for your cousin.

LINDA: What? Oh not our Simon with the dodgy eye. Tom everyone thinks he's trying to get off with them, he could see both ends of a bus at the same time.

TOM: No I've fallen for Fritz.

LINDA: Oh you always do it don't you?

TOM: What? What do I always do? What?

LINDA: Fall for the straight blokes. Bloody hell I mean why can't you homos stick to your own sort? I mean it ain't as if there ain't enough of you to go around. Every time I try and get off with a bloke he turns out to be queer.

TOM: Fritz is gay.

LINDA: Bollocks.

TOM: He is, he's taking me to Spain with him.

LINDA: Yeah right.

TOM: Yeah right. He had me on this coffee table not three minutes hence.

LINDA: What? You bastard!

beryl enters with paper.

BERYL: Any room at the inn for an ex prozzy?

LINDA: Oh don't you start an' all Beryl.

TOM: God, couldn't you at least be happy for me?

LINDA: No you shagged my Freddie.

the headline on beryl's paper is a picture of freddie with the

caption 'he's out'.

TOM: Fritz. Can't you even get his name right? Oh my God, what? What? He's out? The press got onto his sexuality pretty quickly didn't they?

BERYL: No Tom, that's Freddie Windrush the most dangerous man in Britain.

TOM: But...

BERYL: Escaped from prison and on the run.

TOM: Oh my God, oh my God.

BERYL: I read his life story, Inside the Mind of a Psychopathic Looney Tune.

TOM: You said he was your cousin.

LINDA: Well I couldn't tell you who he really was could I? You'd have hit the roof!

TOM: Oh I'm so sorry Linda. Oh was that really out of ord? Oh forgive me for over reacting but I've just been humped by Hoxton's answer to Hannibal Lecter!!

LINDA: Well you're welcome to him mate. I don't want nothing more to do with him.

BERYL: There's a twenty grand reward out for his arrest.

LINDA: Really?

BERYL: I hate to think what he's doing now. He's probably strangling some innocent virgin and drinking her blood for afters. Oh I've got to go, left some kidneys in my slow cooker. Cheerio.

beryl exits as freddie enters from the toilet.

FREDDIE: That's better. I love a good tip out. (To Beryl) All right darling, got any scars? (She shreaks and runs out) I heard a bit of shouting when I was on the khazi. I take it Tom's told you.

LINDA: Vile.

FREDDIE: I'm sorry it had to be like this Linda it's just his gash is bigger than yours.

LINDA: Vile.

FREDDIE: Looking forward to Spain Tom?

LINDA: Vile.

TOM: Will you stop doing that, that's very annoying. Um what if Damoose fails her audition and we won't be able to afford it will we?

FREDDIE: Then I'll rob a bank. I can rob banks in my sleep. I'll do anything for you Tom. I'll rob one now.

TOM: No the thing is Freddie, Fritz, Fritz is that my agent rang and she said I've just been offered a really huge part in Harbour Lights and I'd be silly to turn it down.

FREDDIE: But it's shit.

LINDA: You didn't tell me, you don't tell me nothing no more.

FREDDIE: Please come with me to Spain Tommy baby. I don't think I can face life without you. (Cries)

TOM: (To Linda) Watch this, watch this. I'm going to give the performance of a life time, watch. (Cockney hard guy) Oi, slag, I'm the daddy now. (Hands him a hanky) Wipe them. Right now get in the bathroom and draw a bath.

FREDDIE: But I hate drawing.

LINDA: Oh so do I, can you do colouring in?

TOM: Shut it Hughesy. And you, don't you piss on my head and tell me that it's raining. Now get in the bathroom, you worked up quite a sweat earlier on didn't you, you jailhouse slag.

FREDDIE: Sorry daddy, but you said my BO turns you on.

TOM: Yeah well it don't any more do it, now get in the bathroom.

FREDDIE: Consider it done. I am your obedient little puppy and no mistake.

TOM: Yeah and if you touch your thing whilst I'm not looking you'll have another bloody thing to look forward to right. Now get out you slag.

freddie exits to bathroom.

TOM: Oh Lindy I'm so scared. I feel like I'm in an episode of Charlie's Angels. But I

figure if there's twenty thousand pounds to be got I don't see why I shouldn't be the one to get it.

LINDA: Oi, and me, I got him here.

TOM: Or is this really cruel?

LINDA: Oh sod that, we're skint.

TOM: Yes.

POLICE STATION

a camp dizzy blonde policewoman answers the phone.

POLICE RECEPTIONIST: Hello police station, Chantelle speaking how can I help you?

TOM: Hello Chantelle I'm calling about Freddie the Stick Windrush.

POLICE RECEPTIONIST: Oh yeah?

TOM: Listen, listen we've got him here in our flat.

POLICE RECEPTIONIST: No? That's outrageous. Bye then.

TOM: No, no hang on, don't you want the address?

POLICE RECEPTIONIST: Oh go on then we're not busy.

TOM: Right 69a Paradise Passage, Kentish Town.

POLICE RECEPTIONIST: Oh tell us something we don't know.

TOM: What? You already knew?

POLICE RECEPTIONIST: Oh yeah darling. In fact we've got the Rapid Response on their way over. Should be round just about now.

LIVING ROOM

the rapid response team come

crashing through the french windows.

MAN: Where is he?
LINDA/TOM Bathroom!

the men run through. we hear machine gunfire. the rapid response team come back in.

LINDA: What were his last words?
OFFICER: Miaow.
TOM: What Freddie said Miaow?
OFFICER: No Freddie's fine. It's your cat that got in the way.

freddie comes through in a bath towel.

FREDDIE: Write to me Tom, I love you baby.
LINDA: Oi and what about me?
FREDDIE: Your pussy's in a bit of a mess.

he is taken away. linda is fuming then she realises something.

LINDA: Oh he meant Elaine.

LINDA'S BEDROOM

tom wakes linda.

TOM: I had a bad dream Lindy.
LINDA: Oh come on, come and get in with me.
TOM: Oh good. I dreamt I was the cat from Coronation Street and everyone was being really horrible to me. Audrey Roberts said I was talentless. Rita Fairclough said I had a really unconvincing purr.
LINDA: Pair of what?
TOM: No, purr. Prrr. Prrr. And then Freddie turned up and tried to drown me in one of Betty's hot pots.
LINDA: Oh poor Tom. I wonder what brought this on?
TOM: What do you bloody think brought this on.
LINDA: Oh this is like The Sound of Music isn't it?
TOM: Yeah so like it. Great analogy Linds.
LINDA: No because all the little kiddies get scared and they get into the bed with the nun and she sings 'Down Town.'
TOM: Oh just think we could have been twenty thousand pounds richer today. What would you have done with your half of the money?
LINDA: Well I'd have given some to you and some to daddy and I'd have spent the rest on clothes and world peace.
TOM: Really? Well I would have bought a theatre and I would have produced and starred in my own plays and people would have come from miles around to marvel at my showbiz genius. Oh I feel better now. Time for sleepykins.
LINDA: Night then.
TOM: Night, night. I wonder who turned Freddie in? Maybe it was one of the neighbours who saw him smashing the window. Oh it's a concurrent kaboodle and conundrum.
LINDA: Here talking of neighbours, I saw Beryl earlier, off on her holidays again. Fortnight in Mauritius on Concorde if you please.
TOM: Bet that cost her an arm and a leg.
LINDA: Mmm.
TOM: Mmm. Well night then.
LINDA: Night.
TOM: Kiss Percy. (Holds up his teddy)
LINDA: I said to her, I said 'I bet that cost a pretty penny.' She said 'Yeah twenty grand.' God.
TOM: No.

the penny drops.

TOM: What?

Episode Five

DiRTy THiRTy

LIVING ROOM

tom comes in with the post.

♂ TOM: Happy Birthday to me. Happy Birthday to me. Happy birthday you sexy bastard. Happy birthday to me. (Rifling throught the mail) Bill, bill, bill, bill, bill. Oh God, that's bloody crap. (Phone rings, answers) Hello Birthday boy speaking, don't sing happy birthday too loudly I'm feeling a little bit fragile!! Martin who? No I think you've got the wrong number. Yes well must dash loads of presents to open! I'm not a wanker! (Puts phone down)

linda comes in carrying a video.

♀ LINDA: Nuisance phone calls? Oh I hate that. I mean I don't mind if they get a bit filthy because then it's a two way street, do you know what I mean? But when they ring up just to be rude it's a waste of time.

♂ TOM: Do you know what I hate Linda La Hughes?

♀ LINDA: Female squidgy bits?

♂ TOM: No I hate it when you oversleep on your birthday and your flat mate can't even be arsed to offer you hearty congratulations.

♀ LINDA: Oh I hate that. I used to share a flat with this girl right, well it was more of a cell actually. And she always used to forget my birthday and I was livid. I mean it's not on is it Tom?

♂ TOM: No it isn't. And what are you doing with one of my videos. Bucks Fizz live at the Bradford Alhambra. Little bit highbrow for you isn't it? Postman Pat's not in it.

♀ LINDA: I thought it was Silence of the Lambs didn't I? I wanted something a bit feel good you know, cheer myself up.

♂ TOM: Well we haven't got Silence of the Lambs.

♀ LINDA: But I thought you were in it.

♂ TOM: No, I was in the musical. 'Silence!' at the Swan Theatre Worcester. I closed the Act One finale with 'Help Me I'm Down a Hole.' (Singing) Help me I'm down an hole, so far away from home. At the end of my tunnel I see some light. I'm someone's dinner tonight. (Speaking) So I'm just going to sit here until you say it.

♀ LINDA: Say what?

♂ TOM: Well think back to that time you were in the cell and that girl didn't say to you Happy Birthday.

♀ LINDA: Yeah but that weren't her fault Tom, she'd just come back from having electric shock treatment. I mean she couldn't remember nothing, stupid bitch.

♂ TOM: All right well maybe my mother was rushed to hospital thirty years ago and told to strain really hard.

♀ LINDA: Oh I had to do that when I was constipated. At least I thought I was constipated.

♂ TOM: Maybe she had something in her tummy.

♀ LINDA: Tell me about it. I pushed and

GiMME GiMME GiMME

pushed for five and a half hours and gave birth to a gonk. Don't ask.

♂ TOM: My birthday, you stupid cow.

♀ LINDA: I'll never forget my thirteenth birthday it was the day I became a woman.

♂ TOM: Aren't you even going to say Happy Birthday to me?

♀ LINDA: I done a little strip for the boys in the prefab.

♂ TOM: Oh stop it, stop it.

♀ LINDA: That's what they said. I'd only got down to my trainer bra and pants and they chucked up in the art sink. Homos.

♂ TOM: I give up. Well I'm going back to bed. If you can't even be bothered to say Happy Birthday to me.

♀ LINDA: Here knock one out for me babe.

♂ TOM: (At the door) Linda? Linda what's this in the hall, there? What's that?

♀ LINDA: What's it look like?

♂ TOM: It looks like a trolley with cake and presents and twiglets and gifts and things. Oh Lindy you remembered.

he wheels the birthday trolley in.

♀ LINDA: Oh I had you going there didn't I? Time for your birthday kiss. (Throws herself on him)

♂ TOM: No! No! Oh that was bodily fluid.

♀ LINDA: Oh shut up, what's a little tongue action amongst friends?

♂ TOM: Okay presents out. No time like the present. Get my little pun, no time like the present.

he bursts out crying and runs from the room.

TOM'S BEDROOM

tom surveying his face sadly, in a mirror. linda comes in.

♂ TOM: Look at me. I've got lines. No longer will I be able to play juvenile leads. Have I turned grey over night, will you just check?

♀ LINDA: Shall I look down below?

♂ TOM: Get your sweaty digits off my crotch you dirty minded mare.

♀ LINDA: Blimey I hope I ain't going to be this vile when I hit thirty.

♂ TOM: You're thirty-six.

♀ LINDA: Bollocks, I'm twenty-eight.

♂ TOM: Stone.

♀ LINDA: Oh why are you in such a bad mood?

♂ TOM: That's my pejorative. Last night I had a dream that I was the leading man in an ITV series called Vets in Cirencester. And I wasn't happy unless I was up to my elbow in a cow's backside.

♀ LINDA: I've had dreams like that.

♂ TOM: When I awoke this morning.

♀ LINDA: You'd had a little spillage?

♂ TOM: I realised two things. One – that I'd hit the big three oh, and two – that I'm a failure at absolutely everything.

♀ LINDA: Oh cheer up. We've got loads of people coming round later.

♂ TOM: Have we who? Who?

♀ LINDA: Well I rang everyone in your filofax but not everyone was available. I don't think I gave them enough notice.

♂ TOM: Oh when did you ring them?

♀ LINDA: About six months ago.

♂ TOM: Oh yeah well that will be it you see. Not enough time, yeah they're all hideously busy. It's fiendishly difficult finding a window. So who else is coming?

♀ LINDA: Well I know I'm going to be there, I'm really looking forward to it.

♂ TOM: You don't count. You're already here.

♀ LINDA: And Jez and Suze and Beryl.

♂ TOM: Oh!

♀ LINDA: Oh Beryl was over the moon you wanted her here, she had a little cry actually. Actually she got quite hysterical, I had to give her a slap. But I mean you've got to admit it Tom, I've got a flare for organising birthday do's.

♂ TOM: Yes. You're a real little Meg Matthews aren't you? I mean look at this place, the very image of Studio 54. Decorations all over the place. Oh nearly split my head open on the glitter ball there. Oh that dry ice really gets on your lungs doesn't it? Better chuck him out he's dealing drugs.

♀ LINDA: Who?

♂ TOM: Get out. Go and enjoy your little party thing.

GIMME GIMME GIMME 105

linda exits tom opens a present. it's an outfit.

LIVING ROOM

linda eating the birthday cake. jez and suze come in dressed in bucks fizz outfits.

SUZE: Hi cats.

JEZ: We're on the sniff for the birthday boy. The big hands pointing to party, the little hand's pointing to time. What do you know? It's party time.

SUZE: Where's Tomosexual?

♀ LINDA: Party's off, he don't want to know.

tom comes in in his outfit. the four of them are dressed as bucks fizz.

♂ TOM: Oh thank you Linda. Oh this really suits me. Once again you've proved your flair with up to the minute fashions.

JEZ: Come on Tom, it's for our party piece.

SUZE: Yes don't let the fact that we've been up since five o'clock this morning practising put you off or anything Tom.

♂ TOM: No I won't, no.

♀ LINDA: Oh leave it, he don't deserve it.

JEZ: Come on Linda, let's. I love your legs in that mini skirt Linda.

♀ LINDA: Oh all right then.

♂ TOM: Look what is going on?

JEZ: Who is the best pop group in the world?

♂ TOM: Um Boyzone, is it Boyzone? Boyzone are coming, oh I'm thrilled.

♀ LINDA: Oh shut up, one homo out of five don't make it right you know.

SUZE: No it's the top pop group of the eighties. Hit it daddyo.

bucks fizz plays on the stereo. they peform it for him. tom switches the music off.

♂ TOM: No, no, no, no, no. No.

JEZ: Look come on Tom, you haven't seen the best bit yet. Look.

he rips off the ladies' skirts.

♀ LINDA: Do you know? It's at a time like this a girl wishes she wore pants.

♂ TOM: What is all this nincompoopery you twit?

♀ LINDA: You said you wanted to wake up with Bucks Fizz.

♂ TOM: The drink!

♀ LINDA: Oh.

♂ TOM: Jez, Suze, much as I appreciate your camp good will and your surreal sense of eighties disco, I'm afraid I cannot celebrate with you today. For on this very day seventeen years ago, my entire family was wiped out in a car accident on the outskirts of Kidderminster.

♀ LINDA: Eh?

♂ TOM: Sssh. Sssh. You see we were returning from filming Ask the Family and father took his eyes off the wheel and let's just say I was the only one wearing a seat belt.

♀ LINDA: Yeah but I thought that they...

♂ TOM: Just be quiet please.

SUZE: Tom that's dreadful.

♂ TOM: Yes I know.

♀ LINDA: But I thought that they...

♂ TOM: I just asked you to be quiet. An aunt took me in but we didn't see eye to eye. She was three foot nine. So I was destined to spend the rest of my puberty in an orphanage.

SUZE: I wish you'd told us this Linds.

♀ LINDA: No but I'm sure that...

♂ TOM: The reason Linda said nothing is that she was sworn as she is sworn now, to secrecy. Linda. I thank you for your rare awareness on the issues surrounding confidentiality. So if it's all the same with you guys I'm just going to chill, relax, be with my memories of my dear departed muter unt fater.

the doorbell rings.

SUZE: I'll get that Tom, probably someone for the party, I'll tell them to go away.

♂ TOM: No, no bless you, but I'd appreciate the few minutes walk to the door alone just to gather myself in. To reflect. To mourn.

tom exits.

♀ LINDA: Could someone give us a hug?

suze leans in. linda pushes her away.

♀ LINDA: No not you.

she grabs a feel of jez.

FRONT DOOR

tom opens the door to his parents, sheila and vernon.

SHEILA & VERNON: Surprise!

♂ TOM: Oh could you just wait there for a second please. Shit, shit, shit, shit, shit.

he closes the door on them. the letterbox goes up.

SHEILA: What have I told you about swearing.

LIVING ROOM

tom runs in to disperse the others.

♂ TOM: Right thanks very much for coming. Thank you, thank you, you'd both better go now, thanks very much goodbye. Goodbye.

♀ LINDA: Who was at the door?

♂ TOM: Um, carol singers.

SUZE: Yeah but it's only February.

♂ TOM: Oh God did I say carol singers? I meant Carol Vorderman.

SUZE: My!

♂ TOM: She's come round to give you a lesson for spelling and sums and things. Go, go, get out, get out.

suze and jez leave.

♀ LINDA: Well where is she?

♂ TOM: No you stupid Yak. My mother and father.

♀ LINDA: I thought you said they were dead?

♂ TOM: Hide anything, anything that says I'm gay.

linda holds up a sign that reads tom's gay.

♀ LINDA: What like this?

♂ TOM: Yes. Bin it. The only reason I told that Ask the Family story is because I have the most boring parents in the whole world.

♀ LINDA: Do you mean to tell me your parents don't know you're a poof? I mean what are they? Blind?

♂ TOM: Yes they know I'm gay. When I was eighteen I fell madly in love with the man from our ice cream van.

♀ LINDA: Oh did it go anywhere?

♂ TOM: Alderley Edge and Timperney.

♀ LINDA: Well hang on a minute, if they know you're gay, then why are we hiding all this stuff?

♂ TOM: Because they're not over the moon about it. They're quite prudish when it comes to sex. And unlike you they don't enjoy having things rammed down their throat.

LIVING ROOM, LATER

sheila is knitting. vernon reading the paper. tom is mortified. linda loves it.

SHEILA: And the Masons at forty-three have decorated again. Aquamarine in the bathroom and Birmingham beige in the lobby. Half a million she won on the lottery and she's still buying No Frills lemonade. Vernon don't scratch love. I changed our fabric conditioner and we think he's allergic. Vernon.

VERNON: So how's the old acting going Tom?

♂ TOM: Oh marvellously, you know perhaps a new job at the RSC fingers crossed!

♀ LINDA: Oh you must be so proud of him, he's so talented.

SHEILA: We watched out for you in Daylight Robbery. Can't say as we saw you. I said to Enid, I said what's that all about?

♂ TOM: My God you are hopeless aren't you? You know the scene in the building society?

TOM
'No! No! Oh that was bodily fluid.'
LINDA
'Oh shut up, what's a little tongue action amongst friends?'

Well I was in the queue applying for a mortgage.

SHEILA: Tom if you were an extra in it, why don't you just say so.

TOM: Because I wasn't an extra, I had a line but they had to cut it because of the running time. And it was a beautiful line too, ruined the whole series the fact that they cut it. Shall I act it for you, shall I?

LINDA: Oh listen to this, it is brilliant.

TOM: (Acting dreadfully) No.

LINDA: Isn't he wonderful. What are you knitting Mrs Tom?

SHEILA: Poncho. It's for a woman I meet on my toy bus. I drive a toy bus for kiddies with special needs. There's a lot of brain damaged kids out there with nothing to play with.

LINDA: They don't know they're born these days do they? I mean all I had to play with when I was little was a tiny pink box.

TOM: Well I didn't even get that I was a very deprived child.

SHEILA: Oh shut up moaning. We gave you a bike didn't we?

TOM: All I ever wanted was a great big purple chopper to get my hands on.

LINDA: Outrageous isn't he? Isn't he filthy, isn't he filthy Vern?

TOM: No a chopper bike you preposterous bitch.

VERNON: We got you a bloody chopper, but you wouldn't be seen dead on it.

TOM: No you got me a bloody shopper. Great big pink thing with white baskets on it. Is it any wonder I spent my teenage years locked away in my bedroom reciting Shakespeare to mine own mirror image? You made me an outcast!

VERNON: Are we calling that artex?

LINDA: No it's just cement with cracks.

SHEILA: Jennifer at number nine has had the whole house artexed. Bandying it about at the Campaign For Kosovo Coffee Morning like she's the big I am. I said, I said. 'It's a good job she's not on the front line, bombs dropping, houses collapsing and she'd be flicking through her photos of before and after.' So is your boyfriend going to put in an appearance today or what?

TOM: Don't ask me questions about my sexuality, change the subject.

SHEILA: Where is he? Have you split up? What, can't keep a bloke now? I'm ashamed for you.

TOM: No I have got a boyfriend, I have, Linda tell her about my boyfriend. Tell her about my boyfriend.

LINDA: What? Oh yeah, yeah he's lovely. Yeah he's so quiet you'd hardly know he was here.

SHEILA: So Linda do your mum and dad come and stay much?

TOM: Stay?

LINDA: No sadly daddy's in an iron lung and mummy's in heaven with the angels. Yes, she collapsed in a paddling pool in Pinner.

SHEILA: Oh.

TOM: Sorry could I just clarify something here. Did you just say that you were staying?

VERNON: No, no we brought the caravan. We only want access to the bathroom.

TOM: Well we haven't got one, sorry.

SHEILA: I saw it on the way in.

TOM: Oh really? Really? Linda did you know we had a bathroom?

LINDA: Eh?

SHEILA: You'd never guess he was from my womb.

TOM: Don't say that word.

SHEILA: I mean I only breast fed you and now I can't use your bloody toilet.

TOM: Oh. Have you just come round to list all your body parts? It's so embarrassing, I don't know why you bothered.

SHEILA: We haven't just come to see you. We're off to a party later. Fancy dress.

LINDA: Oh, oh I went to one of them when

I was ten. I wanted to go as a good time girl but daddy made me go as a pig.

SHEILA: Hey Tom, did I tell you? Elspeth Yule's got a pot bellied pig! Oh you'll laugh when I tell you.

TOM: Linda, Linda bedroom please.

LINDA: Oh he's on the turn.

SHEILA: No Tom hang on, she's got this pig right and you'll never guess what it did.

TOM: Nobody's interested. (They go)

SHEILA: Well your father's interested aren't you Vernon?

VERNON: What's that love?

SHEILA: Elsbeth. Pig.

VERNON: Oh yes very interesting.

LINDA'S BEDROOM

tom drags linda in.

TOM: God this is so mortifying. I haven't been this embarrassed since I bumped into Louise Woodward on the tube and said 'I thought you were marvellous in The Hand that Rocks the Cradle.'

LINDA: I don't know what you're whittering on about. They seem really lovely.

TOM: Oh God me whittering on? Me whittering on? My mother makes me look like Helen Keller.

LINDA: She reminds me of Mummy.

TOM: She's not obese.

LINDA: Mummy wasn't always. In her heyday she was Miss Isle of Dogs.

TOM: I feel five years old again. Was your thirtieth this disastrous?

LINDA: How many times have I got to tell you? I'm twenty-eight. Get my passport I'll prove it to you.

TOM : You haven't got a passport. You're not allowed one. The one and only time you tried to leave the country you were caught because you had contraband stuffed into every orifice.

LINDA: That nice man made me take all my clothes off.

TOM: It was a strip search. Why do you think he made you bend over and put a rubber glove on, because he fancied you?

LINDA: Can you blame him?

TOM: You would try it on with anybody wouldn't you?

LINDA: And what's wrong with that?

TOM: Why there's nothing at all wrong with that.

LINDA: Oh Tom.

TOM: No, not me. I want you to come on to my father. That should send them packing.

HALLWAY

tom opens the door to beryl.

BERYL: Happy Birthday to you. Happy Birthday to you.

TOM: Oh piss off.

he slams the door in her face and goes into the bathroom where vernon and sheila are freshening up.

TOM: Dad, dad?

VERNON: Yes?

TOM: Linda would like a word with you, haven't got a clue what it's about. But she'd like to see you in her room. Alone and now.

VERNON: Oh right oh. (Goes)

TOM: It's been lovely seeing you again.

SHEILA: You say that as if we're about to leave.

TOM: Really? Really? I've got to go through to the lounge and prepare for my hundreds of guests arriving. You can take this opportunity to have a nose about a bit. All right? Try Linda's bedroom. Lots of lovely knitwear in there for you. In your own time.

LINDA'S BEDROOM

linda sitting on her bed with her foot up on a stool. vernon comes in.

VERNON: Linda?

LINDA: Come on in Vernon, close the door. Forgive me for lying like this in such a revealing skirt only I tripped on my heel earlier and I think I've sprained my ankle.
VERNON: Oh. Shall I have a look at it for you?
LINDA: Would you Vernon? Have a little poke about? Oh. Forgive my feminine glisten. Only I was bouncing naked on a pogo stick earlier and I haven't had a chance to shower.
VERNON: Does that hurt?

vernon feels her ankle.

LINDA: Hurt's a very strong word Vernon. Can conjure up all sorts of images. Maybe you should try a little higher.

his hand creeps up her leg.

LINDA: Oh my G string. It's like a satin cheese wire.
VERNON: I like a woman with legs.
LINDA: Oh, some men say they're my best feature. Them and my lilly white ass. What do you say Vernon?
VERNON: Well I'm rather taken with your tits.
LINDA: Oh.

HALLWAY

tom pushing his mother up towards linda's bedroom.

TOM: Would you please go into Linda's bedroom now? Go on mother get a move on.
SHEILA: Did I tell you, our Carmel's started her menopause?
TOM: Oh I wonder what's in Linda's bedroom, come on.
SHEILA: She had a hot flush in the middle of Argos. Came out with a long slot toaster, she'd only gone in to get out of the rain.

TOM: Oh do shut up. Linda?

he pushes her into linda's bedroom. vernon and linda are under the quilt. having sex.

SHEILA: Will you look at that.
TOM: Oh you silly bitch, I didn't mean you to go through with it, I just meant you to scare him off.
LINDA: Oh shut up!
SHEILA: No really Tom, our Carmel's got that exact same bedspread. I can't get over that.

LIVING ROOM

beryl chatting with sheila. tom gobsmacked on the chair.

BERYL: And then in 1973 I got Munchausen's Disease by Proxy which ain't a barrel of laughs.
SHEILA: Her at fifty-two had that. Chopped all the heads off my ornamental gnomes. Cost me an arm and a leg.
TOM: Aren't you, shocked?
SHEILA: Eh?
TOM: You just caught your husband shagging my flat mate. Don't we at least get a hint of a raised eyebrow?
SHEILA: Oh put a sock in it Tom, you're always yapping you boring sod. Have you got kids?
BERYL: No I toyed with getting a goat but it's cruel in a flat.
TOM: Me always yapping on? What about you, you gabby old cow?
SHEILA: You are not too old to be put over my knee young man, do you hear?
TOM: You just can't handle the truth can you?
SHEILA: No it's you who can't face the truth Tom Farrell. I mean where's the man of your dreams you're forever prattling on about? Where's this fantastic acting career you're supposed to have? You're living with a social reprobate, some bloody catch you are.
TOM: Well I have got a boyfriend, I have actually, here, here there's a photograph of us, there, there.

SHEILA: You can't even lie convincingly it's no wonder you can't act.

♂ TOM: But if I can't act, what was I doing in Daylight Robbery then?

SHEILA: You were standing in a queue in the background Tom. It's hardly Julie frigging Andrews, is it? You'll never cut the mustard lad and do you want to know why?

♂ TOM: You evil witch.

SHEILA: Because you're selfish. You don't listen to other people. You think of nobody but yourself. You don't know that (Snaps fingers) about other people's emotions.

♂ TOM: Well at least I'm not dead from the neck down.

SHEILA: Oh you are so funny Tom. Get the Pollyfilla out, you're cracking me up.

linda comes in glowing. she passes sheila on her way out.

♀ LINDA: Hi mummy.

♂ TOM: This is your fault. I'm probably from a broken home now. If I was still at school I'd be having free meals. I'd have my own special little queue in the canteen. And all the bullies would crowd round and they'd taunt me and poke fun at me and say 'Hey you Child of divorced parents! You get free meals! You pooh your pants! You like boys! You looked at Tommy Cassidy's willy when he was in the toilet. That's why he hit you. That's why he hit you.' Oh God why am I telling you this?

♀ LINDA: You all right Beryl? You look a bit peaky.

BERYL: I'm off my nut dear. Dropped a pill about an hour ago. I'm sitting on something. It's your birth certificate Linda.

♂ TOM: Give me that. Give me that. Going on about... 1960? You're thirty-nine!!

BERYL: Oh bloody hell, I'm tripping.

vernon and sheila come in in fancy dress.

♀ LINDA: Now here's your fancy dress costume, let me guess. Let me guess. Denise Van Outen and Jamiroquai.

SHEILA: No Peters and Lee.

VERNON: Now Tom your mother's told me about the row and well you're old enough to

know lad, so you know you're gay like?

♂ TOM: Oh really?

VERNON: Yes well we've got an alternative sexuality as well.

♂ TOM: Have you?

SHEILA: Tom we're swingers.

♀ LINDA: Oh fuck a duck.

SHEILA: Well actually for the past six years I've been bonking the ice cream man.

♂ TOM: My ice cream man?

SHEILA: Yes.

♂ TOM: Oh you bitch! Swingers?

VERNON: Doesn't that make you proud?

♀ LINDA: He might not look much Tom, but underneath it he's a right little dynamo, ain't he mummy?

SHEILA: Come on Vernon we'll be late for the wife swapping party.

BERYL/LINDA: Where?

VERNON: Anyway we love you warts and all Tom. Can you still love us?

tom is stunned into silence.

SHEILA: We'll take that as a no then. Come on Vernon. You've had your fun today. It's time I had mine.

VERNON: Hey Tom.

♂ TOM: Don't come near me. Don't come near.

VERNON: I only want you to tell me you love me.

♂ TOM: Oh yeah you loved me so much you didn't even buy me a present did you?

VERNON: Oh we did. We booked you a male escort at great expense actually. There you are Linda that's the address of the party in case you fancy a change of scenery.

vernon and sheila go.

♀ LINDA: Well I hope you're feeling guilty. Banging on about how boring they were and all the time they'd booked him a prozzy. They must really love him.

♂ TOM: Beryl, got any more of those pills left?

BERYL: Plenty.

♂ TOM: Give them to me please. Thank you.

♀ LINDA: I've never been invited to an orgy before. I suppose they didn't want to put the other ladies to shame.

suze and jez come in. tom is knocking back a bottle of pills.

SUZE: Hi cats.

♂ TOM: Look at me, look at me. I'm taking an overdose. Watch me, watch me.

SUZE: Wow this party's really swinging!

BERYL: Tom they're multivitamins.

♂ TOM: Right I'm going to put my head in this oven then. And no one try and stop me.

BERYL: We're not.

JEZ: Tom, it's electric.

♀ LINDA: Right. How do I look?

ALL: Vile.

♀ LINDA: Right I'm going. See you later Tommy.

tom is squeezing his head in the juicer.

♂ TOM: Right who wants some brain juice? Who wants some brain juice?

SUZE: Oh yes, get some beakers quick.

SHARED HALLWAY

linda comes out and finds a sexy man lurking there.

♀ LINDA: Oh.,

MAN: Hi I'm from Spunky Hunks for Hire. I'm looking for Tom.

♀ LINDA: Oh, I don't know if you're familiar with the old Play Away presenter Toni Arthur? Only she was a bird with a bloke's name.

MAN: Right.

she extends her hand to shake his.

♀ LINDA: Tom Farrell. Pleased to meet you!

Episode Six
GLAD TO BE GAY?

NIGHTCLUB

linda and tom dancing. an ugly guy, neville gives tom the eye. a woman brushes past linda and touches her accidentally. linda headbutts her.

♀ LINDA: Oi! Fat cow. Ugly people deserve a good slap. Get off me don't touch what you can't afford. Oh Tom.

OUTSIDE THE CLUB

linda being kicked out. tom and neville follow. a cab driver, maddie, stands by her cab having a ciggie.

♂ TOM: Get up you drunken great dragoon. Come on we've got to get you home. Come on. I say! Young woman? Are you a taxi?
MADDIE: Where are you going?

♂ TOM: Paradise Passage, Kentish Town.
MADDIE: Oh hop in.

♀ LINDA: Oh look at you, ain't you lovely. Ain't you little? You're like a little China dolly wally.

♂ TOM: Get in you slag.
NEVILLE: It's all right I've got a sister with special needs.

♀ LINDA: Here, they're homosexuals, you don't mind do you?
MADDIE: No.

♀ LINDA: They're harmless.

maddie has photos of her kids on the dashboard.

♀ LINDA: Oh look she collects pictures. Do you collect pictures?
MADDIE: No they're my twins. Pearl and Dean.

neville hums the theme music.

♀ LINDA: Who's that?
♂ TOM: I don't know, I'm not with him.
♀ LINDA: Oi, trade, keep it shut.
MADDIE: Kentish Town?

TOM'S BEDROOM NEXT MORNING

tom wakes up to see neville staring down at him.

NEVILLE: All right mate?
♂ TOM: No, no!
NEVILLE: What?
♂ TOM: Nothing, nothing, nothing, nothing.
NEVILLE: Oh was you having a bad dream?
♂ TOM: Oh I think I still am, I think I still am.
NEVILLE: Oh Mr Tongue wants to say hello.
♂ TOM: No, no! I haven't brushed my teeth yet.
NEVILLE: Oh don't worry about that Tom, I did it whilst you were asleep. You had a bit of spam in your molars.
♂ TOM: Would you get dressed and leave please? I've got to go and get the post.
NEVILLE: Done it.
♂ TOM: What?
NEVILLE: Nothing urgent, just some bills.
♂ TOM: Give me that. Would you please get dressed and get out. I've got a very important audition to get to.
NEVILLE: What's the audition for?
♂ TOM: The Charlotte Church Experience.
NEVILLE: There's nothing about this in your filofax.
♂ TOM: I never said you could look in that.
NEVILLE: I love it when you get angry. (Picks his nose)
♂ TOM: Give it to me. Oh will you stop picking your nose. It's utterly disgusting.

NEVILLE: My last boyfriend used to hate me doing that as well. 'Don't pick your nose your head will cave in!' Funny isn't it?

♂ TOM: Yes, yes it's hilarious yeah. Get out please because I've got to get dressed.

NEVILLE: All right.

♂ TOM: What are you staring at?

NEVILLE: Oh who got out of bed the wrong side this morning? Tom!

♂ TOM: Do shut up.

NEVILLE: Shut up yourself. Here Tom.

♂ TOM: What?

NEVILLE: We just had our first row. Oh.

♂ TOM: They're mine.

NEVILLE: I'm wearing your slippers. They're quite a snug fit actually. If we ever split up can I keep them?

a knock at the front door.

♂ TOM: Now you've really got to get out, that will be my errant lover, who's heard that I'm having an affair and he's come round baying for your blood. Quickly jump out of the window.

NEVILLE: No, you told me last night you hadn't had a relationship since 1992.

♂ TOM: Well he bears a very long grudge.

HALLWAY

linda coming to answer the door. neville springs out and pushes her out of the way.

NEVILLE: Leave this to me, I'm a security guard!

♀ LINDA: Not so bloody loudly!

neville opens the door. one of beryl's punters waits outside.

NEVILLE: Linda, I think I'd better deal with

this. Get over it pal, it was seven years ago, he's mine now.

MAN: I'm so sorry, I was looking for Beryl.

NEVILLE: Oh so that's your little nickname for him is it? Very imaginative.

♀ LINDA: Oi wanker, Beryl lives upstairs. Get out of it. (To punter) Hi.

MAN: Hi.

beryl slaps another punter down the stairs. she is dressed in leather.

BERYL: Get down, get down, and don't do it again. Oh hi Linda.

♀ LINDA: Are you paying for it?

MAN: Is that really naughty?

BERYL: Stay there.

LINDA'S BEDROOM

linda comes in. she gets the fright of her life when she sees tom behind her dressing table.

♀ LINDA: Urgh! What are you doing?

♂ TOM: I'm hiding. Shut up.

♀ LINDA: Oh God my heart. Here I think Beryl's gone back on the game. Remind me if I ever get as big as her never to wear skin tight rubber. Who are you hiding from?

♂ TOM: The trade. Well I mean I call him trade. I mean trade tends to conjure up images of scaffolders in hard hats or men who can name all the players in Man United. Not some gormless half-wit with the sex appeal of a Cyclops.

♀ LINDA: Here my Auntie Ivy was a Cyclops. Or Auntie Eye as we used to call her. You could never tell whether she was winking or blinking poor cow. Here did we have a good time last night?

♂ TOM: Don't you remember anything?

♀ LINDA: I do remember one Christmas when Daddy laughed because all I got was a pencil sharpener.

♂ TOM: No about last night you prattling pig. You were all over that poor taxi driver like a rash. Kept going on about how us birds should stick together. Then you started singing an impromptu version of 'Only Women Bleed.' And you were so pissed you kept forgetting the words. So it was 'only women, what do women do again?' And then you dragged her back here for some Tequila Slammers.

♀ LINDA: Well that's bollocks. I don't do women friends, do I? They just get bitter because of my looks. Now will you get out, I want to get back to bed.

♂ TOM: No I've got to wait until he's gone. Oh my God, what if he doesn't go home. Oh no. I need to go wee wee. My bladder will stretch to the size of a space hopper.

♀ LINDA: The British are crap at one night stands. They're so depressed about sex.

♂ TOM: Repressed.

♀ LINDA: The amount of times I've woken up with some bloke screaming, 'What have I done? What have I done?' So was he any good? Did he move your earth?

♂ TOM: He was a bit toothy.

♀ LINDA: Well at least you've had a bit of filth. I ain't had it in weeks. The next bloke I meet is going to need a pick axe and a Davy lamp to break his way in.

♂ TOM: I don't hear any noises. Perhaps he's gone already? I should be fearless, shouldn't I? What would David Jason do in a position like this? Because he's rather fearless in a Touch of Frost.

♀ LINDA: Oh I love that. 'Oh Rodney you plonker!' You know what that's the only thing with homos in that I actually like.

♂ TOM: Homos? Homos? David Jason doesn't play homos.

♀ LINDA: Del Boy and Rodney? They've been living together for years, they love it.

♂ TOM: They are brothers.

♀ LINDA: Look Tom, just because you woke up with a monster, don't take it out on me. You made your bed mate.

♂ TOM: Oh I give up.

linda goes to get back into bed but finds that maddie is there.

♀ LINDA: Oi you cheeky bitch, how long you been there?

MADDIE: All night. Oh what time is it?

♀ LINDA: Oh get out, lying there with all your bits hanging out.

linda runs out.

LIVING ROOM

linda comes in. tom is making tea.

♀ LINDA: Taxi twat was in my bed all along. Can you believe that?

♂ TOM: Oh were you having a little sleep over? Oh, the girls at my school did that. They used to love them, sitting there talking about Purdey cuts and make-up. 'Tom, Tom, how's my haircut looking?' 'Tom, Tom why don't the boys dance at the school disco?' 'Tom, Tom, why are you wearing Beverley's bra.' Oh...

♀ LINDA: You sad git. You should have been outside knocking a ball about and talking about wanking. I never liked sleep-overs. And I think my feelings were known on the subject because I was never invited to any which was great. So, where's the vile trade?

♂ TOM: He's gone, isn't that marvellous?

♀ LINDA: Cor, I wish she'd do the same. (Shouts through) Hurry up I want to go back to bed! (To Tom) What are you doing?

♂ TOM: I'm doing a mail out. I'm warning everyone in the business that I'm on television this Sunday night. Listen to this, just listen. It is with the greatest of pleasures that I, Thomas Farrell, playing age range 16 to 49, announce my appearance on the top rated BBC show Songs of Praise. Please note that during 'To Be a Pilgrim' I get three close ups and look straight into camera.

♀ LINDA: When did you do that?

♂ TOM: Well do you remember when I saw that film crew by Our Lady's by the traffic lights? Well I got chatting to the best boy and he said he'd slip me in the back way while no one was looking.

♀ LINDA: Hurry up! Blimey.

♂ TOM: And I photocopied all my reviews from my Am. Dram. days and also I'm sending in two photographs, look. One sort of matinee idoly you see, like that. And then this one's more sort of character based. Like that. (Writing on envelope) so that's that. For the attention of Sir Richard Attenborough.

LINDA
'Oh my G string. It's like a satin cheese wire.'

maddie comes in dressed.

♀ LINDA: Cor about bloody time.

MADDIE: Hiya! Anyone mind if I fly that kettle on? I'm absolutely parched.

♂ TOM: You help yourself Maddie. Did you sleep well?

MADDIE: After a fashion. (Winks at Linda) Is it all right if I phone my fella?

♀ LINDA: Oh that poor man, having to put up with the likes of you, you dirty stop out. Does he hit you?

MADDIE: No.

♀ LINDA: Why not? Hey there's a perfectly good phone box down the end of the road, bloody Northerners.

♂ TOM: You can phone whoever you want Maddie.

MADDIE: Oh tar kid. Did you have a good time with Neville last night Tom?

♂ TOM: Oh that was his name was it, Neville? Well let me tell you having sex with Neville was rather like sitting in a Robin Reliant on the M6 in the pouring rain listening to Gardeners Question Time. And not just any old Gardeners Question Time actually.

neville enters from the garden with flowers.

♀ LINDA: Tom.

♂ TOM: Shut up. It was the sort of Gardeners Question Time where they're discussing the pros and cons of a rather irksome lobelia from darkest Peru.

♀ LINDA: Tom.

♂ TOM: I said shut up. You see the problem with him was that he wasn't a very big boy. Not very much to look at in the underwear department. In fact it put me in mind of a Walnut Whip. So no having sex with um, um, what was his name again?

NEVILLE: Neville.

♂ TOM: Neville, thank you very much.

NEVILLE: I picked some of these, I'll put them in a vase.

♂ TOM: No not that one, that's tiny – you need a bigger one!

NEVILLE: I'm going.

MADDIE: Oh his mobile's off. Can I phone my mate? Oh Linda give us a ciggie.

♀ LINDA: No.

MADDIE: You should be on the stage you, you're dead funny.

♀ LINDA: Get off.

♂ TOM: Yeah thanks but I already am. Hang on what's this, what's this? (Reading a review) However for me the low point in Salad Days was Thomas Farrell's spring onion which brought tears to my eyes? That should say high point. Right Linda would you turn and face me please. Tongue out. Thank you.

he uses her as a stamp wetting machine.

MADDIE: (On Phone) Hiya Tracey it's me love. Listen I have got some earth shattering gossip. Last night right, guess what I did? I had sex with a woman. Can you believe that? It's this woman I picked up in my cab Linda they call her. I know, I know. Look listen I've got to go. The tea's ready, yeah I'm still round her gaff. I'll call you later. (Phone down) Now anyone take sugar? Linda sugar?

♀ LINDA: I don't want nothing in me. I'm going back to bed.

she runs out.

LINDA'S BEDROOM

linda smoking anxiously. tom comes in.

♀ LINDA: I love smoking me. Mummy gave me my first ciggie when I was ten and I've never looked back.

♂ TOM: Everything okay Lindy? Well I must say this has come out of the blue hasn't it?

♀ LINDA: Tom, you know I smoke.

♂ TOM: Give me a lesbian, gay and transgendered hug will you.

♀ LINDA: Get off me.

♂ TOM: One has to be careful when one is

coming out. If I had my time over again I don't think I'd have chosen to tell my parents on top of the Blackpool Tower. It was very windy, had to do a lot of shouting. A couple of security guards had a bloody good chortle. And a school party, and a group of elderly monks.

♀ LINDA: Tom, I feel like one of them experimental bunny rabbits. Stuck in the lavatory with lipstick on. I feel abused. I wouldn't mind but no-one was watching.

♂ TOM: Well now I know why you were always so vile about dykes. Because you were in that great Egyptian river, denial.

♀ LINDA: Tom you've slept with a bird, does that make you a lesbian? No. I mean look at my posters, I love men.

♂ TOM: Maybe you're bisexual, oh God nobody's safe.

♀ LINDA: There's no such thing as bisexual, it's just greediness. Tom I can't be a dyke I won the prize in Borstal for girl least likely to wear dungarees.

♂ TOM: But, but Lindy you could come on the Gay Pride march with me.

♀ LINDA: No I can't do marching. I got thrown out of the majorettes for misuse of my baton.

♂ TOM: Oh come on Lindy. We're here, Lindy's queer, get used to it!

♀ LINDA: Tom, how can I be a dyke? I mean look at me I'm gorgeous.

♂ TOM: Loads of lessies are gorgeous Lindy, look at... Thelma from Scooby Doo. Now I've organised a little trip to a queer café. Oh no we can't, we can't leave your girlfriend here alone.

♀ LINDA: Don't call her that.

♂ TOM: Oh I know we'll take your girlfriend with us, yes. Maddie?

♀ LINDA: (Sucking thumb) Mummy. Mummy. I want my mummy.

LIVING ROOM

tom comes in to see maddie.

♂ TOM: Maddie, I just can't tell you how empowering I'm finding it being in a queer only space, so bless you.
MADDIE: Is Linda all right? she seems a bit off with me.

♂ TOM: Oh she's like that with everybody. Now would you like to join us for a spot of lunch at a little lezzie taverna I know in Clerkenwell? Or have you eaten enough off the table of love?
MADDIE: Last night was brilliant. I don't know what our Phil's being doing wrong all these years, but Linda was just fantastic. Talk about turbo tongue. I think she enjoyed herself. Mind you I felt a bit sorry for the neighbours, she's a bit of a howler isn't she?

linda has come in and heard this.

♀ LINDA: The size of your nose, I must have thought it was a little penis!
MADDIE: Hello darling. I didn't see you standing there.

♀ LINDA: Don't you call me darling. I ain't your darling, I ain't nobody's darling.
MADDIE: Have I to go then?

♀ LINDA: I think it's wise.
MADDIE: Look about last night. Well what I'm trying to say is, I just think you're amazing. I married our Phil when I was sixteen and pregnant, and he's the only person I've ever slept with till last night. I don't know what to say. I'd love to see you again. I've been a bit silly really haven't I? Broadcasting it to all and sundry. I've slept with a bird. Like it's some kind of novelty. Whereas for you it's a way of life. I'm sorry, I hope you don't think I've been patronising, I'll be off. Oh I can tell I've really upset you. Look if you ever change your mind. Call a taxi. See you. (Leaves)

♂ TOM: She was so nice wasn't she? She was like every nice nurse you've ever seen on Casualty. The minute they get stabbed you're crying your eyes out and you're yelling at the screen 'Not her! Stab the other one! Stab the vile one!'

GIMME GIMME GIMME

♀LINDA: God, one little mistake and I'm tarnished for life. Jeez, I sniffed some glue when I was in the Brownies. Does that make me a drug addict? No. I wore an A line skirt in the seventies, does that mean I've got no taste now? No. I sleep with one woman and all of a sudden I'm branded a tennis player.

♂TOM: Well just give me five minutes and then I'll whisk you off to some lovely bender hot spot, all right?

♀LINDA: I'm not going anywhere with you. I'll show you I'm not gay. I'll show the lot of you. I'm going out.

♂TOM: I suggest you get dressed first. (She goes) Shall I call you a taxi? Oh gay people are so funny.

STREET

linda calls to a man in his car.

♀LINDA: Excuse me, do you want to shag me?

HOTEL BAR

linda approaches a man on a bar stool.

♀LINDA: You looking for a lady? See I think you're really gorgeous right, and I haven't had it in ages. So what say we step outside for a little bit of summertime loving?

a security guard approaches it's neville.

NEVILLE: That's enough madame.
♀LINDA: Eh?
NEVILLE: Oh hello.

she thumps him.

♀LINDA: Oh piss off you, you poofy homo!

SHARED HALLWAY

tom coming home with linda. beryl's punter is still knocking about.

♂TOM: Get in here now!
♀LINDA: Oh you still here? You've been waiting ages.
MAN: I think I must have been an incredibly naughty boy, what do you think?
♂TOM: Linda!
♀LINDA: I think I'd better go in.

LIVING ROOM

tom leads her in.

♂TOM: Keep your lips firmly shut and sit down.
♀LINDA: Bit of a challenge.
♂TOM: You see a tone and you've just got to lower it haven't you? It's been a funny twenty-four hours in the life of Linda La Hughes hasn't it? I mean first you try your hand at nightclub violence. And then you pull a penis free cab driver.

♀ LINDA: Tom could we just put that down to me being off my box?

♂ TOM: And then I get a phone call from Kentish Town Police Station informing me that Miss Linda La Hughes has been arrested for soliciting.

♀ LINDA: Yeah and like I said to them. 'Do I look like a solicitor? No.' And what do they do, what do they send me? A bloody solicitor. I said to them I said 'Go on arrest her.'

♂ TOM: No, no, no, no. Soliciting is what prostitutes do.

♀ LINDA: And as my solicitor said, 'I ain't no prozzy because I didn't want paying'.

♂ TOM: Oh.

♀ LINDA: God just how thick are you?

♂ TOM: Well we'll just sit here until I get an apology.

♀ LINDA: What for? I got let off.

♂ TOM: Yes and in order to convince Neville to drop the ABH charge, I've had to agree for him coming round here for dinner tonight. Oh yes that's very funny isn't it? Go on laugh, yes a very sensible thing to do. Well I think I'll change my mind. Yes supper's off I'll give Neville a ring. Then you'd go to court wouldn't you? And you'd go down. And you'd have to do your bird. And then you'd have to do loads of birds wouldn't you? But you'd quite like that. The bike of C wing. Always dropping your soap in the shower and calling yourself Larry, yes. (On phone) Hello, hello Neville?

♀ LINDA: No, no, no. I'm sorry Tom.

♂ TOM: Sorry didn't quite hear that.

♀ LINDA: I'm sorry Tom.

♂ TOM: Sorry a little bit louder please.

♀ LINDA: (Booming) I'm bloody sorry, all right? What more do you want?

♂ TOM: Well you can prove it can't you? You can finish my mail out.

♀ LINDA: Oh how many are there?

♂ TOM: Well I've done five, so you've only got four hundred and ninety five to do all right? Letter, reviews, photographs and then write down their names and addresses there.

♀ LINDA: Oh God but I hate writing.

♂ TOM: Just do it!

he goes. she gets to work. beryl slips through heading for the french window.

BERYL: Hello Linda.

♀ LINDA: Bloody hell Beryl you nearly gave me an heart attack then. What you doing?

BERYL: I've got to go and be filthy to an MP in Westminster. Apparently there's great call for granny porn.

♀ LINDA: Well why don't you go out the front door like normal people?

BERYL: Well I've got a punter waiting there. I can't let him see me.

♀ LINDA: That poor man, he's been there all day.

BERYL: Oh he wanted humiliation he's getting it.

♀ LINDA: Beryl, wouldn't it be more humiliating if you went out the front door?

BERYL: Linda I could eat you!

♀ LINDA: Yeah well that's a bit of a sore point.

beryl goes the other way.

LINDA
'There's no such thing as bisexual, it's just greediness.'

LINDA'S BEDROOM

linda bored rigid with the mail out.

♀ LINDA: I can't do this.

KITCHEN

tom and neville eating soup.

NEVILLE: I do think jokes about the handicapped can be really funny.

♂ TOM: Would you like some more soup from my tureen?

NEVILLE: What is it again, something weird isn't it?

♂ TOM: No it's just cauliflower.

NEVILLE: Oh no it gives me terrible wind cauliflower. That and chilli con carne. Oh. (Farts)

HALLWAY

linda pops her head out. the punter is still there.

LINDA: Hi. She still not back? That's a bit humiliating isn't it? I bet I could find you something to keep you occupied.

MAN: No offence, but I like my mistresses old.

LINDA: Well I'm knocking eighty, I just do a lot of exercise.

his eyes light up.

LINDA'S BEDROOM

the punter doing the mail out.

LINDA: Hurry up.

MAN: Yes mistress. Sorry.

KITCHEN

tom and neville finishing off their main course. neville farts a lot.

NEVILLE: No if I'm going to be honest, my favourite food is the much maligned pilchard. My ex-boyfriend used to say 'Knock a pilchard knock a pal'. Classic quote. Oh sorry.

TOM: Would you excuse me? I've just got to go and get my gas mask.

NEVILLE: Tom you're drinking rather a lot tonight. Have you got a problem with the sauce? Shall we get you to a counsellor?

TOM: No I was rather hoping that by getting pissed you'd suddenly become attractive.

NEVILLE: I couldn't go out with you if you was a bit of an alcoholic Tom.

TOM: Oh really, well then yes I am, yes.

NEVILLE: Only kidding I love you warts and all.

TOM: You can't have a relationship with me, you can't. I'm a very heavy smoker.

NEVILLE: I don't mind.

TOM: You see I couldn't light any naked flames around you, you'd blow me into the next street up.

NEVILLE: Well give up then.

TOM: Why should I bloody give up? It's nothing to do with you.

NEVILLE: Tom, Tom it's everything to do with me. I'm your boyfriend.

TOM: You're not my bloody boyfriend. I wouldn't go out with you if you were the last woman on the planet.

NEVILLE: Oh well in that case I don't want to have a relationship with you, thank you very much. I don't even want to sleep with you, so there.

TOM: Thank God for that. Really. (Beat) Why? I'm gorgeous!

NEVILLE: I was a virgin until last night.

TOM: Oh were you? I've never been anyone's first time before. What was I like, was I fantastic? Yeah I expect I was pretty good wasn't I? Did you like my body? What's your favourite bit? Apparently I've got fantastic deltoids. They've been written about in the cubicles at Charing Cross. Oh God I wish you'd told me I was breaking you in, I'd have stayed awake.

NEVILLE: I'm going.

TOM: But you haven't shared your ruminations about my body yet.

NEVILLE: Forget it Tom, it was never going to be.

TOM: But hang on! How many people have you been out with, with a birthmark the same shape as Merthyr Tydfyl?

NEVILLE: Tom it might have been my first time, so what do I know? What I just wanted to say, you're a crap shag.

LINDA'S BEDROOM

the punter getting dressed. linda lounging on the bed.

MAN: Did I work hard mistress?

LINDA: Well you got a treat for your labours didn't you?

MAN: I didn't believe you were eighty at first, until you took your clothes off. (Getting wallet) So what's that then, fifty?

LINDA: Hundred, hurry up.

MAN: Can I come again?

LINDA: No I'm knackered, piss off.

LIVING ROOM

linda brings through all the mail outs.

⚥ TOM: Oh my God. My God you've done them all. God your handwriting's improved. You're getting the B's the right way round.

♀ LINDA: I enjoyed every minute of it.

⚥ TOM: And you smell unusually nice. You didn't have to go to any trouble for me you know.

♀ LINDA: It ain't for you mush, I'm going out.

⚥ TOM: Well it's lesbian night at Billy Jean's on the high street.

♀ LINDA: I don't care what you say mate, I know I'm straight.

⚥ TOM: Yeah fine, whatever.

♀ LINDA: You can't

wind me up anymore. I am what I am.

⚥ TOM: Okay. Well have a lovely time then. You great big lezzer.

she punches him.

LINDA'S BEDROOM

tom comes in with the breakfast tray.

⚥ TOM: Good morning!

linda appears from under the covers.

♀ LINDA: Morning!

maddie appears too.

   MADDIE: Morning!

♀ LINDA: Oh no!

GIMME GIMME GIMME   121

Episode Seven
SOFA MAN

sofa advert.

a cheesy tv presenter called rick cheesecloth bounding through a sofa store.

STORE

RICK: (On TV) Hi, I'm Rick Cheesecloth and let me tell you, I know a lot about sofas. Why? Because I speak to thousands of our happy customers who buy our top of the range seating arrangements every single day. (Sits) This feels wonderful and it's only four nine-nine. Yes, four nine-nine! And if I buy this weekend I pay nothing for twenty-five years. But what do other people look for in a sofa?

TRENDY WOMAN: I need a sofa that's going to stand the test of time. And be fashionable too.

YOUNG MUM: With three triplets under the age of nine, we need a sofa that can beat that bounce test. And be handily wipe clean.

DRUNKEN LUSH: My sofa's my best friend. Cheers!

RICK: So whatever your sofa needs, hurry down to World of Sofas. Today!

tom & linda.

LIVING ROOM

tom and linda having breakfast. linda switches the advert off.

♀ LINDA: Oh shut up. Silly git. I'd like to knock him out. Give him some of that. (Clenches fist)

♂ TOM: Quiet, I'm reading my stars!

♀ LINDA: Is the moon in Uranus?

♂ TOM: Pisces. A telephone call brings good news. And it's an excellent day for travel. What are you again?

♀ LINDA: Stunning.

♂ TOM: Leo, avoid wearing mini skirts you look like a stupid fat cow in them. Well it's spot on then.

♀ LINDA: Spot on? Spot on? Freak!

♂ TOM: It's just a saying. Like mutton dressed as lamb.

♀ LINDA: Well here's another one. Kiss my arse.

♂ TOM: It's barely eight o'clock in the morning. I don't want to have to consider your lumpy bare behind. You're putting me off my porridge. I've got images of stretch marks shooting across my brain.

♀ LINDA: Stretch marks? The skin of my cheeks is as tight as a tambourine. Bang it baby!

♂ TOM: Oh Linda please! You're bringing on one of my heads.

♀ LINDA: (Aroused) Oh?

♂ TOM: One of my headache heads. I didn't have to be up this early you know.

♀ LINDA: Well don't look at me. I never made you get up.

♂ TOM: Oh no? I'm supposed to sleep through a twenty million decibel rendition of 'Hit Me Baby One More Time' at seven o'clock this morning?

♀ LINDA: You want to get some ear plugs Thomas. The walls in this flat are wafer thin. The things I hear you get up to of an evening. Strain, strain, strain. Then you call out somebody's name.

♂ TOM: Oh don't be ridiculous.

♀ LINDA: Who is Dennis Norden by the way?

♂ TOM: That's libellous and anyway I could be wearing ear plugs, a stainless steel balaclava and a small horse on my head and I'd still hear that **cacophonous** crap pounding through my walls.

♀ LINDA: Pardon me for breathing. I just thought you might want to support me on my big day.

♂ TOM: Your big day? Your big day? You're starting work on a production line in a factory. You call that a big day do you?

♀ LINDA: Well it is for me mate. Oh I can't wait. It's going to be just like the Rag Trade, do you remember that? 'Everybody out!'

♂ TOM: Yes well I could never do manual work, I'm far too middle class.

♀ LINDA: Bollocks! You're just like me moosh, common as muck.

♂ TOM: I'm nothing like you. I've worn jodhpurs.

♀ LINDA: What?

♂ TOM: Jodhpurs. They're a sort of upper class shell suit.

the phone rings.

♂ TOM: Oh, oh, oh my horoscope said a telephone call brings good news.

♀ LINDA: Oh shut up, it's probably my boss wanting to know the size of my new uniform. (On phone) Hi? Thirty-six double D. What's your inside leg? Oh right. Hang on. (Hands it to Tom) It's your agent.

♂ TOM: Oh, oh, oh, oh. Hi Norma, hi. No I'm always up at the crack. Nothing like the early hours to shove back the settee, slip on a jock strap and have a stab at a couple of star jumps. So how can I help? Oh great. Great. Yes, yes place, time. Oh hang on I need a pen, hang on I'll just get my PA to pass me a pen. PA?

♀ LINDA: Pee off.

♂ TOM: She's got a wonderful sense of humour. Yes thank you, thank you that will be all Mrs Bridges. Right okay your pistol's pointing me wise, so shoot from the hip. Yeah, yeah great lovely. Yeah, okey dokey, pig in a pokey. Yeah. Okay that's lovely. Yeah. How much will I be paid? Lovely. Lovely okay well tell the director I'll see him on the set at ten. Ciao bella, Ciao. (Phone down) Well slip me a fish and call it Wanda. If I haven't gone and got myself a job. My horoscope was right, I don't believe it!

♀ LINDA: What is it? Are you going to be a dirty screw in Bad Girls?

♂ TOM: No, no it's an advert! Do you remember when I almost got that insoles commercial? I nearly was the face of Odour Eaters.

♀ LINDA: I know, some adverts are brilliant these days aren't they? What's it for?

RICK'S WINNEBAGO

close-up on tom doing dire acting.

♂ TOM: But most of all, I want a sofa that says I'm an individual.

rick coming out of his toilet.

RICK: Well that sounded top notch. I was only tinkling so I heard every word.

♂ TOM: Well I love your winnebago. Does everyone who works in adverts get one like this?

RICK: Only the greats, Zeffirelli, Pauline Quirke. Me. You really have to have queered your pitch and said Talent For Sale to end up with trappings like this. I hope you're not uncomfortable with my use of the word queer there, Tom?

♂ TOM: No, no I use it all the time.

RICK: Stick with me kid, I'll give you a lift home in my limo.

FACTORY

linda on a mash potato production line with a sexy guy ron and a scary freak with red hair and glasses daisy.

DAISY: (Singing) It's the same the whole world over, it's the poor who gets the blame. The rich who takes the pleasure, ain't it all a bleeding shame? (Speaking) I don't

LINDA
'Think like a slut, dress like a slut.'

half get bored with this mashed potato you know. I wish we could do sausages like them lot over there.

♀ LINDA: I don't know what it is about sausages. But whenever I see one I come over all funny.

DAISY: Do you Linda? Eh, eh? Do you?

RON: You're making some nice big lumps there Linda.

♀ LINDA: Oh thanks. I've often been complimented on the size of my lumps.

DAISY: Here Ron, don't you think me and Linda look like twins?

♀ LINDA: Piss off, do we!

DAISY: Though you've got the sight in both eyes obviously.

♀ LINDA: Here Ron, is she a bit backward only between you me and the post box, I overheard this bird in the bog and she said there was a new girl started today with red hair who was a bit thick.

RON: You don't want to take any notice of gossip Linda. Tongues can be vicious things.

♀ LINDA: Oh I know.

DAISY: You ain't half good fun Linda. Ain't she good fun Ron?

♀ LINDA: I'm the good time that was had by all.

DAISY: You got a man Linda? I bet they're queuing up for you ain't they? Eh? Eh? Eh?

♀ LINDA: Yes Daisy they are but at the moment I'm young, free, single and slack. What about you Ron?

RON: What have I got a man in my life? Yes.

♀ LINDA: Oh bloody hell! Everywhere I go I'm surrounded by homos. I want to go to another section!

RON: I was only pulling your leg Linda. The man in my life is my dad.

♀ LINDA: Oh Ron you can pull my leg anytime you want. You can pull anything you want mate, I'm very supple.

DAISY: Is your dad tall Ron? I always pictured him being tall for some reason. I'm mad like that Linda honestly, I always picture people being tall.

♀ LINDA: Great.

RON: He's about my height.

DAISY: Oh that's a lovely height.

♀ LINDA: Oi you dirty bitch, stop flirting over the conveyor belt. God you're so blatant. So Ron do you live with just your dad or your dad and your wife?

RON: I'm not married.

♀ LINDA: Oh really? What do you look for in a lady then? Apart from the obvious. Do you like a nice big chest? Filthy personality?

RON: I have to admit I do like redheads.

♀ LINDA: Really? Well I'm red all over, collar and cuffs.

DAISY: You're naughty. You are, you're naughty.

♀ LINDA: I know, bend me over and spank me Ronnie baby, I'm bad.

she spurts mashed potato over her breasts.

LIVING ROOM

linda comes in to find tom and rick having a drink.

♀ LINDA: Hi honey I'm home!

♂ TOM: Hi, hi. This is Linda my room mate, she's huge in mashed potato.

RICK: Rick Cheesecloth. Voice of the nation.

♀ LINDA: Linda La Hughes, Voice of the Beehive fan club member. Here don't take this the wrong way mate, but you don't half look like that prat out of them sofa adverts. God I can't stand him. I'd like to give him a good slap.

♂ TOM: No, no, no you're right it is that prat, it is him. It's Rick, it's Rick, be nice to him please.

RICK: (Touches Linda's hair) Have you ever thought of doing something with that? It's really quite extraordinary.

♀ LINDA: I know. Mummy said it was my morning glory.

RICK: I think I'm going to have to hide behind the sofa. Ugly lady alert.

TOM: Yes I know, I know.

RICK: Is it a triffid? Is it a dalek. No it's Linda!

TOM: We've finally made contact with life on Mars.

RICK: I think I'm going to throw up, it looks like a cross between Chris Evans and Olive from On the Buses.

LINDA: Oh I get it. I get the picture. You're just being vile to me because you want to be on your own. Well have fun, you dirty great pair of homos. (Exits)

RICK: How did she know? How did she know?

TOM: Know what? She doesn't know. I don't even know. Know what exactly?

RICK: I'm usually very popular with the ladies.

TOM: Oh look please just sit down and try and relax will you?

RICK: I suppose I am a bit on edge. I'm a huge celebrity and I'm taking a giant step for mankind sort of risk here. But I find you more enticing than a three seater banquette with adjustable arm rests Tom. Would you happen to have such a thing as a sofa bed in your passion palace? I've an overwhelming desire to pull something out and double its size.

LIVING ROOM

tom sitting with new hairdo.
linda enters.

LINDA: What you done to your hair? You look like thingy Hitler. Heil.

TOM: Rick says it really suits me.

LINDA: Oh wise up. And would you mind telling your boyfriend the next time he uses the bath to lock the door? I went in to go to the toilet and my knickers were round my ankles and my cheeks were on the rim before I even realised he was there.

TOM: Rick went to public school. He's very physically uninhibited.

LINDA: My uncle Billy was physically uninhibited and he got arrested for it.

TOM: Rick wouldn't flash at school girls.

LINDA: Billy wasn't a flasher he was just absent minded.

TOM: What? So absent minded he forgot to put his pants on?

LINDA: We've all done it.

linda suddenly notices a brand new pink leather sofa.

LINDA: Argh! Where the bloody hell did that come from?

TOM: It's one of Rick's freebies. Isn't it gorg? And it was only three nine nine. Yes three nine nine.

LINDA: Urgh. Give me a ciggie.

TOM: No I've given up.

LINDA: What?

TOM: Rick says 'Kiss a smoker, kiss an ashtray.'

LINDA: I say kiss a Rick, kiss a prick. Oh! (She slips off the sofa)

TOM: If you're going to sit on that you need to sellotape these to your buttocks then you won't slip off apparently, there we are.

puts sellotape on her bum.

LINDA: It reminds me of that time we were on that day trip at Borstal and the girls superglued me to the back of the bus. We were half the way to Giddlywitch before the driver could hear my screams. Bless them.

RICK: Borstal Linda? Did you say you went to Borstal? Young offenders should be shot on sight in my book.

TOM: Yeah yeah I agree, yeah. Hanging's too good for them isn't it Rick? Did you see Dead Man Walking? Had me peeing my pants that did.

LINDA: I didn't say Borstal you deaf bastard. I said Portsmouth! It's where I come from. Can't you tell by my accent?

RICK: I love Portsmouth, love the bloody place. I was the panto king there in the eighties. Did Babes in the Wood a couple of times with Gary Glitter. Where's my coffee Tom?

LINDA: Oi, stop bossing him about.

RICK: Linda butt out or get pretty, one of the two yeah. Oh for heaven's sake Tom if it's going to take all day forget it.

storms out.

TOM: I've just done it. He isn't always like that you know. When we're alone together he's a very different person.

LINDA: My Auntie Susie was married to someone like that. Seventeen different personalities. It was a bugger to buy Christmas presents for because you never knew which one you'd get.

TOM: God that's so interesting. No wonder you can't get a bloke.

LINDA: Ah but I have got a bloke. His name's Ron, he's gorgeous, do you want to see his picture?

TOM: No I'd rather cosh myself over the head with a hostess wagon frankly.

LINDA: I nicked his filofax and I'm going to get him round here later to get it back. That's my plan. (Gets photo out) Oh ain't he gorgeous Tom? That girl he's with is Daisy from me line. I don't know why he's got his arms around her, she's as thick as shit. (Tom has gone) Tom? Tom?

LINDA'S BEDROOM

linda comes in from work out of breath. she chucks the filofax on the floor.

LINDA: Come on in Ron, the filofax is in here somewhere. I'll find it in a minute.

ron and daisy come in in cycling outfits.

RON: I'm so sorry there wasn't room for you on the tandem Linda.

DAISY: You're a really good runner though Linda.

LINDA: Oi, I never said you could come in, I only said he could come in.

DAISY: Isn't she a good runner Ron, eh? Eh? Nice and bouncy.

LINDA: Come and sit next to me on the bed Ron.

RON: This is a lovely bedroom Linda.

LINDA: Oh thanks. I've got an eye for colour. I think I could be on that Changing Rooms, I'd make a packet.

DAISY: It's like a big pink flower. I'm mad like that Linda, honestly. I think everything's like a big pink flower.

LINDA: Oi, you can't keep it schtum for five minutes can you?

RON: Is that my filofax?

DAISY: It certainly does look like a filofax. But I can't be sure, what with my eye.

LINDA: I can't bend down Ron you see because I've got this lace body stocking on with Velcro round the crotch. You want to hear the noise it makes when it opens, it's like a thousand little lips kissing.

DAISY: That sounds lovely Linda. Bend over, I for one would be really interested to hear that.

LINDA: What are you? Some sort of lezbo?

RON: It's all right I think I can get it.

LINDA: No, no I'll get it.

RON: No it's all right.

he bends over. she jumps on top of him.

LINDA: No, look. Oh, oh I've come over all funny.

DAISY: Come on Ron, time to make tracks.

LINDA: No. Don't you want to stay for a drink Ron?

RON: No I think I'd better get Daisy home.

DAISY: See you Linda, and if I don't see you through the week I'll see you through the window.

RON: Bye Linda.

LINDA: Bugger.

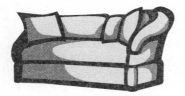

KITCHEN

linda and tom eating dinner. linda messily. she is wearing her factory hat.

TOM: Oh for goodness sake. Do you have to eat with your mouth open?

LINDA: How else am I supposed to get it in?

TOM: And do you have to wear that god awful hat every waking hour? Do you sleep in it as well?

LINDA: Yes it reminds me of my boyfriend.

TOM: Stupid fat pig. You haven't got one.

LINDA: I remember when you used to be nice to me. I remember when you were a laugh.

TOM: Still am. What do you call a nun with a washing machine on her head?

LINDA: Strong.

TOM: Sister Matic. Now kindly get out. I think Rick wants to talk to me about something special.

LINDA: God he's always round here. Ain't he got his own bloody home to go to?

TOM: Well yes he has, but I think that's what he wants to talk to me about. Because tonight Linda I think he's going to ask me to move in with him.

LINDA: You've only known him five minutes!

TOM: Well in gay years that's a lifetime. Linda can't you just picture it? Me and Rick in a small Essex mansion, pansies in the garden, puppies on the porch. A small brook babbling by.

LINDA: You're not going to say yes are you?

TOM: Well you don't think I'm going to spend the rest of my life in this shit hole with you do you?

LINDA: Why not? (Crying)

TOM: Oh stop it, stop wailing like a banshee. It's really unattractive. You're getting snot all over the macaroni cheese.

LINDA: I ain't got an hankie. Give me a hankie.

TOM: Don't you tempt me. I'll dip it in chloroform and stuff it down your slavering little gob.

LINDA: Stop picking on me. You can't leave me Tom, you can't. You're my flatmate.

TOM: Exactly. Not your partner.

LINDA: Oh please Tom! Please don't leave me!

TOM: Oh get off me, this is dry clean only.

RICK: (Coming in) Oh God that is such a revolting sight.

♂ TOM: Yes isn't it, isn't it?

♀ LINDA: You! I hate you, you long streak of piss. I'm going round to my boyfriend's! Ron loves me. He'll take me in. (Exits)

RICK: There's nothing quite as nauseating as a big fat insipid piggy, pasty pre-menstrual slag, don't you agree?

♂ TOM: Not really no. Well hey ho, goodbye single lifestyle. (Going through books) Delia Smith's One is Fun. Oh no it ain't, Delia in the bin. Single Ball Action by Michael Owen. In the bin.

RICK: Tom when I said I wanted to talk to you I did mean some time this year.

♂ TOM: Oh I'm sorry. Right okay I'm all ears now. That's a funny expression isn't it Ricksy? I'm all ears. Imagine if we were all ears. We'd look like...

RICK: Oh shut up Tom there's something I've got to ask you.

♂ TOM: Right okay. Shouldn't you be down on bended knee or something?

RICK: Stop fussing Tom. You're like a girl.

♂ TOM: Yes sorry, sorry. I just want everything to be just right okay?

RICK: Now there comes a point in every man's life when you step back and take stock. You wonder whether certain changes need to be made in order to feel more content, centred, secure. I want to make those changes Tom. Yes I really do.

♂ TOM: Oh so do I, so do I.

RICK: But I want to ask you, before I go ahead and organise anything, so I may as well come out with it. Tom?

♂ TOM: Rick?

RICK: Do you think it's time I had a facelift?

♂ TOM: Is that it? Is that the question?

RICK: Well of course it's the bloody question. What else do you think I was going to ask you? Whether or not you'd move in with me? Oh God, oh yes really good idea. I can really see the wife approving of that.

♂ TOM: Oh God, well you know. I just thought our relationship had got to that stage where we could, what, what, what, what, what

did you say? What? Your wife? Are you married?

RICK: Why do you think I'm round here all the time? I can't have you bouncing around on my four poster bed in the west wing. She'd hit the roof.

♂ TOM: But you're gay.

RICK: What on earth makes you say that?

♂ TOM: Well sleeping with me was a pretty big pointer.

RICK: Oh Tom you silly sausage. I'm a straight man who sleeps with men. Okay? I'll phone the clinic now.

♂ TOM: Actually no don't call the clinic. What I'd really like you to do actually is stand up, take your mobile phone out, extend the aerial a little bit and then shove it right up your saggy, arrogant, misogynistic, homophobic arse. How dare you assume that I'm like you! How bloody dare you! I don't hate women, I don't hate gay people, I don't hate people. And most of all I don't hate myself. Now get out!

RICK: I'll come back when you've calmed down.

♂ TOM: I won't bloody calm down so don't bother coming back. I like the men in my life to be strong, to stand up for what they believe in. Not to be so far back in the closet they're in fucking Narnia!

he is on his own. he starts to cry.

♂ TOM: Lindy?

LINDA
'I'm the good time that was had by all!'

STREET

woman, baby & linda. linda skipping to ron's house. she stops at a zebra crossing to tickle a baby's face. as she skips across the road

she swings her bag and knocks the
baby flying from its
mother's arms.

RON'S FRONT DOOR

linda knocks. daisy answers.
moving oddly.

♀ LINDA: You!

DAISY: Oh hi Linda. How can I help you?

♀ LINDA: You four-eyed, ginger-headed bitch!
Do you know what really irritates me about
you? Your breathy voice and the way your
head bobs up and down.

DAISY: I can't help it.

♀ LINDA: Really?

DAISY: Yeah. Look.

she pulls back the door to show
that ron is giving her one
from behind.

RON: Oh hi Linda. What's up?

♀ LINDA: I just came to say I'm going to be
late for work tomorrow. I've got an
appointment. With a modelling agency.
Someone spotted me in the street and told
me I was really beautiful.

she runs off.

LIVING ROOM, NIGHT

tom and linda having a drink.

♀ LINDA: Tom can I ask you something? Will
you be honest with me?

♂ TOM: Yes.

♀ LINDA: Am I doing something wrong?

♂ TOM: Can I be honest with you?

♀ LINDA: Yes.

♂ TOM: Yes. You're not demure enough you
see. You need to be more demure. I tell
you what you need you know. You need a
crash course at the Tom Farrell Academy of
Flirting. Look I'll show you. We're in a wine
bar and I'm a business man, in pinstripe and
brogues. It's mid-evening and Richard
Clayderman is tinkling in the corner.

♀ LINDA: Use the bloody toilet!

♂ TOM: I'm on my second bourbon and dry

and oh look. A lovely lady has come in, I
wonder who she could be? Hello.

♀ LINDA: Hi.

♂ TOM: How are you? (Waves)

♀ LINDA: No straight men don't wave like that.

♂ TOM: Look it doesn't matter. Hello!

♀ LINDA: Hi.

♂ TOM: My name is Kenneth.

♀ LINDA: Oh Kenneth. That was my mother's
name.

♂ TOM: Would you care to join me?

♀ LINDA: Am I going to get a shag out of it?
This is so boring.

♂ TOM: Well you're not making an effort.
Make an effort. Right okay. What do they
call you?

♀ LINDA: The bike, but it's just jealousy.

♂ TOM: No what is your name?

♀ LINDA: Britney.

♂ TOM: Oh and what do you do for a
living Britney?

♀ LINDA: I chew corn for gummy parrots.

♂ TOM: Are you doing anything later?

♀ LINDA: You hopefully.

♂ TOM: This is ridiculous. Men don't like their
women to be aggressive. You've got to be
more innocent, you've got to be more virgin
like okay? So we'll try it again. Right, so
okay Britney what's a nice girl like you doing
in a place like this?

♀ LINDA: I'm a virgin.

♂ TOM: Right?

♀ LINDA: No. See I'm boring you. You was
having a much better time when I was being
filthy. Come on Tom, men like a bird that
can make them laugh and get them stiffed
up. Come on Kenneth, how big is it? Can I
feel it?

♂ TOM: Oh for goodness sake. I'm not playing
this anymore.

♀ LINDA: Well I'm not surprised you're
bloody crap.

♂ TOM: Yes well I'm not used to chatting up
girls, am I?

♀ LINDA: All right then well I'll be the bloke
and I'll chat you up. Right, so it's a gay
bar, lots of white t-shirts. All right mate?
My name's Mick, what's yours?

♂ TOM: I'm Thomas.

♀ LINDA: Excellent. Did it hurt?

♂ TOM: What?

♀ LINDA: When you fell from heaven baby.

♂ TOM: Oh thanks, thanks. Er do you work?

♀ LINDA: I'm a builder. I make houses. Big ones, small ones, flats, love it.

♂ TOM: I've always wanted to pull a builder.

♀ LINDA: Well tonight's your lucky night mate.

♂ TOM: Have you got anywhere where we could go?

♀ LINDA: Yeah I'm working on a flat round the corner. I've got the keys in my pocket. Feel.

♂ TOM: Oh yes. I don't usually do this you know, I get quite nervous. You hear such horror stories don't you?

♀ LINDA: What's the matter, don't you trust me?

♂ TOM: Well I oughtn't but I'm tempted.

♀ LINDA: It's all right baby, I ain't going to hurt you.

♂ TOM: Oh I feel a little bit tipsy. Ooops. (Bends over)

♀ LINDA: Oh nice arse.

♂ TOM: Oh thanks.

♀ LINDA: Yeah can I feel it?

♂ TOM: Oh yeah of course you can Mick.

♀ LINDA: Cor, I can't wait to get you back in that flat.

♂ TOM: Be gentle with me.

♀ LINDA: Gentle? I don't know the meaning of the word.

♂ TOM: Come on let's go.

he drags linda towards the door then stops.

♂ TOM: Oh no, no my God. Oh my God, what am I thinking?

♀ LINDA: What?

♂ TOM: I forgot my drink.

he grabs it then pulls her out.

CURRICULUM VITAE

NAME: THOMAS THESSALONIUS FARRELL

AGE: 32 (Playing range: 16–92)

TRAINING: 16 years under the personal tutelage of Sheila de Groot – the original face of Dairylea cheese!

3 years at the Poor School.

ROLES INCLUDE:

Corpse Number Two in SILENT WITNESS (BBC)
Rumours that my scene wasn't shown because I fell off the slab are completely unfounded. Amanda Burton is a fantastic, chameleon-esque actress. An inspiration. I loved her in all those Northern Irish Screen Twos in the seventies, forever banging on a door and crying 'Mammy! Mammy! Daddy's been grabbed by the Provos!' She's a real practical trickster. Daubing dog dirt on my Winnebago door and pretending to come at me with a crow bar every time I stepped foot outside! Miss you Mandy!!

Victim Number Three in SILENCE! (Swan Theatre, Worcester)
The musical version of Silence of the Lambs. Wincey Willis was wonderful as Clarice Starling. And Matthew Kelly wasn't half bad as Hannibal – though I wasn't totally bananas about the Abergavenny accent, Matty! I brought tears to a lot of eyes with my act one finale 'Help Me I'm Down A Hole'.

Assistant Social Worker in SOMEONE'S STOLEN MY BABY (ITV)
The fantastic two-parter starring Sarah Lancashire. She is another practical trickster. When she came up to me in make-up and whispered 'If you don't stop stalking me I will be forced to call the police. You're scaring me,' she did it with such conviction that it was almost as if she meant it! Now there's true acting talent. She's got it. She's like Su Pollard without the specs.

Osbert in WHO WILL DANCE WITH DAPHNE?
(Hen and Chickens Theatre)
I love the fringe. It's my second home. I disagree with the critics. I think paraplegia is a wonderful topic for farce. And Juliet Stevenson really knows how to work both an audience and a motorised wheelchair.

TTFarrell

BERYL MERIT

Identical twins Beryl and Cheryl Merit toured their Vaudeville act around the provinces through the majority of their childhood, their most famous song being 'A Sailor In Capri Pants Once Showed Me His Kazoo'. An acrimonious rift occurred between the two following an incident in which Cheryl sewed a lychee into one of Beryl's undergarments before they were presented to the Pope on their eighteenth birthday. Beryl had less success alone and ended up working the windows in Amsterdam through the fifties and sixties with her live floorshow 'Lesbos in Lederhosen'. Returned to England in the seventies to become maid to infamous pensioner prostitute Reeney Screens, Madame of the Hackney House of Pain.

JEZ AND SUZE CELERY-BOWLES

Jez and Suze met when they collided during a do-se-do at the Ice-Breaking Salsa Night at the 1994 Accountants' Convention at the Droitwich Spa Travelodge. They soon discovered they shared a love of long division, The Archers, and the poetry of Pam Ayres. Within weeks they were married. Suze was brought up on a farm, and as a result often whiffs a bit of wee. Jez's years at boarding school means he sometimes like his wife to dress up as a roly poly schoolmaster called Mister Britches. Suze is adamant that their new-born baby Leigh is not just an accessory — the handbag straps on his romper suit are just a heck of a lot easier to use than baby-reigns.

LINDA'S LUSTS

- Liam Gallagher (til he had the baby. I hate the smell of poo.)

- Robbie Williams (til he turned into Frank Sinatra)

- Danny from Hear'say (til I auditioned to be Kym's replacement and he said my knees were like grey plasticine)

- Now I like all the fellas in Footballer's Wives. Particularly the really violent one who looks like a rhino and knocks his Mrs about.

TOM'S PIN-UPS

- Sir Simon Shepherd in anything.
- Sir Derek Jacobi in a tunic in I, Claudius.
- Little Leo Di Caprio in trunks in Titanic.
- David Furnishings (goes with Elton John).
- David Beckham's body with the personality of Anthony McPartlin.

SERIES

BBC1 had been keen to take the second series and we'd resisted, basically because we were worried that we'd have to sanitise the show for a more mainstream audience. However, they let us do what we wanted in series three and still stuck us on BBC1. I did worry slightly that Lorraine Heggessey, the Controller of BBC1, hadn't seen the show, but she came to one of the recordings with her fella and chortled away in the green room.

I suppose another change in this series was that Tom became a bit more stupid. I found it funny when James would play Tom getting something wrong, but with complete conviction – so we found more opportunities to have Tom being as equally stupid as Linda.

DOWN AND OUT IN KENTISH TOWN

Ann Mitchell had expressed an interest in playing something in Gimme when she came to a recording of the second series. She wanted to play one of Linda's screws, which I thought was a fab idea. This episode marks the third and final appearance of Simon 'Peak Practice' Shepherd. We were slightly worried we wouldn't get him, so I was poised to change it to A.N. Other celebrity if he was unavailable.

THE LOLLIPOP MAN COMETH

Tom finally gets his big break in a West End show. At the time the Almeida Theatre in London always seemed to be doing shows in old buildings with film stars in them, hence Tom Cruise performing in a converted fire station. I'm afraid that the poem at the end is not my own work. The poem was written by Miss Kathy Burke, a contender for the next poet laureate if ever I heard one.

SECRETS AND FLIES

Eagle-eyed viewers may notice that when Linda talks to Zippy in her bedroom she is holding a small tennis court in her hands. This was on Miss Burke's insistence, as the stage direction read 'Linda is holding court'.

GIMME GIMME GIMME

THREE

TRAUMA

Please note that Kathy Burke is a very lazy actress. Whilst filming the first two series I noticed that she was at her happiest when not required to do too much movement in a scene. So, I conceived this episode with Linda in bed for the whole of it, then what did she go and do? Moan the whole time that her arse was going numb. There's no pleasing some people.

This episode featured Tom getting another job, amazingly. (He seemed to do a lot of that in series three. Running out of ideas maybe? Never!) Here he plays alongside the very funny Frances Barber, who at the time was appearing in my record-breaking musical Closer To Heaven. (Though what records it actually broke, I am not at liberty to say).

DECOY

I have become quite addicted to Crossroads. Lines like 'My mother died thinking she was me!' don't come along every day (except on that show). Because of the level of acting talent on display therein I thought it was the natural home for a man of Tom Farrell's talents. Suddenly I'd found a show where he might conceivably get a job, so when I decided to finally split Tom and Linda up for good, there was only one way it could go.

Kathy was always keen on revealing that Linda was bald underneath those gorgeous ginger locks, so she got her dream come true!

SINGING IN THE DRAIN

Su Pollard took me out for lunch a few years ago and asked me if I'd be interested in working with her on something. When I suggested getting her in Gimme, she seemed pretty unimpressed. Still, she is a trouper and turned up, and did it all in one take!

Rumours that James Dreyfus had a special lectern in the singing lesson to keep his script on are exactly that – rumours!

I originally wrote the part of Louie to be played by one of the dancers from my successful West End hit musical Closer To Heaven, Louie Spence. But I stuck the scene in at the last moment, and so I had to take that part at the read through. The lovely producers decided that I was probably cheaper, so I ended up doing it. I asked my mum if any of her friends had spotted me in it, and she answered, 'Well they probably wouldn't recognise you, because you've put on so much weight.'

WHITHER GOEST THOU NOW, GIMME GIMME GIMME?

At the end of DECOY, Tom is living in Nottingham whilst Linda is rotting away in the flat on her own. Will there be any more Gimmes? Who knows? At the moment there are no plans for making any more. I was aware of repeating myself during the third series, and I always think it's better to quit while you're (kind of) ahead. Also, Kathy has given up acting for a while, to concentrate on her directing. It is conceivable that we will all get together and make the odd one-off special, or even do a stage show, but I doubt we will see another whole series of Gimme.

If we're all skint in a few years time, however, please ignore the previous paragraph.

I'd like to take this opportunity to thank Kathy and James for giving the show such a special place in my heart, and to the other 'regulars', Ros, Brian and Beth, for their commitment to saying crap dialogue with 100 per cent conviction! To Liddy and Tristram, Sue, Francis, Mark, John and the entire crew, thank you all for helping to get my twisted view of the world out there onto the small screen.

Episode One
DOWN AND OUT IN KENTISH TOWN

LIVING ROOM

Linda anxious on the couch with miss twitch her old screw.

MISS TWITCH: Well who'da thought it Linda? That after all these years we'd meet again.

she waits for linda to light her ciggie.

MISS TWITCH: I was the hardest screw in Borstal, wann'I Linda? (Linda nods) There's no need to look so scared. Not now you've been so nice to me and allowed me to live in your back garden!!

out of the window we see a man by a tent.

MISS TWITCH: That's my young man. Handsome, inn'e?

♀ LINDA: Really?!! We always thought you were a dirty old dyke.

MISS TWITCH: Never confuse being the hardest bitch in B Block with being a dirty old dyke! How's your knee-caps?

♀ LINDA: Oh they're great thank you – they've healed up lovely.

MISS TWITCH: Shall I bring my young man round for a spot of supper tonight Linda?

♀ LINDA: Well how long were you thinking of staying?

MISS TWITCH: Why? You got a problem with that?

♀ LINDA: No! No! It's just that I'll have to have a word with my flatmate.

MISS TWITCH: He won't mind will he Linda?

♀ LINDA: Well...

MISS TWITCH: Will he Linda? Still no oil painting are you dear? You offend me.

linda wets herself.

MISS TWITCH: Wipe that up.

miss twitch exits. tom enters.

♂ TOM: Morning, morning. Oh – I had the most amazing dream! I was in a cutting edge Channel Four late night soap called 'Benders'. And I was in it. And Sir Simon Shepherd was in it. And it was really sort of in yer face queer drama with a capital 'q'! You know what I'm gonna do?

♀ LINDA: I know what I'm gonna do, heave.

♂ TOM: I'm going to write it all down. Because if the work won't come to me, godammit, then I'll create the work myself! The muse has entered me and is throbbing for release. Linda? Pass me my Pentel and click out my nib. I feel like squirting some serious ink!

♀ LINDA: I wrote a book once. 'Keen Teens'. Actually it was more of a photo shoot. Actually... it was more of a porn story. Actually I didn't write it, I was in it. It's in my special pink box somewhere!

TOM: Actually d'you know what? Pen and paper is so last century. I think I'll just yank out my Dictaphone. (Dictates) 'Benders'. By Thomas Thesalonius Farrell.

LINDA: Daddy spilt some egg mayonnaise on the snap of me bending over. Well at least he said it was egg mayonnaise. (Sniffs) I think it smells more like coronation chicken.

TOM: A four hundred and forty four part comedy drama vehicle for Sir Simon Shepherd and Thomas Thesalonius Farrell!

LINDA: No Tom! Don't go near the window!

TOM: W-w-w-w-why not?

LINDA: Because... Because. Did you know Tom that an hundred and seventy-five per cent of all drive-by shootings happen near french windows?

TOM: Twiggy preserve us! One is no longer safe in one's own home!! God it's like living in that really scary movie, isn't it? What's that really violent film? What was it called... 'Chocolate Orange'!

LINDA: (Produces teeth) Oh look – Mummy's teeth!

TOM: Ah. Tea?

LINDA: No I think it's gravy.

TOM: (Sniffs) Curry?

LINDA: (Sniffs) Daddy! Oh look, Mummy's Dutch cap! Uncle Tyrone used to make me wear that for my extra special treat!

TOM: (Dictates) Maybe the baddie in 'Benders' could be shot at the french windows. It would make a real statement about the futility and utter lack of serendipity in Blair's Britain.

LINDA: (Wearing cap) You took the words right out o'my mouth.

TOM: I dedicate this script to Julia Mackenzie and the entire cast of 'Fresh Fields'. If it wasn't for you I'd still be selling popsocks in Dolcis. Thanks for the inspiration guys! You know. If I pull this off and Sir Simon Shepherd is cast alongside me...

LINDA: Huh – you'll pull him off?

TOM: Fingers crossed! Well, a chum of mine from drama school, well he tried to poison me a couple of times so perhaps 'chum's' the wrong word, but he said that

he'd slept with Sir Simon. What do you say to that?

LINDA: I'd say he had an over-active imagination. Mummy had one of them. Oh no she never – it was an under-active thyroid. Here it is! (Produces jam jar)

TOM: (Dictates) 'Scene One. Tom stands naked but for a dickie bow and a pair of galoshes, whilst being approached from behind by the marvellous Sir Simon Shepherd. What's that lovely perfume you're wearing Simey? Simon: You Tom, you.'

LINDA: (Produces mag) Oh here it is! I knew it was here somewhere. Oh I was so peachy!

TOM: 'Simey slowly unbuttons the buttons on Tom's Burberry Bell-bottoms and...'

LINDA: Oh look at me licking me baps and slapping me doughy buns. Ah!

TOM: 'Simon slowly glides his hands over Tom's pert morello cherry-esque nipples, as Tom winces in... is that pain? No dear reader, 'tis ecstasy!'

LINDA: Oh in this one I'm opening me oven and showing me runny flan.

TOM: Oh for goodness sake!

LINDA: It was set in a bakery!

TOM: (Grabs mag) Give that to me! (Reads) 'Naughty Saturday girl Linda's enough to make any man's dough rise.' Well not mine!

LINDA: Well that's 'cos you're an 'omo!

twitch's young man enters through the window and gets a glass of water. he leaves.

TOM: Oh! Oi, what d'you think you're doing? You can't just walk in here and pillage us of our supplies of H2 bloody O! (Approaches window)

LINDA: No Tom, don't go to the window.

Please don't go to the window. Tom – don't go to the window!

♂ TOM: What have you done? You foolish foolish child!

♀ LINDA: I've opened our back garden up as a campsite.

♂ TOM: D'you know, sometimes Lindy I think you're a few crumbs short of the full biscuit. (Calling out of window) Away! Get away from here! Shoo, you... you... you gypsy type person! Shoo! Get away! You all smell of poo-poo bottoms! Go!

♀ LINDA: No Tom – no no please don't Tom – honestly Tom – one of them's an ex-screw from me Borstal Tom.

♂ TOM: What?

♀ LINDA: She broke me kneecaps once Tom.

♂ TOM: What?!

♀ LINDA: She's not a very nice person, Tom!

♂ TOM: What?!! You're joking. Oh my...

miss twitch appears.

♂ TOM: Oh. Oh hello. Hi. Um – help yourself to anything you should need! There's a lovely cushion there or something! And... give her the couch. Give her the couch. Take the couch. Here you are...

MISS TWITCH: Shirley Twitch. Fingers to her friends.

♂ TOM: Oh, why's that?

she shakes his hand. bones crack.

♀ LINDA: This is my flatmate Tom. I was just telling Tom what a lovely screw you were.

MISS TWITCH: I never laid a finger on any of my girls.

♀ LINDA: Not without a knuckle duster.

♂ TOM: So er... tell me Miss... Miss Fingers. Er – are you still a screw?

MISS TWITCH: No Tom. These days... I guess you could say I'm a philanthropist.

♂ TOM: Oh my god, I used to collect stamps too! How many do you have?

MISS TWITCH: You taking the piss?

♂ TOM: No! No!

MISS TWITCH: Are you scared of me Tom?

♂ TOM: No! No! You remind me of a sort of very big fluffy cuddly bear called Nancy, Miss Twitch.

MISS TWITCH: See you at eight. (Leaves)

♂ TOM: Okay Bye bye! Go easy down them stairs! Yeah!

♂ TOM: What's happening at eight? Huh? What's happening at eight?! Eh? What's happening at eight?!!!!!

♀ LINDA: All right Tom – calm down! Her and her fella are coming over for a bit of dinner.

♂ TOM: Over my dead body! I know how to get rid of these unwanted visitors.

♀ LINDA: Well that's what you said about your little problem mate. But you're still scratching away, ain't you?

♂ TOM: (Into phone) Hello is that the council? Well yes I suppose it must be. You sound frightfully vulgar. Now listen, I have four words to say to you. Vagrants. Lawn. Get. Rid! No of course I don't hate travellers. The first record I ever bought was 'Caravan' by Barbara Dickson. I am not a fascist! I've still got a 'Coal Not Dole' sticker on my ballet bag. I was practically the blueprint for Billy Elliot. Oh I know, wasn't it? Oh I know, I know – I love that film. Oh god, which was your favourite bit? When he kissed the boy? I know – mine too. Ahhh...didn't your heart just... I can do the dance, listen to me, I can do the dance, listen...

TOM

'I am not a fascist! I've still got a 'Coal not Dole' sticker on my ballet bag. I was practically the blueprint for Billy Elliot!'

tom dances. beryl enters.

BERYL: I didn't know Tom was epileptic Linda. Shall I phone for Doctor Quimley?

♀ LINDA: No, he's doing that film – the one with the little boy.

BERYL: The Sixth Sense? 'I see dead people.'

♀ LINDA: No, that one set up north or Iceland, y'know – where they talk weird. She was in it. Julie Wotsit.

BERYL: Andrews?

♀ LINDA: Bloody hell – was that her? She's gone right common.

BERYL: I'm nipping out on the camp site, catch some rays. (Exits)

TOM: (Into phone) Well now listen to me! If my back garden becomes a Butlins-style holiday camp I am holding you personally responsible. Before you can say Ruth Madoc there'll be knobbly knees contests, donkey derbies on Gaiety Green, a man called Freddie standing in the toilets with his pecker out. Or was that just my experience of Butlins? Hello? Hello? Oh big fat hairy bollocks!

KITCHEN

linda making pot noodles. tom watching.

LINDA: So all you do is just pour on some boiling water and then just leave it to stand for a couple of minutes. And then in the meantime, you may as well have a cigarette and a finger. (Eats Chocolate Finger)

TOM: Sorry to bother you Nigella... but I'm going out – all right?

LINDA: No Tom, you can't leave me on my own with her!!

TOM: I am going to Spud-U-Like to continue toying with my Benders.

LINDA: My Aunty Wey-Wey wrote her suicide note in a Spud-U-Like. On the steamy windows. With her tongue. Freak.

TOM: Oh for goodness sake!

suze and jez enter

SUZE/JEZ: 'And hoorah, we're off to sunny Spain, Y Viva España!'

JEZ: Ole!

SUZE: Oh Linda, we're so excited about staying at your camp site!

JEZ: I'm moist, feel!

SUZE: I'm like a dripping sponge!!

TOM: I'm sorry. You're treating staying in your own back garden as a holiday?

JEZ: Well, we fancied the Algarve, but as Suze is with child, flying is out of the question.

SUZE: I'll say. I went on the chair-o-planes at Margate and got air rage. Demanded to see the stewardess. I'm not in my right mind!

JEZ: So we thought, how about a couple of hours under canvas?

SUZE: Oh I've spent many a happy holiday in the New Forest. Stroking a pony. Waking each morning to a cheeky little thoroughbred nibbling my muslin flaps.

JEZ: So tell me Linda, how much is it again?

LINDA: Well seeing as you're my neighbours, how about five hundred?

JEZ: Right...

TOM: Excuse me – sorry – you are paying to stay in your own back garden!!

JEZ: (Exits) Come on Suze. Holiday time! (They exit)

TOM: I feel like Mavis Nicholson in 'One Flew over the Cuckoo's Nest'.

LINDA: That was Jack Nicholson wasn't it Tom?

TOM: Not at the Sheffield Crucible Lindy. Catcha later!!

as tom goes twitch enters. she wears a grubby ballgown. her fella si is with her. he wears shades and dreadlocks.

MISS TWITCH: You!! Stay where you are!!

LINDA: Oh, Miss Twitch!! Don't you look lovely? You look like a pretty little princess!

MISS TWITCH: It's a little something I used to wear for the Borstal Balls.

LINDA: Oh I used to love those Borstal Balls. They used to get really sweaty. We used to call them the sweaty ba...

MISS TWITCH: Tom! Not going anywhere are you?

TOM: Sadly Miss Twitch I have a prior engagement to do some writing at a potato-based eating establishment.

MISS TWITCH: Meet my young man. Si.

SI: Hi. How do you do?

♀ LINDA: Si! That's an unusual name innit? Si. It's like gasp.

SI: Believe it or not it's short for Simon.

♂ TOM: Oh. Cut glass diction. So tell me, what did you do before you dropped, like a young man's slacks, out of society?

SI: I was an actor.

♀ LINDA: Oh really?! Tom's an actor!!

MISS TWITCH: You said you was a writer. You lying to me?

♀ LINDA: Well he's bi-job-ual inn'e. He's a bit of both.

♂ TOM: Yes. It's a fiendishly tricksy business, isn't it Si? You probably haven't had the luck or the talent that I've had. You know – I've done everything... um, telly, ads, theatre, film..

♀ LINDA: Pop videos.

♂ TOM: Pop videos.

♀ LINDA (OOV): Yes.

♂ TOM: I was Wedding Guest With Bell's Palsy in 'Tragedy' by Steps.

♀ LINDA: He's played a lot of people with afflictions, haven't you Thomas?

SI: Actually I had a reasonable amount of success.

♂ TOM: Listen kid. I used to think street theatre was 'success'.

SI: Well then you're a bit of a sad git, aren't you?

MISS TWITCH: Si's been on the telly, int ya Si?

♂ TOM: I know who you are! I know who you are! You're Worzel Gummidge, aren't you! Oh! I can do him. I can do him! Look! 'Cup o'tea and a slice o'cake, Aunt Sally!'

SI: No Tom, I'm not Worzel Gummidge.

♀ LINDA: 'Ere – d'you remember when I was on the telly, Miss Twitch?

MISS TWITCH: Yeah – when we thought you'd escaped.

♀ LINDA: But I hadn't, had I. The other girls had hidden me under the floorboards.

♂ TOM: What – alive?!

♀ LINDA: No Tom, they wouldn't be that cruel. They'd chucked an hair dryer in the bath so they thought I was a gonner. But I'm a fighter in'I Miss Twitch?

MISS TWITCH: It was the saddest day of my career when I felt your pulse.

♂ TOM: So, tell us about your little telly moment then.

SI: I was the lead in a medical romantic drama.

MISS TWITCH: What was it called again Si? Something catchy. 'Piano Practice'?

SI: No. 'Peak Practice'.

♂ TOM: 'Peak... Peak Practice'? Did you say 'Peak Practice'? Well don't be so ridiculous. The only Simon that was in 'Peak Practice' was the wonderful, the inspirational, the phantasmagorical Sir Simon Shepherd.

si takes glasses and hat off. it is indeed simon shepherd. tom is gobsmacked. linda drops a penny!

SI: Can I use your bathroom? I need to spruce myself up a bit.

♂ TOM: Oh my God! Are you really Sir Simon Shepherd?!!! I don't believe... I've always wanted to... can I touch your... (Faints)

♀ LINDA: Well pick him up!! I thought you were a bloody doctor!!

KITCHEN

tom, linda, twitch and si having supper.

SI: Well originally I left the series to pursue other things. I did a couple of episodes of a dreadful sitcom, the name of which escapes me. It was about a couple sharing a flat. She was sex mad, he was a disillusioned actor.

♀ LINDA: Bloody hell, they put some crap out these days, don't they?

♂ TOM: Don't they!

LINDA

'Oh in this one I'm opening me oven and showing me runny flan.'

SI: And then after that, work kind of dried up. One day I was signing on at the local dole when I met the lovely Miss Twitch. We fell in love, didn't we? And after that it seemed churlish to return to T.V.

♀ LINDA: And how did you end up a tramp Miss Twitch?

MISS TWITCH (Shouts) Get your clothes off now Hughes and get in them cold showers!

♀ LINDA: It's La Hughes now. La Hughes!

SI: Darling, it's time for your medication. You really have to lie down.

MISS TWITCH: Oh it's so cold out there, Simey. Can I lie in here Simey?

SI: Fingers. We're talking. We'd keep you awake. And there's all those people queuing for the campsite.

we see a queue of people in the living room.

MISS TWITCH: Can I have a lie down in your bed, Linda?

♀ LINDA: No...

♂ TOM: Yes. Yes you can. Go! Go! Simon and I need to be alone to have a little chinwank. Er wag! Wag! Chinwag!

LINDA'S BEDROOM

twitch and linda.

MISS TWITCH: I love your dress sense Linda.

♀ LINDA: Think like a slut, dress like a slut. Bye.

MISS TWITCH: (Restrains her) I never had a daughter. And I think it might be a bit late to start thinking of babies now.

♀ LINDA: A bit?!

MISS TWITCH: Maybe. Maybe you could call me Mummy. Try it Linda.

♀ LINDA: I don't want to.

MISS TWITCH: You never had a Mummy did you?

♀ LINDA: Yeah, you met her.

MISS TWITCH: She wasn't your real mummy Old Dolly.

♀ LINDA: Yes she was.

MISS TWITCH: Nah!! She was just some old bird you wouldn't leave alone. I'm not saying she wasn't good to you, 'cos she was. Her whole family was. Treated you like one of their own. But your real mummy dumped you on 'em 'cos she couldn't stand the sight of you. Ain't that right?

♀ LINDA: That's a lie!

MISS TWITCH: Your real Mummy was a witch.

♀ LINDA: No!!

MISS TWITCH: From the neck up, she had the head of a horse.

♀ LINDA: You're lying to me! Why are you lying to me?!

MISS TWITCH: I'm sorry Linda. I thought you knew! Did no-one ever tell you?

linda looks in the mirror. a horse looks back.

♀ LINDA: Noooooooooo!

MISS TWITCH: Haha!! Got you!! You were always so gullible!! You silly bitch!

LIVING ROOM/KITCHEN

♂ TOM: This is your Camp Manager speaking. And when I say camp, I mean 'camp' as in site. Not as in 'Get you bitch mother!' The ladies lavatories are blocked. I repeat, the ladies lavatories are blocked. Kindly ablute your doings in that mulberry bush o'er yonder!

he goes inside to simon.

♂ TOM: I'm glad I've got you on me ownsome lonesome, because I believe we have a mutual friend in common.

SI: Really? Who's that?

♂ TOM: Cliff Higginbottom? We did a sandwich course together at the RADA. He was on ciabattas. I was on baps.

SI: Oh that poisonous old queen! He spread rumour after rumour about me being a raving poofter! You've got to pity the rancid fruit. You've got to pity even more the thick twats who believed him.

TOM: (Laughs) You know. You look sphincter-clenchingly beautiful in the dusk of this eventide light.

SI: I said to him, I said 'Clive. There's nobody that likes to drink from the fur cup more than I do.' I mean, I've got nothing against the old Nancy boys, per se. Our business would fall apart without shirt flaplifters, quite frankly.

TOM: God, your... your hair is so'... so hairy, isn't it? And your eyes are like two azure paddling pools of love.

SI: Tom, can you keep a secret? I mean, you won't tell Fingers?

TOM: Well if you don't want anyone to hear it, you're going to have to whisper it into my ear. (He leans in) That's not quite close enough. I have rather a crooked cochlea. In fact, I'm going to have to sit on your lap. (Does so) In fact, you're going to have to put your hands round my waist. Oh no.. no I'm slipping! (Si falls on top of him) Oh Master Shepherd! Is that your crook I feel in the small of my back?

SI: All I was going to say Tom is that I I'm really itching to get back in front of the cameras.

TOM: My God! I've got a brilliant idea! You can be the lead in Benders! It's this T.V. series I've been writing! Look, look, here – (Gets scripts) here, look – you play Simon, and I'll play... oh gosh, what a coincidence – Tom. Tom... all right. Let's er, plunge straight in with Scene Two shall we... so you are...

SI: In the shower, naked.

TOM: Yes.

SIMON: And you're on the toilet.

TOM: Yes I am, right. But er, don't do 'Cor that smells!' acting coz I'm only tinkling. I always sit down to tinkle. Okay?

SI: (Pretends to shower) 'Say Tom. D'you wanna join me? You look like you could do with a good soaping up.'

TOM: 'Okay Si. Should I keep my trunks on or off?'

SI: 'Oh, I think off Tom. Don't you?'

TOM: 'Whatever you say Simon.'

SI: Off go the trunks then.

TOM: Well I'll just mime that for now.

Actually sod it – in for a penny, in for a pound. (Pulls pants off)

SI: Look, look – there's a very strange stage direction.

TOM: Is there?

SI: Yeah. It says that we kiss.

TOM: Oh really? Gosh, gosh – that's strange, isn't it. Must be a typing error, I suppose. Look um, shall we just do it anyway? I'm game if you are, you know.

SI: No – look, look – I'm reading further on here...

TOM: What?

SIMON: Is that physically possible with a bar of soap?

TOM: Um... two words, Simon – patience and practice. Right? Now come on – um, are you going to kiss me or not?

SI: You're a boy! I'm not kissing a boy!

TOM: That's where you've got it all wrong Simey. I'm no boy. I'm man. (Grabs Simon's face) All man!

tom kisses si they fall onto sofa.

SI: Steady, tiger, steady.

TOM: Come on, come on!

SI: D'you know, Tom, I think you've released something dormant in me.

TOM: Then let's do it again! And this time use your tongue! It's there for a reason, godammit! (Kisses Simon)

SUZE

'I've spent many a happy holiday in the New Forest. Stroking a pony. Waking each morning to a cheeky little thoroughbred nibbling my muslin flaps.'

miss twitch enters with linda.

MISS TWITCH: Get him off! Get him off my man.

LINDA: Get off him Tom! Get off him guy!

tom jumps off simon.

MISS TWITCH: Well well well. Linda Hughes. Si. Get out there and pack the tent up, we're leaving.

♂ TOM: Simey ain't going anywhere, Miss Twitch I'm afraid I have woken something hitherto a-slumberin' within him. I think you'll find that he's jumped ship, sexuality-wise! Go on, Si. Tell her. With you at my side, she don't scare me no more!

MISS TWITCH: Is this true Si? You gone all poofy on me?

SI: Yes, It is true that Tom's awoken something in me, yes...

MISS TWITCH: I'll kill you for this..

starts to strangle linda.

SI: No, no, no Fingers, Fingers, Fingers – it's not my latent homosexuality... I want to be an actor again!! I read this script...

♂ TOM: You like it?

SI: No, It's dreadful! But it's awoken in me my desire to act again! 'Peak Practice' have been banging on about me going back for

pitching the tent in the car park of a GP's surgery in the Peak District?

MISS TWITCH: Oh Si! Si! (Hugs him)

♂ TOM: No! But I felt tongue! You used your tongue. Don't do this to me Simey! I love you Simon Shepherd!!

MISS TWITCH: Oh shut up! (Punches Tom)

SI: Come on, Twitchy.

simon and miss twitch exit.

♀ LINDA: Phew!!

LIVING ROOM, LATER

tom plays notes on stylophone.
linda comes in.

♀ LINDA: How's the series going?

♂ TOM: Oh marvellously. I've reworked the entire thing into a big musical. It's called 'Hey Big Bender!' So, ahem, where have you been?

♀ LINDA: Judging the Glamorous Granny Competition. I wish I'd never bloody started that camp site.

jez and suze enter room.

JEZ: Thanks for a lovely holiday Lindy.

SUZE: Who would've thought it, eh? Me winning the competition for the Prettiest Pregnant Person on the campsite.

JEZ: And wasn't it funny, Linda, when you walked past and they asked if you were going to go in for it?

SUZE: Because although you look pregnant, you are of course vomit inducingly ugly.

♀ LINDA: Get out o'my lounge. Go on, piss off! (They go)

♂ TOM: Well, well, well, well, well, well, well, well well.

♀ LINDA: Funny old day wannit?

♂ TOM: I can think of many transient verbs to describe today Linda. Painful. Humiliating. Frightening – very, very frightening. But not by any stretch of the imagination was it funny!

♀ LINDA: What, just coz Sir Simon Shepherd didn't fancy you?

♂ TOM: Bollocks! When we kissed there was definite trouser movement! (Looks out the window) Linda. How much are you charging per tent?

♀ LINDA: Five hundred.

♂ TOM: But, but there must be over a thousand tents out there.

♀ LINDA: Three thousand nine hundred and seventy-one.

♂ TOM: God! D'you know what this means? D'you know what this mean? It means I'm rich! Rich! (Cackles) Rich! Oh shit – you're rich. Damn. What are you going to do with the money?

♀ LINDA: Spend it!! But, if you do sex with me, I'll give you half.

♂ TOM: What position d'you want then?

♀ LINDA: Space hopper!!

♂ TOM: Come on!!

he grabs her head and bounces up and down on her.

♀ LINDA: Harder! Harder!

♂ TOM: Oh yes! We're rich. We're rich. Rich!

beryl enters.

BERYL: No dear, I'm rich. If I may draw your attention to your tenancy agreement, Section 5, sub-section 35A, and I quote. 'In the event of my back passageway being used as a camp site, all proceeds from said venture will go to Ms. Beryl Merit.'

beryl puffs on cigar then exits.

♀ LINDA: Oh well you've started now, it seems a shame to stop.

♂ TOM: Yeah true. Come on – bounce it bitch, bounce it!

he continues to bounce up and down on top of her.

SIMON
'Well originally I left the series to pursue other things. I did a couple of episodes of a dreadful sitcom, the name of which escapes me. It was about a couple sharing a flat. She was sex mad, he was a disillusioned actor.'
LINDA
'Bloody hell they put some crap out these days, don't they?'

Episode Two
THE LOLLIPOP MAN COMETH

CONVERTED FIRE STATION

a theatre audience arriving. the poster says 'tom cruise in the life cycle of salmon' by jacob salami we pan down the cast list. finally arriving on tom's name.

DRESSING ROOM

♂ TOM: … Nicole Kidman, Kevin Spacey, the lovely lovely Jessica Lounge. One by one all the major Hollywood players are coming over here to do theatre. Stick a star in a play and you've got B.O.S Bums on seats! Box Office Smash! I'm so clever with letters!!

♀ LINDA: You got me here under false pretentions. You said there'd be loads of fellas here and there ain't!

♂ TOM: Even Anna Friel – would you believe it – recently played Lulu in the theatre! I didn't even know she could sing. Let alone do Scotch. 'You know you make me wanna shout!'

♀ LINDA: Mummy met Lulu in the sixties. She threatened her with an Irn Bru bottle. I bet that ain't in the play!

♂ TOM: Why shouldn't Tom Cruise, the well-known heterosexual, want to do some physical theatre in a converted fire station? Hmm?

♀ LINDA: Daddy still refuses to have 'Boom Bang-a-Bang' piped through his iron lung. He may be brain dead Tom, but he's got principles!! (Sniffs)

♂ TOM: You're probably smelling the sweat of an old fireman.

♀ LINDA: Oh. An old flame of mine used to be a fireman. Actually, he was more of an arsonist. He could only get it up to 'Relight My Fire' by Take That.

♂ TOM: Oh for goodness sake will you stop pacing around please! One's very twitchy around one's opening. One needs peace, calm, serendipity. Not a roly poly red-headed racoon racing around in a ra-ra skirt!

♀ LINDA: Wash your mouth out, this is a mini!

♂ TOM: Oh my God! Look! Look! Look! Look! I'm shaking. One can hardly hold his mascara brochette still. Oh my God! That reminds me of the time The Wombles opened a Petsmart in Poulton Le Fylde and I got so excited I wet myself!

♀ LINDA: I used to get like that every time I seen Emu. Oh wann'e gorgeous! Two long legs with a bush on top. Where's Tom Cruise? I wanna meet Tom Cruise!! What's he like? Is he a right bastard?

♂ TOM: Well how should I know? I've been rehearsing with his stand in. Yakashoto Shakamoto prefers it that way.

♀ LINDA: Sack o'shit o'what-o? What you talking about?

♂ TOM: My director. She's a Japanese genius. She says The Other Tom is holding back his performance till the opening night. So I've been rehearsing with his understudy. Stan Boardman. Not that we've done much rehearsing. That's one of Shakamoto's leit-motifs. She doesn't like to over-rehearse the crowd scenes.

♀ LINDA: Oh. What So is you like… an extravert?

♂ TOM: No, I have dialoje. I've got very good dialoje in fact. Dialoje as written by one of the finest wordsmiths whatever to have graced the Great British stage!

♀ LINDA: (Gasps) Jim Davidson?!!!! Oh Is he here as well?!!!!!!

♂TOM: No, it's Jacob Salami. The enfant terrible of agitprop theatre! Made his name with his three second play 'Blink!', in which – I might add – Linda Robson was a bloody revelation. She had me in tears you know. Even now thinking about it can set me off. (Cries)

♀LINDA: Oh don't Tom! That reminds me of the time when I spilt a cup o'tea on my Flange. It ballooned up to twice its normal size. I never knew a kinder goldfish Thomas.

♂TOM: Dear Lord in Devon above. If I might be half as good as Dame Linda Robson tonight I might die a very happy man. Amen. Right, now, Lindy. Before we go any further, I implore you not to mention the Scottish play!

♀LINDA: Uh what – 'Brigadoon'?

♂TOM: No, 'Macbeth'! You mention 'Macbeth' in the theatre it's professional suicide. You would never catch me saying that word in the theatre.

♀LINDA: What word?

♂TOM: 'Macbeth'. When Vanessa Redgrave was playing Madame Edith in the stage version of 'Allo 'Allo. She said 'Macbeth' on the opening night and she nearly choked on her own talent!

♀LINDA: My Aunty Vilma had seven years bad luck. All coz she walked under a stepladder.

♂TOM: Really? See, I'd never do that. I'm far too superstitious. (Walks under a stepladder) So what happened to her then?

♀LINDA: Well her side of the family are quite big-boned and the fat cow got trapped in the middle of them. Mind you she was quite handy if you needed something off a very high shelf. She got a job up Soho, bought herself a see-through body-stocking and a python. Called herself Snatch and Ladders.

♂TOM: I should remember this moment you know, it would make a fantastic scene for the opening musical of my life.

♀LINDA: Who'd play you?

♂TOM: Possibly Ross Kemp.

♀LINDA: I wonder who'd play me?

♂TOM: Well, they could always bring back Babapapa...

♀LINDA: I'm stuck between Liz Hurley and Courteney Cox. A position most lezzers would envy.

tom is stretching at pole.

♀LINDA: Ugh! What you doing?

♂TOM: I'm just stretching. God! I always find it helps to grab onto a thick fireman's pole and really open myself up as much as possible. I can work up quite a sweat doing it you know. Sometimes it hurts. But I quite like that. Cos you know what they say. No pain – no gain!

♀LINDA: I thought you said there was gonna be loads of people here and there ain't, I thought I'd be squeezed up against somebody but I'm not! (Gasps) Is they invisible Tom? (Gasps) Have they got X-ray vision? (Gasps) Can they see through my clothes? Can they see my ladygarden?

♂TOM: Just, just shut up would you? The rest of the cast if you must know are crammed into a tiny room down the corridor. I mean Lord knows why. I came in here, plonked my stuff down and they all decided they preferred the other room.

♀LINDA: I should have been on the stage you know. When I did a play at Borstal, Screw Driver said to me that I had the biggest jugs o'custard she'd ever seen. I played the custard lady. 'Hello, I'm the custard lady. Does anybody want custard?' And then Big Bertha from B-wing would say 'Yeah, I want custard. Splash it over my tart!'

♂TOM: Oh shut up will you! You evil selfish chugnut! I don't want to hear about your feeble attempts at performingness, thank you very much. God, I am a classically trained actrine of the highest calibrations and this is my evening! I don't even know why you're here!

♀LINDA: Coz you asked me! 'Keep me company!' you said 'No-one's talking to me!' you said. 'I'm all on my own' you said. See? The truth comes out when you're pissed.

♂TOM: That's utter tosh, I'm hugely popular in this company. I'm everyone's shoulder to cry on. Everybody's rock.

knock on door

VOICE 1: (OOV) Wanker!!

VOICE 2: (OOV) Break your neck Farrell!!

VOICE 1: (OOV) Yeah you great tit-head!!

♂TOM: People are so kind. Yeah, that's a sort

of first night tradition, you see. It's a sort of thesbian knock and run. Yeah? Now for my lip relaxants.. Ma, ma, ma. Me me me, me, me.

LINDA: I don't need nothing to relax my lips baby. Mind you after a couple o'vodkas they're usually flapping around like flip-flops.

TANNOY: Testing, one, two, three.

LINDA: Aaaagh!! Tom, the walls taliking!

TOM: Oh shut up – it's just the tannoy you gout-ridden gibbon!

TANNOY: Ladies and Gentlemen of the 'The Life Cycle of Salmon' company, this is your ten minute call. Ten minutes to go until curtain up, ladies and gentlemen.

TOM: Ma ma ma ma ma ma va va va. Vee vee vee vee vee vee vee. Ma va va va va Right. That's enough of the vocal warm up, I think it's time for a physical warm-up now, I think. Very very physical show. Star jumps, forward rolls, tumbles – might be called upon to do them at any moment you see so this is a crucial part of my preparation. Stand back please, stand back – right... here we go and... (Slaps his chair) Back again... There – that's enough of that I think.

LINDA: D'you wanna go through your speech again?

TOM: Yes, yes. That's a very good idea, Right. Now – you give me my cue line which is... 'You! Passing Person! Have you anything to say on the matter?'

LINDA: Oh no, no I can't remember all that!

TOM: Well, just say 'Have you anything to say on the matter?'

LINDA: Ready?

TOM: No, wait, wait one minute please. Okay now – you're playing Tom Cruise. You're a salmon so keep completely still – all right? Don't move a muscle.

LINDA: An old boyfriend of mine used to say that to me. He worked nights at the abattoir.

TOM: Right. So I'm meandering through...

LINDA: Oh – If you smell anything untoward, don't worry, it's just me vanilla surprise. It tends to drip when hot.

TOM: Eugh! Eugh! Eugh! Eugh! Eugh!

LINDA: Me ice cream!

TOM: Eugh! So I'm meandering through, and you say...

LINDA: Cor, you dunn'alf walk like a fairy don't ya?

TOM: Just give me your cue line.

LINDA: I've forgotten it.

TOM: 'Have you anything to say on the matter?'

LINDA: No, I'm just standing here. I'm Tom Cruise apparently.

TOM: Just say 'Have you anything to say on the matter?' then I will say my line.

LINDA: Right. Ready?

TOM: No.

LINDA: Oh see you cheat! You slipped it in when I weren't looking!

TOM: (Clasps Crotch) I did no such thing!

LINDA: Your line!

TOM: What?!

LINDA: You said 'No!', that's your line!

TOM: I didn't say it in context!

LINDA: Oh there's so much to take on. My brains mashed guy! Oh that poor Tom Cruise!

TOM: 'Have you anything to say on the matter?'!!

LINDA: That's my line!!

TOM: Say it!!

LINDA: Have you anything to say on the matter you nonce!!

TOM: No!!

LINDA: (Claps) Electric Tom, electric!

TOM: Oh – do you think so?

LINDA: Yes.

TOM: Do really think so – oh thank you! (Showbiz kisses her)

LINDA: Ah you were brilliant you know, you are, you're brilliant. You're just like that bloke in that film.

TOM: Ah – which film?

LINDA: You know that film that one you love!

TOM: Oh. 'My name's Leisl, I'm sixteen and I don't need a governess!' (He curtsies)

LINDA: No, no it ain't that one you like – it's that one Mummy likes. Oh what's it called? Oh it's lovely, it's got a really little pretty name like a little pet.

TOM: Er... 'Terms of Endearment'?

LINDA: No.

TOM: 'Babe'?

LINDA: 'The Bitch'! That's it, you're like that

bloke in 'The Bitch'! Ah, Mummy took me to see that when I was ickle.

♂ TOM: Wasn't that Oliver Reed?

♀ LINDA: No it was definitely Mummy. I can remember the tang of her Victory V's.

♂ TOM: Well I am horrified, look. (Makes horrified face)

♀ LINDA: No wonder you don't get no work.

♂ TOM: I'm sorry – I am horrifed that 'The Bitch' was the first film you ever saw.

♀ LINDA: Well that's where you're wrong, you pouff, coz the first film I seen was 'Sluts on Skis – Fun and Games on and off The Piste.' It was a little home movie Mummy made.

♂ TOM: Oh do shut up! God! How's my make-up looking?

♀ LINDA: Er...you can't tell you've got any on.

♂ TOM: Really? Shit. Bugger. Bog roll. Right. (Cakes himself in slap) Oh, and d'you know what you have to do when you're stage acting?

♀ LINDA: Fart silently? I can do that. Listen.

♂ TOM: No! 'You put two red dots in the corner of your eyes. (He does them) Right, in fact, they won't be able to see those from the gods I'll just make them a tad bigger, alright? (Turns to Linda and shows her) There you see, do you know why we have to do that?

♀ LINDA: So it looks like someone's punched you out?

♂ TOM: No, no – it draws people to your eyes. It's clever isn't it?

♀ LINDA: Really? I'm having some o' that. (Daubs her clevage)

♂ TOM: Now just in case no-one can see me from the Gods (Cakes brown make-up on) Oh oh oh – and another thing that you have to remember when you're stage acting, right, is if you're playing a character that's over the age of say, fifty-two, you have to put talcum powder all over your hair. Ha-ha! It's great isn't it? Now, I wonder how old my character is, 'cos d'you know I'm not really sure...

♀ LINDA: Well, what's your name?

♂ TOM: Why?

♀ LINDA: Well 'cos if you was called something like Latasha you'd probably be young. And black. And a girl.

♂ TOM: Well, no I'm called Passing Person. And I know that because the salmon yells out at me 'Passing person!' and I answer.

♀ LINDA: What's your costume like?

♂ TOM: Well this is where I started to hit upon something you see. I'm in a white coat right, in a white coat – and I do a lot of meandering, a lot of passing by, passing to and fro. So. I'm in a white coat, I'm doing a lot of passing to and fro, so I brought this along because I'm obviously... a lollipop man!

he grabs a lollipop stick.

♀ LINDA: Oh! Well I'd say your character was probably ancient then..

♂ TOM: Oh well... lots and lots of talc then! (Covers himself in talc) Oh no, oh no – it's made my face go all white. So what do we do now?

♀ LINDA: We put more brown stuff on!

♂ TOM: That's right Lindy! My, you're getting the hang of this.

♀ LINDA: Oh, someone's put a note through your door. Shall I read it?

♂ TOM: Yes, go on.

♀ LINDA: 'You're shit'.

♂ TOM: What, what? Oh no – that's s-h-i-t ha-ha! 'So Hot It's Tom'. Ha-ha! Oh, those cheeky little pranksters! Oh I've been looking forward to this moment my whole life! I must admit I was doubtful whence taking this on. I mean – one line! But as they said at the audition...

♀ LINDA: 'No other mug'll do it.'

♂ TOM: 'There are no small parts. Only small actors.'

♀ LINDA: Look at your leading man.

♂ TOM: Well I know. He only comes up to my ankles. (Laughs) Well, I think the sun is well and truly over the farmyard wall. Partakez-vous a glass of showbiz tincture?

♀ LINDA: Oh yes.

♂ TOM: Oh! Hang on, before you do that would you please kiss my lucky little Dick?

♀ LINDA: Oh yes. Hello. (She kisses mascot)

I had a lucky milk bottle you know. Somebody put it through the letterbox and mummy said it was lucky it didn't kill me.

♂ TOM: Well how could a milk bottle kill you? Surely it just plonked on the mat!

♀ LINDA: And who slept on the mat? Plus it was on fire.

♂ TOM: Oh.

♀ LINDA: (A toast) Down the back o'me throat and make me giddy!

♂ TOM: Yes, here's to 'The Life Cycle of Salmon' having a massive long run, me getting lots of recognition for it, and becoming huge!

♀ LINDA: Bisto!!

♂ TOM: Ha-ha-ha-ha-ha!

they drink.

♂ TOM: That's nice isn't it? Well, they're mighty fine at Costcutters. Now! On with the boots!!

♀ LINDA: So, what's this play about?

♂ TOM: No idea. It's set on a boat.

♀ LINDA: Oh I almost forgot. Your agent phoned.

♂ TOM: Oh fantastico, tan spastico! Is she going to come to the aftershow party?

♀ LINDA: No, she says she couldn't come. Said something about the decorators.

♂ TOM: Oh, buggerlumps! Decorators? What's that all about?!

♀ LINDA: I dunno, she just said she'd rather watch 'Paint Dry'.

♂ TOM: Well yeah. She's just taken on Handy Andy. He's opening in his play tonight, yeah. So, there's a spare ticket if you want to go up front.

♀ LINDA: No, you're all right mate, I'm not a big fan o' fish.

♂ TOM: But what happens if I forget my line? I'll need you there to yell it out at me!

♀ LINDA: Tom, you ain't gonna forget your line. It's one word, three letters. No! Okay?

♂ TOM: Oh my god!

♀ LINDA: What?

♀ TOM: Oh my god my mind's gone blank. Oh my god I can't remember anything. Oh my god I'm having a panic attack! I'm having a panic attack.

linda slaps him.

♂ TOM: Ah! Oh!

the director and interpreter enter.

♂ TOM: Yakashoto, hi!

yakashoto begins a long-winded speech in japanese. tom and linda look at each other. yakashoto continues.

INTERPRETER: Director say. The soft whispers of morningtide wind in the windchime mean that very special songbird come down from mountain to drink from pool of beauty. When bird lay egg in nest at brow of foothills, ...bird that born have wings to fly higher. Ride that bird far far away. Bird young. Bird free. Bird you.

♂ TOM: Right. So does that mean I should ditch the talc or not?

yakashoto looks at linda - says something coarse in japanese.

INTERPRETER: Bugger me Yakashto, no wonder you're a comedy genius. Break a leg Tom! (They go)

♂ TOM: Did you hear that? Did you hear that? 'Break a leg'. Christ, what a bitchy thing to say.

♀ LINDA: I know. The Norwegian nonce.

♂ TOM: These slacks are a bit tight round the gusset. You can tell I'm not Jewish can't you?

♀ LINDA: I love a nice Jew, Thomas.

♂ TOM: Yeah.

♀ LINDA: All the nuns in my convent were Jewish.

♂ TOM: Were they? Were they?

♀ LINDA: Well, all except Sister Brian May, the headmistress. Ooh she was a vicious cow!

flashback.

SCHOOL CHAPEL

schoolgirl linda sniffing glue. sister enters.

SISTER BRIAN MAY: Linda Hughes! Why aren't you at netball?

♀LINDA: 'Cos Sister Contraception's a big lezzer and she keeps looking up my skirt.

SISTER BRIAN MAY: Sister Contraception is a holy creature. And the only skirt she'd look up would be Our Lady's. Dirty... dirty... child! Now... Father Dick will be along shortly to take confession. Will you be confessing?

♀LINDA: Nah, I'm gonna sell my story to the Catholic Herald.

SISTER BRIAN MAY: You're going the same way as your mother. And she was evil, Linda, evil! She was the child of Satan Linda. And you know what we do to girls like that...

♀LINDA: This skirt stays on!

SISTER BRIAN MAY: They go to Borstal! But not before they've had a taste of my cane. Touch your toes!

linda whimpers and bends over.

SISTER BRIAN MAY: Oh stop whinging, you miserable little cow!!

DRESSING ROOM

linda and tom lost in thought.

♂TOM: And they say one's schooldays are supposed to be the happiest of one's life.

♀LINDA: Yeah – bollocks! Were you happy at your school, Tom?

♂TOM: Oh!

flashback.

SCHOOL PLAYGROUND

tom as schoolboy, with two skallies barry and gary. they have a ciggie. tom has huge hair.

GARY: Smoke that.

♂TOM: What is it?

BARRY: It's heroin.

GARY: Yeah, we're heroin addicts.

♂TOM: No, I can't. If I smoke that I'll imagine great big Mars bars chasing me down the street.

BARRY: Smoke it you big pansy or I'll tell the whole school you tried to get a grope o'me knackers.

tom takes a drag. he coughs his guts up.

GARY: You big girl.

♂TOM: Leave me alone!

GARY: You must be a girl, you've got girl's hair!

BARRY: Yeah, you sit down to wee!

♂TOM: It keeps the rim clean!

GARY: (To Barry) Stub it out on his arse.

BARRY: No, I'm not touching his arse!

♂TOM: Oh be gentle with me!

GARY: Stub it out on his arse!!

barry tuts and makes to do so. we hear tom scream.

DRESSING ROOM

linda is stubbing cigarette out.

♂TOM: Aaaaaaaghgghghghgh!!!! Stop that at once! (Swivels to mirror) Oh no! I've gone as white as a sheet. Time for more make-up methinks. (Weird music on the tanoy) Oh my God that's my opening music. Oh no, I need to go wee wee.

♀LINDA: Go in the sink.

♂TOM: Dare I? Dare I?

♀LINDA: Oh go on Tom, we've all done it.

♂TOM: Yes, oh all right.

he climbs onto the sink and tries to wee!

♂TOM: I can't go! I can't go!

♀LINDA: Here y'are, have some more to drink – that'll shift it.

♂TOM: Yes, yes that'll help, that'll help! (Drinks) Turn on the tap now Lin – turn on the tap.

♀LINDA: I ain't sticking me hand down your rear, I'll lose it! (Drinks)

♂ TOM: Well just, just distract me then. Just do something distracting and then perhaps it'll come out of its own accord.

♀ LINDA: Okey dokey. (She mimes)

♂ TOM: What in God's name are you doing?

♀ LINDA: I'm miming I'm stuck in a box, oh look, here's a door. Oh look I can walk through it, I'm walking down the street – oh look, there's a disco! Come on let's shaft! (Dances)

♂ TOM: Oh! Oh god, this is ridiculous, I obviously don't need to go. Pull me off.

♀ LINDA: Eurgh!

♂ TOM: Off the sink! Come on.

she puts her arms around his waist.

♀ LINDA: One two four!

he won't budge.

♂ TOM: Tickle me Lindy, Hurry, try and tickle me!

TANNOY: Passing People to stage left to walk across the back of the stage please. The Passing People in white coats to stage left.

LINDA
'I don't need to relax my lips baby, after a couple o' vodkas they're usually flapping around like flip flops.'

♂ TOM: Oh my God that's me, that's me – quickly hurry up and tickle me!

she tickles him. he pulls the sink away from the wall – it is still attached to his rear.

♀ LINDA: Cover it up with your coat.

♂ TOM: Brilliant, brilliant. Can you tell?

♀ LINDA: No. It just looks like you've got a really fat arse. And it'll come in handy if you get nervous, won't it?

♂ TOM: Brilliant, brilliant, right. My stick! My stick! My kingdom for my stick.

♀ LINDA: (With stick) Oh good luck Tommy baby!

♂ TOM: I can put more make-up on on the way down.

♀ LINDA: Yes.

♂ TOM: Right. Come and watch me from the wings. Come and watch me from the wings.

THE STAGE

a salmon lies on a rock. behind, a group of four people walk past in white coats.

SALMON: Flush! Flush! Against the tide! Flush! Flush! Again I jump! Against the tide I slowly float. You – Passing Person! Do you have anything to say on the matter?

tom crashes onto stage with his lollipop.

♂ TOM: All right – don't push me!!

SALMON: You, Passing Person! Do you have anything to say on the matter?

tom can't remember. he looks to linda in the wings.

♂ TOM: Linda! What's my line? Tell me my line!

♀ LINDA: No!

♂ TOM: Tell me my bloody line!

♀ LINDA: No!!!

♂ TOM: Don't be so unfair! This is the biggest night of my career. And all I'm asking you to do is prompt me the one line of dialogue that we went through in the dressing room beforehand. Now. Are you going to give it to me or not?

♀ LINDA: No!!

SALMON: Okay, that's it! Bring the goddamn curtain down will you?!

♂ TOM: We're in a converted fire station love, there isn't a bloody curtain!

the curtain comes down quickly, knocking tom over. behind the curtain the salmon takes his head

off. it is not tom cruise.

TOM: Who are you? You're not Tom Cruise!

SALMON: Oh shut up, I was cheaper!

DRESSING ROOM

tom storms in with a broken lollipop stick and linda.

TOM: Well I mean what sort of a production is this anyway? They're so desperate to get bums on seats that they lie and make out a top Hollywood star is in the show. I mean at least I've got nothing to be ashamed of.

LINDA: And there was no need for that director to smash your lollipop over your head.

TOM: Director? She couldn't direct a stray pube disappearing down a plughole!

LINDA: And who was that bird who said she wanted to kick your head in?

TOM: Narinder? Wardrobe mistress! Fancy having an affar with a wardrobe! She's never liked me since the day I said 'The yellow of your sari's clashing hideously with your sari, love!'

LINDA: And who was that bloke who said he wanted to garotte you with a skipping rope?

TOM: The producer. Let me tell you something about producers shall I? They're only interested in making money. They wouldn't know art if it came up behind them in a cul-de-sac and slapped them round the face with a branding iron.

LINDA: And who was it that came up behind you and slapped you round the face with a branding iron?

TOM: It was just an irate member of the audience. Look! What's the biggie? I came on. I did it. I came off. I mean, that's half the bloody battle love. (Gasps) What's this? (Grabs bill stuck on mirror) They've billed me for the bloody sink. I don't believe it, the buggers! A hundred and ninety pounds! That's a year's wages!

suddenly yakashoto's angry voice is heard over the tannoy.

INTERPRETER: Director say, Tom Farrell – if you're still in the building. And I know you are there you camp pillock, I've got one word to say to you. Why?

TOM: Why what? Why what? See – she makes absolutely no sense at all. No wonder this whole show's gone cock-a-hoop with her at the helm? I am surrounded by amateurs!!!

LINDA: Well, we'd better go home Tom. They said they were gonna set the rottweilers on you if you weren't out of here in five minutes.

TOM: I feel fantastic! Ah It must be the aftershow high. Oh Lindy – share with me more champagne, I'd like to go out there and do it all over again except I can't because...

they hear a pack of dogs at the door.

TOM: Quickly Linda – go down on that pole!

LINDA: All right, where is he?

TOM: See, this is all your bloody fault 'cos you mentioned the Scottish play! Brigadoon! Brigadoon! Briga-bloody-doon!!

he slides down pole. she follows him and gets stuck.

LINDA: I'm stuck, I'm stuck. My arse is too big for the hole. I'm stuck, I'm stuck. My legs are wrapped right round this pole. I think I like it! I think I like it!

she wriggles on the pole. a big smile on her face.

Episode Three
SECRETS AND FLIES

SOUTH LONDON GRAVEYARD

a funeral like at the beginning of 'secrets and lies' but there are two coffins. later we find zippy, a young black man being comforted by the priest.

PRIEST: Such a terrible blow. To lose one's parents like this. Even though they were your adoptive parents, I know how close you were to them. Do you have any immediate plans?

ZIPPY: Yes – I'm going to find my real mum.

we see zippy from the front. he has big red hair and specs.

ZIPPY: I'm going to find my mummy!

LIVING ROOM

tom and linda. he has a picture of her as a baby.

♂ TOM: (Sings) 'You must have been a beautiful baby! You must have been a beautiful child' What went wrong, eh Lindy? What went wrong'? How did this bundle of peachy skinned fun become this amorphous great wobbling mass of sadness and cellulite, hmm? Oh, I was a bonny wee laddie, as we say in Merthyr Tydfyl. It's no wonder I won first prize in the school contest for biggest hair in class.

we see picture of little boy with big curls.

♀ LINDA: I thought you were making me a cup of tea!

♂ TOM: All right! All right! Keep your hair on.

♀ LINDA: And crisps. I want crisps!

♂ TOM: Okay, okay, okay. I've only got one pair of hands, you know. I'm not an octopus! Je ne suis pas octopuse! Though I did play an octopus once, in 'Underwater Calypso' at Ventnor Rep. Gave great tentacle. Had a washing-up bowl on my head with pairs of tights hanging off it, all done in dayglo paint. Wore a black bodystocking and it was all done with ultra violet lighting. Like this...

he gets the washing up bowl and puts it on his head and jumps across the room.

♂ TOM: But you've got to imagine lots of brightly coloured tights hanging off it and Dervla Kirwin coming up behind me dressed as a seahorse. Oh how I loved her cheeky Irish craic!

♀ LINDA: D'you mind? I'm eating!

we hear knocking on the door – a heavily pregnant suze enters. she has coal on her cheeks.

♀ LINDA: Oh whadda you want?!

SUZE: Hi Linseed Oil. Hi Tom des Garcons! Oooh – cool hat!

♂ TOM: Why have you blacked up? Can I just say a) I find that offensive and b) ridic! What does Jez think about all this nonsense?

SUZE: Take a chill pill Tom. I've been eating coal!

♂ TOM: Oh right.

SUZE: D'you mind if I take a seat? I've locked myself out and Jez is abseiling off Tate Modern for Donkeys in Crisis, so.

♀ LINDA: Great.

SUZE: Left my keys hanging on my lifesize cut-out of Benezir Bhuto. Honestly I am so forgetful.

♀LINDA: Oh my Aunty Nittie was like that. She once locked me in the boot of her Beetle when she went to Malaga for a fortnight. I nearly died!!!

♂TOM: Yes they say never to leave dogs in a car on a hot day.

♀LINDA: Them handcuffs! That gag! Psst, psst, psst – have you seen the size of her?

♂TOM: It's rude to whisper.

♀LINDA: (Loudly) Have you seen the size of her?

SUZE: I am pregnant.

♀LINDA: Oh. Pregnant is it, eh? And that means?

♂TOM: She's having a baby!!

♀LINDA: Oh.

SUZE: I'm about to drop at any moment.

♀LINDA: Eurgh! 'Ere – when you is pregnant... does that mean you're not allowed a bevy? You know, of the alcoholic variety?

SUZE: I'll say. May lead to difficulties later in life.

♂TOM: Did your mother drink while she was carrying you Linda?

♀LINDA: Oh yes. She'd have me in one hand and a can of Guinness in the other. She used to shove things down me romper suit. Used me as a handbag. I was the only one in nursery with straps.

♂TOM: Shut up. As if you went to nursery! I mean, as if! Your parents probably tied you to a pole in the back yard and chucked you bits of raw meat every other day.

♀LINDA: Well a girl's got to eat!

the doorbell rings. they look around room. linda looks at suze.

SUZE: Well I can't get it, I'm pregnant.

♂TOM: I can't get it, I'm homosexual.

♀LINDA: Oh so I suppose I've got to get it 'cos I'm the only one here who's normal!

linda pushes suze on her way out.

SUZE: Do you mind if I use your bedroom, Tom? I um – I feel a little sleepy. (Exits)

♂TOM: I felt a little Sleepy when I did Snow White and the Seven Dwarves at Chester. He wasn't that little either, I can tell you.

FRONT DOOR

zippy waits on the doorstep anxiously. the door opens and linda stands there.

♀LINDA: Yes?

ZIPPY: Mummy!!

he puts his arms around linda.

LIVING ROOM

tom and linda peer at zippy on the sofa.

♂TOM: Linda, how on earth can you forget about something like this?

♀LINDA: Well I put it at the back o'me mind, innit?

♂TOM: Linda La Hughes, you put worries about unfinished housework to the back of your mind. Worries about your slacks clashing with your bra-top to the back of your mind – not giving birth!

zippy puts his hand up.

♂TOM: Oh my god, he's got his hand up.

♀LINDA: Up what?

ZIPPY: Excuse me? I'm, er, pretty tired after my journey. Could I trouble you for some refreshment?

♀LINDA: It's David Copperfield. 'Ere y'are – chuck him a bag of crisps.

♂TOM: Oh prodigal son of Lindy's? Here – catch!

ZIPPY: This is a funny little house isn't it? With funny little chairs and a funny little sofa.

♀LINDA: I'll give you a funny little slap in a minute. Cor – he loves his crisps, dun't he?

♂TOM: Yes – I wonder where he gets that from?

linda shrugs.

♂TOM: You know. I used to wish that I'd been adopted. Well most children do, don't they? I used to regularly attack my mother with a potato peeler. Dressed head to toe in her leisure wear and her Doctor Scholls screaming 'You witch Sheila Farrell! Hard to think that someone as talented and artistic as I could have sprung from your dried up old prune of a womb!' Well everyone says that to their mothers, don't they?

ZIPPY: Please Mummy Linda. Can I have some more crisps?

tom chucks crisps over.

ZIPPY: He throws like a girl!

♀ LINDA: I know, he's a right show up inn'e?

♂ TOM: Excuse me – I have won medals for my wrist action, actually. You don't get far in the trombone section of the Boys Brigade without some sort of payoff – d'you know what I mean?.

ZIPPY: Sorry.

♂ TOM: Call me Daddy.

ZIPPY: Is he your husband?

♀ LINDA: It's a long story.

ZIPPY: All right Daddy?

♂ TOM: Hi! So Linda. When did this happen?

♀ LINDA: Oh I dunno. I was about fifteen, I think. 'Ere mate. How old are you?

ZIPPY: Twenty-eight.

♀ LINDA: Liar!! Tom that's biologically impossible. He's older than I am.

ZIPPY: But you are my Mummy! You are!

he starts to cry.

♂ TOM: Aaaah! Shall we venture forth and giveth unto him counsel?

♀ LINDA: Oh go on then. I'm not busy. All right son?

ZIPPY: I've been better.

♂ TOM: Lindy, give him some succour.

♀ LINDA: (Pats his leg) Come to Mummy ickle boy. Aaah!

♂ TOM: Hey kid, kid! You wanna go out and er, shoot some crap?

ZIPPY: No! I don't like sport.

♂ TOM: Gosh, and yet you have a strangely athletic physique, don't you. Is that muscle?

♀ LINDA: Get your hands off him Daddy!

♂ TOM: I'm only making him feel better, Mummy!

♀ LINDA: You wanna watch Daddy! He's one of them homos.

ZIPPY: So?

♂ TOM: Oh. So – you don't mind having a... a gay dad then, eh?

ZIPPY: Well it's modern.

♂ TOM: Yeah, yeah it's great isn't it? It's great actually...(Hugs Zippy)

ZIPPY: Yeah all right, easy mate, easy.

♂ TOM: All right. So Linda. Why did you decide to give this charming boy away?

ZIPPY: Well innit obvious? She's poor white trash.

♀ LINDA: Ah thanks!

♂ TOM: So why did you decide to search out this sad 'ole slapper with the manners of a dray horse, then?

ZIPPY: Well I wanted to fit the final piece into my jigsaw.

♀ LINDA: What – you can do jigsaws?! God, that's brilliant!

♂ TOM: So – do you have anything to ask your new Mama and Papa. I, for my part, have no aversion to being probed.

ZIPPY: So where's your swimming pool? Eugh, is your swimming pool outdoors? Eugh! How common!

♂ TOM: Were you brought up in a house with a swimming pool?

ZIPPY: Yeah – so?

LINDA: Cor, you must be loaded! Is there anything else you would like to know?

ZIPPY: Where does my name come from?

LINDA: Oh. Well. You was named after a person in a book. Literature.

TOM: Oh! So... what's your name? Oh no, let me guess! I'm very good at guessing games. Um...Heathcliff? No, Darcy!!

LINDA: No – well, it was more of a television programme really. It was a very good television programme. I watched it quite a lot when I was preggers.

TOM: Right. Um, well, what's your name?

ZIPPY: Zippy.

TOM: You called a baby Zippy? Are you completely out of your mind?

LINDA: Oh shut up! You still got that bump on your head?

ZIPPY: Yeah.

LINDA: Aaaah – that's where I dropped you.

ZIPPY: You're weird!

LINDA: Yeah well, at least I ain't adopted!

TOM: Linda La Hughes!

ZIPPY: No I mean your... your clobber and that. You're not like a real mummy, are you?

LINDA: Well darling I am spunky.

ZIPPY: Are you pleased to see me?

LINDA: 'Course I'm pleased to see you Zippy. It's just a bit of a shock really. I mean I haven't been this shocked since... well since I give birth to you, really. I thought you were wind. I very nearly called you Fart.

ZIPPY: On my birth certificate, right, it says my father's name was Owen Nistand. Who is he?

LINDA: Well I don't know anyone called...

ZIPPY: Owen Nistand. (Shows Her birth certificate)

LINDA: Oh...(Laughs) No – that says One Night Stand. Your Daddy was a one night stand. I weren't very good at spelling in them days.

TOM: Yeah – so speaks the lady who put the 'dic' in dictionary.

ZIPPY: So you don't know his name?

LINDA: I know very little about him actually, except we met at a party and he was dressed as a pillar box.

TOM: Was it a fancy dress party Mummy?

LINDA: Well this is the worrying thing Daddy. No.

TOM: Well I mean, you must remember something about him, I mean apart from his quirky dress sense?

LINDA: Well... I don't know if this is going to come as a bit of a shock to you Zippy, but if I remember rightly, your daddy was black.

TOM: Are you taking the piss?

LINDA: It's true! I'm not messing!

ZIPPY: D'you think I could be part of your life?

LINDA: Well I dunno. D'you think I could be part of yours?

ZIPPY: Maybe. There might have to be a few little changes though, Mummy. D'you fancy going shopping?

LINDA: Sorry mate I'm Larry Flint. Skint!

TOM

'Linda La Hughes, you put worries about housework to the back of your mind. Worries about your slacks clashing with your bra-top to the back of your mind – not giving birth!'

GIMME GIMME GIMME   157

TOM: Funny – I had you down as a bit of a Helen Hunt.

ZIPPY: Well, may I remind you that I am loaded?

LINDA: Great! Well what are we waiting for then, big boy?

TOM: Yes. I'll just go and grab my poncho!

ZIPPY: Oh and another thing. The homo stays here.

LINDA: (Pushing Tom over) Bye!

tom falls onto the floor.

STREET

linda and zippy outside a shop called sluts r us. he drags her into mummy dearest instead.

MUMMY DEAREST

zippy holds up some big granny knickers. she tells him to fuck off.

LIVING ROOM

tom having tea with beryl and suze.

SUZE: I can't believe Linda's got a kid.

BERYL: No, a body that shape's got to have given birth.

TOM: God. I just find it all so... so unexpected. D'you know what I mean? It's like that old television show isn't it?

SUZE: Bagpuss?

TOM: No, no, no.

BERYL: The Onedin Line?

TOM: No – no, no, no, no. No, no. Each week they had a tale, and they were just like... unexpected. Oh god, what was it called?

BERYL: Do you know if it's a boy or girl?

TOM: Oh it's definitely a boy. He's quite sexy actually considering his gene pool.

BERYL: No! I was meaning hers.

SUZE: No. Do you know how to work it out?

TOM: Yes, the boy's got a little thing sticking out in front... it's about that big...

zippy propels linda into the living room. he has dressed her like a mummy.

LINDA: I feel like that fucking tranny from Coronation Street.

ZIPPY: Mum! Don't swear. Ladies don't swear.

LINDA: And ladies don't sweat neither, but I tell you what mate – I am sweating like a glass blower's arse under all this acrylic.

ZIPPY: Mum!

TOM: You know, you do look like a tranny actually. A really bad tranny. I'm in one of those dreary gay clubs in Driffield. It's a Monday night. The Human League's playing on the jukebox, a couple of rent boys in the corner. Then you, Brian, stood there in your wife's clothes, rolling your own.

LINDA: Oh shut up! It's not funny. I look about ninety.

ZIPPY: I think you look lovely.

BERYL: I think you look quite sexy actually, Linda.

LINDA: Eughhh!

BERYL: Mark you, I went out with a tranny called Brian for sixteen years.

suze is studying linda.

LINDA: What are you looking at?

SUZE: Tom, tell me I'm not going to end up looking like that.

ZIPPY: I'm so glad you're going to be part of my life now, Mummy. What's your favourite TV programme? No don't tell me! Anything with John Thaw. Inspector Morse.

LINDA: No, I like Ant and Dec. Oooh, the dreams I've had about them cheeky chappies.

TOM: I know what they could do with my wonky donkey! D'you know what I mean?!

ZIPPY: You know who Ant and Dec are? Is that coz you watch them with your grandkids – aaaah?

LINDA: Listen here, mush, right? Just remember I was practically a foetus when I had you, right?

ZIPPY: What's for tea Mummy?

LINDA: Oh have a cigarette!

ZIPPY: A real Mummy would make me bangers and mash. Toad in the Hole. You're such a bloody disappointment! Well tell me off for swearing then!

♀ LINDA: Tom? Can I talk to you in the bedroom please?

♂ TOM: Yes, all right.

♀ LINDA: (Pushes Suze) Oh get out my way, bitch!

suze falls backward behind sofa.

LINDA'S BEDROOM

tom and linda.

♂ TOM: Can I just say that you look absolutely revolting.

♀ LINDA: I should be a glam mum like Scary Spice. Tits up here. Arse out there. Max Beesley giving me a lick. I mean, this is not me.

♀ TOM: So what are you going to do?

♀ LINDA: Well get rid of him. He's cramping my style guy!

♂ TOM: Oh I've got an idea! I've got an idea! I did this musical once called Oedipus Rex – do you know it?

♀ LINDA: No.

♂ TOM: Well it's all about this guy called Oedipus. He gouged out his own eyes…with a knitting needle!

♀ LINDA: Well I ain't doing that! They're my best feature! Well, those and my purdy white baps!

♂ TOM: And… and why did he do it? He did it because… oh god, I was only in the second act…I played Oedipus's best friend Billy McNulty… um… oh no – Oedipus gouged out his own eyes because he was totally and utterly traumatised because his own mother came onto him.

♀ LINDA: Thomas, are you suggesting what I think you're suggesting?

♂ TOM: And prithee damsel, what might that be?

♀ LINDA: That I come on to my own son just to give him the elbow?

ZIPPY: (Enters) Sorry to interrupt only that blonde bird – er, her waters have broke. Well do something! She's your mate!

♂ TOM: Well I shall go and build a bridge over her breaking waters, and leave you with your delightful son. Zippy, bon courage mon petit! And bon appetit!

tom exits room. linda smiles meekly at zippy. zippy smiles nervously back.

LIVING ROOM

suze giving birth on the couch. tom livid, beryl perturbed.

♂ TOM: Can't you wipe them up or something?

SUZE: Tom they're my waters. Don't you know what this means?

♂ TOM: Yes my shag pile's getting ruined!

SUZE: I am having the baby!

BERYL: I'll phone for an ambulance.

SUZE: No! I'm having a home birth!

♂ TOM: Not in here you're bloody not! Go downstairs!

SUZE: I can't! Look, phone Jez! Oh give me the phone! Oh god I can't remember the number.

♂ TOM: Let me… I'll call an ambulance.

SUZE: Don't you dare, you bastard!

♂ TOM: God, I've never heard you swear before, Suze!

SUZE: Oh! Oh! It's coming Tom, it's coming! Feel between my legs!

BERYL: Have you got a washing up bowl or something?

♂ TOM: Now is hardly the time to be doing my octopus routine.

SUZE: Sorry?

♂ TOM: Oh if you insist I will.

he puts the washing up bowl on his head and jumps up and down

LINDA'S BEDROOM

linda is holding court.

♀ LINDA: Oh Zippy. I could talk to you till the cows come home. In fact that's what Daddy used to say when I got in of a night. 'Oh look, the cow's come home!' Ah.

ZIPPY: Is granddad still alive?

♀ LINDA: Yes. But sadly his faculties ain't. He often mistakes me for Kylie Minogue. It's a common error.

LINDA

'I should be a glam mum like Scary Spice. Tits up here. Arse out there. Max Beesley giving me a lick.'

ZIPPY: What's his name?

♀ LINDA: Daddy.

♂ TOM: (Enters) Suze is on our couch having contraptions! Legs in the air, tears streaming down her face and there's a little head appearing between her legs!

♀ LINDA: Eugh!! That's weird, guy!

♂ TOM: It's really beautiful actually. Beryl!!

tom exits.

linda puts some jazz on her boogie box. she dims the lights.

♀ LINDA: Are you a fan of... scat? I know how you men hate electric when you're in the mood for loooooove.

ZIPPY: What are you doing?!

♀ LINDA: Ooooh – hot in here, init? Why don't you lose a layer? Mmm – those slacks feel tight. Why not unzip your zip, Zip?

LIVING ROOM

beryl is videoing the birth.
tom is delivering the baby.

SUZE: Aaaaaaaaagggggggh!!!!!

♂ TOM: Come on – push! Push!

SUZE: Aaaaaagghhh!

BERYL: Try and smile Suze!

SUZE: Oooh! Oooh! Something's snagging!

♂ TOM: Oh – Beryl, you couldn't just grab my watch could you?

BERYL: Oh it's got diamonds all over its face.

SUZE: Has it?!!

♂ TOM: No, no – the watch has, the watch has.

SUZE: Oh. Is it coming?

♂ TOM: Oh... I can see the head! I can see the head!

SUZE: Aaaaaaggghhh!

BERYL: You're very good at this Tom. Did you train as a doctor?

♂ TOM: Well I've sluiced out the abortion suite on Where The Heart Is, so I'm as good as really.

BERYL: I'm gonna send this in to You've Been Framed. Would you try and do something wrong Suze? Fall off the couch maybe?

♂ TOM: He's coming, he's coming!

the baby comes out.
tom bites away umbilical cord.

♂ TOM: It's a little boy. It's a beautiful little boy! Look!

BERYL: Drop him! I'll get two hundred and fifty quid!

zippy runs in

SUZE: I wish Jez was here.

♂ TOM: Oh – Why?

ZIPPY: You're all freaks. The lot o'yous! Monsters! Cruel warped demons! I'm out of here!

he runs out of the french windows with his bag.

LINDA'S BEDROOM

linda looks at herself in mirror.

♀ LINDA: You had to let him go. I mean, he may have been rich but he made you feel ugly.

LIVING ROOM

suze knackered on the couch.
tom hugs the baby.

♂ TOM: Have you thought of any names for him yet?

SUZE: Well you know sometimes people name their babies after where they were conceived, like Brooklyn Beckham? Well we're going to call him Lea-On-Solent. Lea for short.

♂ TOM: Lea? Little Lea. Little Lea. That's your name poppet. Yes it is. Yes it is your name – yes. Look at you – you're so perfect, aren't you? Ten tiny little fingers. Nine tiny little t... no, ten... no I was right, nine little toes. Oh you're so quirky, aren't you! Yes you are, yes you are – I could hold this child forever you know. I really c...

the baby wees in his face!

TOM: (Gives baby to Suze) Get this vile little thing away from me!

SUZE: Do you ever want kids Tom?

TOM: Well, parents can be such an embarrassment, can't they? I remember my mother used to have a cerise Honda Express. The queen of mopeds. Dressed in her cerise jerkin, cerise ski pants and cerise moonboots. I tell you, the kids in our school had a field day.

suze yawns.

TOM: Sorry, are you shattered?

SUZE: No, I'm bored. A simple yes or no would have done..

TOM: If I adopted a child that kid would have the piss taken out of it. And I don't wanna be my child's Honda Express.

SUZE: You could have one with Linda.

TOM: She doesn't drive and I don't suit the helmet.

SUZE: I meant a baby.

TOM: Yeah, right!

still it's given him food for thought.

LINDA'S BEDROOM

linda lying on her bed sucking her thumb and scratching her tummy, watching tv.

tom comes in sits.

TOM: What are you doing?

LINDA: Just sat here scratching me trunk.

TOM: What are you watching?

LINDA: Only got one eye on it.

TOM: What's the other eye on?

LINDA: My Di shrine.

TOM: I take it our little scheme worked then?

linda nods.

TOM: You look a bit down in the dumps though. D'you wanna play a little game to cheer yourself up?

LINDA: Like what?

TOM: Well I don't know. We could play um... oh we could play Changing Rooms! You can be Carol Smillie and I can be a distraught neighbour.

LINDA: Great! Now she's Dutch isn't she? I'll just find me clogs.

TOM: No – she's Irish. Comes from just outside Auchtermuchty. Okay? In your own time. (Closes his eyes)

LINDA: Keep 'em closed. Keep 'em closed. And open your eyes!

TOM (Opens Eyes – Shouts) What have you done to my lounge diner? I said no turquoise!

LINDA: Oh you're brilliant at that.

TOM: Yes I know, I know I am. Um, all right – Now we can do 'Big Brother'. I'll be the Irish trolley dolly and you can be the Welsh girl with big hair.

LINDA: Great.

TOM: Right.

they sit down.

TOM: Okay – and go!

they say nothing! linda has her mouth open, tom sits silently, pause, then they laugh and applaud.

LINDA: What now? What now?

TOM: Um – all right – we'll do Coronation Street – all right? I'll be Deirdre Rachid and you can be a non-speaking extra. All right?

LINDA: Okay.

TOM: Okay.

they stand and get into position.

TOM: (Handing Linda imaginary change) And fifteen change. Thanks very much, love. Don't speak – just go!

linda waves and exits. tom waves back. linda comes back in – they laugh and applaud.

TOM: Right. Do you – do you feel better now?

♀ LINDA: Oh yes.

off. we hear the baby cry.

♀ LINDA: Oh how long's that gonna go on for?!

♂ TOM: Would you like any more kids Linda?

♀ LINDA: Oh what you asking me for?

♂ TOM: I'm just... being deep.

♀ LINDA: No. I don't think I've got that maternal highlight in me.

♂ TOM: Ah, I always thought I didn't. But holding baby Lea in my arms this afternoon brought a few things home to me, you know. I mean, who's going to take care of me when I get old? No-one popping by to mop up my wet patch or shave my nostril hair. No-one to slip a farthing to when they sit on my lap. I mean, if I got a lady pregnant, I wouldn't expect her to do anything. I'd do all the work. I wouldn't expect the lady to do anything except give birth.

♀ LINDA: Tom? Are you saying what I think you're saying?

♂ TOM: Possibly.

♀ LINDA: That you want to have an ickle baby?

♂ TOM: Possibly.

♀ LINDA: With me?

♂ TOM: Yes Lindy.

♀ LINDA: Oh well I'm flattered but I'll have to think about it. I am after all, a lady.

♂ TOM: Well, look, why don't you just sleep on it and we'll talk again in the morning, all right?.

♀ LINDA: No, I've thunk enough. What are you waiting for big boy? Let's make babies!!

♂ TOM: Great, great! Lie back! Now throw your legs in the air! Don't you have to slip off your combats?

♀ LINDA: No they've got Velcro round the crotch!

♂ TOM: I'll just go and fill up my turkey baster, all right?

♀ LINDA: Eh?

♂ TOM: Can I borrow this? (Rips Danny poster off the wall)

♀ LINDA: What for?

♂ TOM: Well I mean you don't seriously expect me to shag you do you?

♀ LINDA: Eh?

♂ TOM: Look, just lie still – I'll be literally seconds.

♀ LINDA: Tom, can I have a word with you for one little moment, please?

♂ TOM: (Kneels) Yes mother of my future children-ettes?

♀ LINDA: You've got an headache!

she punches him out.

Episode Four
TRAUMA

HOSPITAL

an empty ward. linda in bed with a saucepan on her head, smoking. the smoke alarm goes off.

♀ LINDA: Nurse!! Nurse!! I'm dying!! Quick nurse, help!!

a sexy male nurse runs in, bart. he switches the alarm off.

♀ LINDA: Is it time for my bed bath yet?
BART: God, I never get five minutes peace with you do I?

♀ LINDA: Well, it's these sheets! They're so clammy. Feel.
BART: Don't make me touch you if I don't have to!

♀ LINDA: 'Ere, do I look sexy in a saucepan Bart? I can see a liddle bit of your anatomy sticking out like a saucepan's handle! And it's not that little!
BART: Please let me go. Please!

♀ LINDA: Oh, please stay and talk to me Bart. I get so bored in 'ere on me own. Please.
BART: You should be proud of yourself. You've made medical history. Look! No-one wants to share a ward with you. We've never known people get better so quick.

♀ LINDA: See? I'm a gin. I mean a tonic.
BART: No more smoking Linda, right?

♀ LINDA: But it gives you vitamins! Mummy said!

he slaps her and leaves.

♀ LINDA: Bloody National Health Service. They all want lining up against a wall and shooting.

tom comes in wearing shades and carrying a basket of goodies.

♂ TOM: (Enters, on mobile) Okay and I'll need a basket of crudités in my Winnebago. I'm with Linda Lusardi on this one. If I haven't got a small carrot inside me, I simply cannot perform. Goodbye. Hi.

♀ LINDA: Hi.

♂ TOM: Hi. Well, guess what? You are feasting your bug-eyed stairods at the dashing new star of 'Doctor Deaf'. Isn't that fantast?

♀ LINDA: Speak English, Tom.

♂ TOM: 'Doctor Deaf'! It's a crime series about a pathologist. But a pathologist with a twist, you see... well, the clue is in the title. 'Doctor Deaf' so she's...

♀ LINDA: A police lady with flicked back hair?

♂ TOM: No, no – she's deaf. I will be playing Boyo Griffiths, the slippery, heroin-addicted pathologist's assistant with a criminal record and an perverted interest in Tamla Motown.

♀ LINDA: So, with a name like Boyo he's gotta be... Portuguese?

♂ TOM: Well, that's what I thought but no, in fact, he's Welsh. Really threw me in the audition, but I just remembered back to when I was stuck in a lift with Lorraine Kelly, so I just simply imitated her. 'Get me oota here ye bastards! Get me oota here ye lousy gets!'

♀ LINDA: Great.

♂ TOM: Yeah. So... tell me why are you in here again? Involved in some major road traffic accident or something? Quelle fromage, as we say on the Consonant.

♀ LINDA: Nah, I fell off a bus conductor. I went arse over tit off the 38 and flick-flacked halfway down Oxford Street.

♂ TOM: Anything broken?

♀ LINDA: An ironmonger's window and possibly me wrist.

♂ TOM: Oh, I've just had an idea, you couldn't just... die, could you? Then I could watch your autopsy and it would be very good research for me.

♀ LINDA: Well, normally Tom, I'd die like that... (Clicks fingers)... but I've fallen in love innit? So d'you mind if I don't?

♂ TOM: Anyone we know?

♀ LINDA: It's one of the nurses in here actually.

♂ TOM: Male?

♀ LINDA: 'Course he's male!

doctor french and students enter

♀ LINDA: Oh here they come. Coming for a poke about.

DR FRENCH: Everybody this is Linda. Linda is... nineteen. She was recently involved in an RTA and has proved to be a most fascinating case. Despite extensive investigations, scans – you name it – we have as yet been unable to locate a brain. She walks, she talks, she breaks wind like a rhino. But she ain't got no brain! This way!

they exit.

♀ LINDA: I wanna see my boyfriend! I wanna see my Bart!

♂ TOM: Bart? Bart! God, there was a guy on our drama course called Bart. God I had a really big crush on him. He had a huge package!

♀ LINDA: Like a pensioner's leg?

♂ TOM: Oh I'll say. We played the cow together in an avant-garde production of Flashdance.

♀ LINDA: I hope you were up the back.

♂ TOM: And on the final night, do you know what I did? I stole his tights. And to this day... when the mood takes me, I slip them on and dance a furtive fandango. The last time I saw him we were up for 'Gerry - The Musical'.

♀ LINDA: Halliwell?

♂ TOM: Adams. I gave a brilliant performance at my audition. Didn't even look at the script. Just walked straight in, and went 'There'sh a boowumb under your sheets. Get ite nie!' That's my Gerry Adams. God that's spooky, because Bart had a boyfriend called Adam.

♀ LINDA: 'Ere, that used to be my nickname up the Hod Carrier's Arms. They used to say 'Anyone ugly, she's 'ad 'em.'

♂ TOM: Every time I hear that name it fills me with bile, Adam! Adam! Bloody Adam!

♀ LINDA: Ere, I played Eve once in the school play. Billy McGinty was Adam. I got pulled off on opening night. I went on as naked as the day I was born. But I didn't look odd as Eve. Mummy made me a downstairs wig out of Brillo pads. Brought me out in a terrible rash. Still not shifted it. It was touch and go whether I''d make it to Infants after that.

♂ TOM: I'm gonna vomit.

tom crosses to window and heaves. bart comes back in.

BART: Drugs Linda?

♀ LINDA: Well, I don't as a rule but seeing as it's you, chop me out a big one baby!

BART: They're painkillers you daft sod. Open wide!

linda laughs.

BART: Your mouth. Swallow.

♀ LINDA: You know me so well! 'Ere Tom – that's my boyfriend Bart! Inn'e gorgeous? Look at that arse!! It's like two grapefruits in an handbag!

bart turns round.

♂ TOM: Bart?!

BART: Tom!!

♂ TOM: What the bloody hell are you doing here?

BART: Working.

♂ TOM: You're not researching a role are you? You're not playing Mitch, the out gay wheelchair bound HIV positive kidney courier with the speech impediment in 'Doctor Deaf' are you? Oh no! They told me Eammon Holmes had been pencilled.

BART: Are you still doing street theatre? With that cardboard Alsatian?

♂ TOM: No, no, no. I have actually just taken a leading role in a... in a new crime series, yeah. I nearly got mobbed on the way in, yeah. Er – 'Doctor Deaf'. Have you heard of it?

BART: What, someone's actually paying you to work?

♂ TOM: Yes! Don't sound so surprised!

BART: You jammy git Tom. I mean no disrespect like, but you've got to admit you were the worst in our year. I mean, the best part of his performance was usually the curtain call.

♂ TOM: So, um tell me how's er, how''s thingamebob? You know your boyfriend. Er – what's his name?

♀ LINDA: Adam.

♂ TOM: Yes, that's it – yes, Adam.

♀ LINDA: You said you wanted to kill him.

♂ TOM: Yes, shut up, shut up, shut up. So how is he then?

BART: Didn't you hear? Um Adam died six months ago.

♂ TOM: Oh dear. Was it a... was it a gruesome long, drawn-out death?

BART: No, reasonably quick.

♀ LINDA: Hang on a minute. Are you trying to tell me he's a bleeding homo?! Shit guy!

♂ TOM: Well er... look um, why don't you come round for supper if you're single. Are you still vegetarian? Because it's amazing what I can do with three courgettes and a palmful of olive oil.

♀ LINDA: I can do it with four.

♂ TOM: Take my card. Buzz me. Okay?

BART: Er, Tom – this is an appointment card for the clap clinic.

♂ TOM: Oh shit is it? Voici my real card. Juji on over when you have a moment and who knows... I might be wearing a little bit of history...

BART: Oh, great. How does um – Tuesday at eight grab you?

♂ TOM: By the short and curlies baby, just the way I like it!

BART: Thanks Tom, I really appreciate that. I'm in bits.

♀ LINDA: So's Humpty Dumpty but I don't hear him complaining.

HOSPITAL, LATER

linda watching tv. jez and suze come in.

JEZ/SUZE: Hi Neighbour!!

♀ LINDA: Oh whadda you want?!

SUZE: We've come to visit you.

♀ LINDA: Well visit me then!

JEZ: Is there anything infectious about you?

♀ LINDA: Only me giggle.

JEZ: Look, we bought you colouring books!

SUZE: Pokemon colouring books!

JEZ: And crayons!

SUZE: And face paints.

JEZ: And an Etch-A-Sketch!

SUZE: Jez that's my Etch-A-Sketch! You promised!!

JEZ: Oh poorly Linda. My precious little prune. You look even worse than usual. Come – let me give you a little hug.

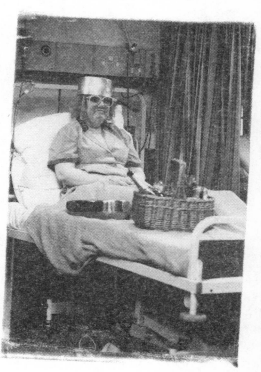

LINDA: Yes.

JEZ: Suze. Give Linda a hug.

SUZE: I don't want to.

JEZ: Please.

SUZE: No she's ugly.

JEZ: It'll turn me on.

SUZE: Really?

JEZ: Mmm.

suze puts down her etch-a-sketch and hugs linda.

SUZE: Oooh Linda. Your skin's so soft. It's like a downy peach.

LINDA: Eurgh! Get off me lesbo slag!

JEZ: Suze isn't a lesbian. She's just very accommodating.

SUZE: I might be a lesbian. Last night I had a very interesting dream about Sue Lawley, actually.

JEZ: Fill me in kitten chops.

SUZE: That's what she said. Oh this is crap!

she throws the etch-a-sketch across the room.

SUZE: So what do we do now?

LINDA: Well, I think you're meant to cry, tell me you love me, give me some money. And then leave.

SUZE: We've never been in a National Health hospital before.

JEZ: It's the only reason why we came.

SUZE: I won't step foot outside the house unless I'm BUPA'd up to the eyeballs.

JEZ: Where's Barbara Windsor?

LINDA: Oh look will you two shut up! I'm tryina watch Tom on the Telly! Is that him?

JEZ: No that's a cheese plant.

LINDA: Oh

TOM: (Enters) Have I been on yet? Have I been on yet? Sorry I'm so late, I decided to take public transport. Just in case anyone wanted to spot me.

LINDA: Did you get recognised?

TOM: Twice! Once by a man who reckoned he'd had sex with me in the Top Shop changing rooms.

LINDA: And the second time?

TOM: No, it was him again. Well I went round the Circle Line three times you see.

BART: (Enters) Are you any looser today Linda?

LINDA: Yeah, they're shooting out o'me like bullets.

BART: (Feeling saucepan) You are still quite tight.

TOM: Barty Barty, Barty. I'm in the next scene. Look! Look. Look.

BART: I'm a bit tied up at the moment, Tom mate.

TOM: Oh all right. Well I'm taping it anyway. You can watch it tomorrow when you come round.

BART: Okay.

TOM: Yes, yes.

bart leaves.

JEZ: Gosh Tom – you are famous. Even the nurse recognised you!

SUZE: And so kind to your fans. Inviting them round.

TOM: Oh my God – that's Gidea Gordogne. Do you remember? She used to be the face of Menu Masters. Oh God she adores me. She loves me. She gave her all in this scene. So did I actually. She's so good at playing deaf.

ON TV

a deaf relatives' room.

janine with a relative.

RELATIVE: Any news?

JANINE: I am sorry, you're gonna have to sign that. I'm as deaf as a post.

RELATIVE: (Signs a crap sentence)

JANINE: I'll bring you up to speed. I'm about to cut open your husband's spleen. By then we should have a clearer idea of why he

was moonlighting at the sewage farm. Boyo, my Welsh Pathologist's Assistant is through those doors preparing the stiff. As soon as we find anything out I'll give you a shout.
RELATIVE: Good luck!!
JANINE: How many times do I have to tell you? I'm deaf!

DOCTOR DEAF MORTUARY

janine and boyo performing the autopsy.

JANINE: Pinking shears. Right, I'm going in. For the purposes of the tape I'm cutting into vital Artery B. Egg whisk. No, no – actually, get me the nail clippers.
BOYO: So, does being deaf make you a better pathologist Janine?
JANINE: I don't know, Boyo, but it sure as hell makes me a better lover.
BOYO: Janine – there is something I have to tell you. I'm a raving homosexual.
JANINE: Sign it!!
BOYO: (Signs a sentence)
JANINE: (Gasps) I don't believe you are doing this to me? You're actually having an affair with Father Parr the hospital chaplain, I don't believe it!!

STREET

tom is stopped by a passerby.

PASSERBY: Excuse me, are you? Oh it is you. Oh I think you're wonderful. Could I trouble you for a... oh I haven't got any paper.

tom produces an autograph book and a pen.

♂ TOM: Ta-dah!! I always come well equipped.
PASSERBY: Could you er... could you sign it to Myra?
♂ TOM: To Myra. Oh such a pretty name. Can't think why it never caught on!

he walks on.

PASSERBY: Tell you the truth I thought you were dead. When are you going to make any more of those marvellous Carry On Films? 'Infamy infamy! They've all got it in for me!'

CORNER SHOP

catholic assistant prices tom's food into a till – she eyes him suspiciously.

♂ TOM: Watch a lot of daytime television do you?
ASSISTANT: Oh – it's you!! Six seventy-two please.

she takes his money and punches him out.

ASSISTANT: Shagging a priest? You dirty bastard!!

tom staggers out of the shop with his groceries. he bumps into a priest.
♂ TOM: Oh I'm sorry.

the priest winks at him saucily. tom makes hasty exit.

TOM'S BEDROOM

tom is dancing round his room to 'beautiful lover' by brotherhood of man. he pulls open one of his drawers and pulls out a pair of american tan tights and sniffs them. he has an idea.

LIVING ROOM

bart sits on the sofa.

♂ TOM: (Pouring wine) So, do you er, still see anyone from our drama college days, mmm? Oh no – my robe is open to reveal my fleshy tabernacles.

tom is wearing the tights.

BART: I did bump into Freddie Clutterbuck the other day.

TOM: Is he still acting?

BART: No. He's a paparazzi photographer now.

TOM: Oh dear sweet Freddie, how I miss him.

BART: He told me to tell you that he still thinks you're an absolute twat.

TOM: Well, I didn't mean to kick him off the stage, you know – is he out of the wheelchair yet?

BART: Yes.

TOM: Now talking of 'Doctor Deaf', have you seen it? And aren't I marvellous in it?

BART: Well, I haven't, but some of the orderlies tell me it's absolutely hilarious.

TOM: (Laughs) Yes, moving swiftly on, um so how are you finding singledom? Great isn't it? Are you shagging anything that moves? You're so like me.

BART: No. I really miss him.

TOM: Who?

BART: Adam.

TOM: Oh God.

BART: Don't you even want to know how he went?

TOM: Oh all right, well if you insist on droning on about your dead boyfriend, I will give you sixty seconds, okay? You now have just a minute to tell me how your boyfriend died without hesitation, deviation or repetition starting... now!

BART: He was working in the States doing an advert for Cheerios and they were filming in a candy store and this gunman ran in in the middle of filming...

TOM: Buzzz. Repetition of filming!

BART: ...waving a sawn off shotgun in the air.

TOM: Forty seconds!

BART: And Adam was pretty scared as you can imagine. And he hyperventilated and he choked on a Cheerio. The whole thing was caught on camera.

TOM: Thirty seconds!

BART: They sent me the video, but I can't bring myself to watch it. If only I'd been there.

TOM: Why? Twenty!

BART: I could have practised the Heimlich Manoeuvre!

TOM: Ten!!

BART: And saved his life.

TOM: Ah – buzzz. Hesitation! I win, you lose.

BART: That wasn't very nice Tom.

TOM: Well then could we change the subject, please!

BART: You really are one of the most vile queens that ever walked the planet aren't you?

TOM: Vile, but alive! I think I'm just gonna sit down now and cross my legs. Look at how brown my legs are, Barty. Look at how brown and shiny they are. I'm gonna let you in on a little secret Barty... I'm wearing tights. And d'you wanna know what else? They're not mine!

BART: Are they Linda's?

TOM: Look at my lovely brown legs Barty. Look at them, kiss them, C'mon – you know you want it. I've fancied you ever since I first clapped eyes on you in dialect class.

BART: Oh my God, you're actually serious aren't you?

TOM: Oh touch me in those naughty places Bart. Go on go on, I love you, go on, go on!

BART: You love me?

TOM: Yes.

BART: What? You'd do anything for me?

TOM: Oh yes, God, anything, anything, anything. Your wish is my command.

BART: Anything at all?

TOM: Yes I would.

LIVING ROOM

tom trots in 'baaa-ing' like a sheep he is dressed in linda's clothes.

TOM: I really had no idea you were into this sort of thing, oh, worshipful master. But hey, I ain't complainin'.

BART: That looks good.

TOM: Does it?

BART: What's your girlie name?

TOM: Tomasina. Tomasina Tool.

BART: How does it feel being a girl, Tomasina?

TOM: Oh, oh God it feels really good being a girl. Very liberating being a girlie!

BART: You wouldn't have such things as... handcuffs, would you?

TOM: (Gasps) Oh God, Oh God, Oh God...Yes, yes, yes. I do! Yes. My lovecuffs! Here, quick – come on. Be gentle with me, be gentle with me!

bart handcuffs tom to the door.

BART: You've been a very, very naughty... girl.

TOM: Have I Mister? Will I be punished? Severely? But I knoweth not what I dideth...

BART: How does that feel? Can you escape?

TOM: No, no... I can't. No, no. I'm stranded, all alone in a strange part of town.

BART: You'd like nothing more than me to kiss you now wouldn't you?

TOM: Oh yes, that would be nice – but I'm a good girl, I am!

BART: Beg me.

TOM: Oh God, go on! Kiss me Barty! Kiss me! Treat me like the dirty bitch that I am!!

bart grabs tom.

TOM: Owwwww!!!!!! God – that hurts, you prick!!

BART: Good! Because I wouldn't touch you with a very long bargepole if you were the last man on this planet. You disgust me. In fact, you make me wish I was straight. In fact I'd shag Linda before I shagged you. And that's bad!

TOM: Where are you going?

BART: Home. But – not before I've called a certain friend of ours.

TOM: What is your problem?

BART: You were bloody vile about Adam.

TOM: God, are you still banging on about him! He's deeeeeead!

BART: (On phone) Yeah, Freddie? Freddie Clutterbuck? Yeah It's Bart.

TOM: No.

BART: Yeah, come over to 69 Paradise Passage. Kentish Town. Rear window. Bring your camera. You might make yourself some money kid.

TOM: No, no you can't do that, you can't do this, I'm a huge star and he's a paparazzo!

BART: Exactly. (Exits)

TOM: Help! Help! Soap star in a conundrum! Help!

HOSPITAL

linda is reading 'the mirror' – tom is headline news.

LINDA: Oh! That is a right show-up. So how long were you there for?

TOM: Not very long. About three days. Jez and Suze had to break in and cut me loose with a chainsaw.

LINDA: My first boyfriend used to tie me up, in knots. Thank heavens I'm double-jointed.

dr french enters.

DR. FRENCH: Hello Linda. D'you want to play a game?

LINDA: This is my boyfriend. Thomas. He's off the telly.

DR. FRENCH: Yah right!

TOM: Yeah right!! Though not for much longer, thanks to your lousy wank nurse Bart!

DR. FRENCH: Bank nurse!

TOM: No I got it right the first time, thank you.

DR FRENCH: (Shows Inksplot) So Linda, what does this shape remind you of?

LINDA: A knob.

DR. FRENCH: (Shows car) And this one?

LINDA: A knob.

DR. FRENCH: (Shows a photo of Jeffrey Archer) And this one?

GIMME GIMME GIMME 169

TOM
'Kiss me Barty! Kiss me! Treat me like the dirty bitch that I am!!'

♀ LINDA: That's a really big knob. You got any more pictures?

DR. FRENCH: No, I think I've shown you enough.

♀ LINDA: D'you go around showing everybody pictures?

DR. FRENCH: Oh, only special people.

♀ LINDA: Ooh, that's a good job innit?

DR. FRENCH: It takes years of training Linda.

♀ LINDA: What, just to go round flashing pictures of knobs? I used to do that in the Brownies.

DR FRENCH: Do you know Linda, I find you fascinating. I think you have a very serious condition. It's rare. So rare, in fact, it's almost unique.

♀ LINDA: That's right, there's only one of me babe!

DR. FRENCH: I think you have Reversed Body Dismorphic Disorder.

♀ LINDA: What's that?

DR. FRENCH: Well usually Body Dismorphic Disorder means that someone quite quite beautiful thinks they're sickeningly ugly and that they don't deserve people being nice to them.

♀ LINDA: And what happens in my case?

DR. FRENCH: Well it's reversed.

bart enters - hands envelope to doctor.

♂ TOM: Oh God. Oh, oh – somebody hold me back! Somebody hold me back! If I get within three feet of that vile queen, I'm likely to do some damage!

DR. FRENCH: So they've finally located it.

♀ LINDA: What, me brain?!

DR FRENCH: I don't believe it.

♀ LINDA: I have got one haven't I? I can do that...

puts arm out and stretches fingers.

DR. FRENCH: I have heard of the phrase 'brains in your arse' but I've never actually seen it in the flesh!

♀ LINDA: Eh?

bart holds up diagram.

♂ TOM: So that's why your bum's so lumpy!

doctor and bart laugh.

♀ LINDA: I'm discharging...Meself. I'm discharging meself!

DR. FRENCH: Oh Linda, we were just playing a trick on you. God, lighten up baby!

♂ TOM: You're all completely mad in this hospital. And you. Thanks to you I've been fired.

BART: There is a God after all.

♂ TOM: I film my final scene as Boyo tonight. And all because they've got me down as a gender-bending, cross-dressing, panties-wearing freak!

DR FRENCH: Linda, do you think it's wise to leave? You still need help!

♀ LINDA: Ah shuddup, I'm getting out of 'ere. It's full of boring homos who don't wanna cop off.

DR. FRENCH: You both need help!

♀ LINDA: Listen mush, don't hate me 'cos you ain't me!

♂ TOM: Yeah!

tom punches bart who falls on top of dr french.

♂ TOM: Oh - er, socks. See? Socks. Men's socks.

LIVING ROOM

tom reading a book. linda comes in - dusting and whistling. she makes for the t.v.

♂ TOM: Come away from there. That is not going on today.

♀ LINDA: It's freaking me out without pictures on it. It's really weird. (Sighs) I read a book once. They all went to the shops. It was great. Do they go the shops in that?

♂ TOM: Do they go to the shops in 'A Tale Of Two Cities'? Why don't you call up Charles Dickens and ask him?

linda laughs.

♂ TOM: Don't pretend you've heard of him.

linda stands, whistles, dusts the telly.

♂ TOM: (Crosses to her) Come away from that evil thing!! Get away!

♀ LINDA: Ah but it's your last ever episode of 'Doctor Deaf' on now!! You haven't told me how they write you out.

tom picks up telly – hurls it from balcony.

♂ TOM: (Turns) Now you will never ever, ever get to find out, will you?

♀ LINDA: D'you wanna put my knickers on?

♂ TOM: For God's sake!.

back garden jez and suze pegging washing out.

SUZE: Jez, look. Tom's head's in the corner of the garden!
JEZ: Really? Wow. Spooky.

the telly has landed in the garden. tom is on it.

DOCTOR DEAF HOSPITAL CORRIDOR

BOYO: I became a pathologist's assistant because I care. I care about people. I care about patients, and autopsies. And murder. Well I'm sorry if that's not good enough for you Janine. But I've got a pretty big heart and I've got one heck of a social conscience.
JANINE: You've also got my body stocking on, Boyo.

reveal boyo in ladies' clothing.

BOYO: I'm not Boyo any more. I'm Boya. I'm a lady. With breasts and bumps and goodness knows what else. And if that isn't good enough for the Saint Aloysius Morgue then it's goodbye from me.
JANINE: I can't let you stay Boyo. Your legs look lousy in those tights.
♂ BOYO: Oh you're a cruel-hearted bitch, Janine.

boyo leaves.

Episode Five
SINGING IN THE DRAIN

TOM'S BEDROOM

tom is reading book called 'how to be middle class'.

♂ TOM: (VO) 'By his early thirties the middle-class person will not go to sleazy nightclubs and get off his tits on Ecstacy..'

♂ TOM: Oh bollocks!

♂ TOM: (VOICE-OVER) 'Instead, his favourite pastime will be hosting dinner parties.'

♂ TOM: Oh – that's interesting, hhmmm. Who shall I call? Who shall I call? (Leafs through address book) There's nobody, nobody. Oh, Jez and Suze.

LIVING ROOM

tom linda jez having dinner suze with massive hair on her mobile.

♂ TOM: Well, isn't this thrilling?

♀ LINDA: Is it chicken?

♂ TOM: No. It's much more middle-class than chicken.

♀ LINDA: Is it cow?

♂ TOM: Oh, shut up Linda. God! I love dinner parties. One feels almost as if one's in an episode of Cold Feet.

♀ LINDA: Oh, I've seen that, that's bollocks innit, they were all wearing shoes.

♂ TOM: Sprout puree? There's plenty left. Now, does anyone have an interesting or amusing anecdote to help this party go with a swing?

♀ LINDA: I remember once when Mummy was cooking dinner and I can't remember whether we had sausages or fish fingers, but I threw them across the room.

♂ TOM: Oh God, how am I supposed to follow that up?

JEZ: I have to say Tom, this food is top notch. It's almost bistro standard.

♂ TOM: Well it's a little rustic French peasant recipe picked up in the Dordogne. Yah. Coq Au Fromage.

♀ LINDA: 'Ere. Has that Suze done something to her hair?

♂ TOM: I'm not a hundred per cent sure.

JEZ: Do you think so? I just thought she'd put on a bit of weight.

♀ LINDA: Nah, she's always been a fat pig.

♂ TOM: Why is she talking to herself? Is she mentally ill?

JEZ: No, she's on the mobile phone.

♀ LINDA: Well who's she talking to? She's been on there for bloody hours.

♂ TOM: Yeah. Oi, you rude bitch – come and sit down! I've been slaving over a hot microwave all bloody day!

SUZE: Well slap her round the face and shove her down the catwalk! Jesus! Oh sorry! Sorry! Sorry!

suze's mobile rings.

♂ TOM: Oh God!

linda chucks it in the casserole dish. it stops ringing.

♂ TOM: So – what are we calling this new hairdo Suze? I think we can rule out the words 'a success'.

SUZE: It's a perm. Well you know what they say. New job, new hairdo.

♀ LINDA: Who says that?

SUZE: Everybody says it Linda. Now will you just stop questioning me! I've had a really hard day!

♀ LINDA: Oooh!

♂ TOM: So, tell me, is your new job anything to do with being an American porn star?

♀LINDA: You did that for a while, didn't you, Tom?

♂TOM: I did a little film called 'The Postman Only Comes Twice'. In a tiny bed-sit in Bury St. Edmunds.

SUZE: If you must know I'm working as a talent scout at Cyclone Modelling Agency.

JEZ: Yeah, she's handling all the top models actually.

♂TOM: Oh well – in the words of Sir Cliff Richard...

♀LINDA: Oh your coq's so cheesy Tom.

♂TOM: 'Congratulations!' Devil Woman!!

SUZE: Jez has got himself a new job too. Haven't you sex giraffe?

JEZ: I have. And, Tom, I've got a proposition for you.

♂TOM: Oh Jez! You're so blatant right in front of your own wife!

JEZ: I've been doing some promo work and I heard about some West End auditions this Friday, and guess what – I've got you one.

♂TOM: Oh my God!

SUZE: What's it called again Jezzy?

JEZ: 'Titus, The Musical'.

♂TOM: I've got a really tight arse, haven't I Lindy? Well I did have 'til the eighties.

JEZ: No, no, no, 'Titus. It's the musical version of 'Titus Andronicus'.

♂TOM: You say that as if it's supposed to mean something. I...?

JEZ: By William Shakespeare.

♂TOM: Who?

♀LINDA: Oh I've seen that. The Wicked Witch is in it, isn't it? That's so scary.

JEZ: Oh yes, and they sing 'Ding Dong The Witch is Dead'!

♀LINDA: Yeah, 'ere, (To Suze) they could play that at your funeral. This sauce ain't got any lumps in it. I want lumps.

♂TOM: Jez this is so kind of you. Is there anything I can do to repay you? Though can I just point out, there is a lady present.

JEZ: Well, You could try being nice to us.

♂TOM: Nice? Nice? I've just cooked you a bloody meal. What more d'you want? Foreplay?

SUZE: Actually Linda. I've just had a thought.

♀LINDA: I had one o'them last year. It's weird init?

SUZE: I'm organising Alexander McQueen's fashion show at the Royal Albert Hall on Friday. How d'you fancy being a model?

♀LINDA: Oh Suze!!

♂TOM: Suze, have you completely taken leave of your senses?

SUZE: I always thought you had a certain something.

♀LINDA: Oh Suze. I don't believe it. Well I do. But I don't know what to say.

♂TOM: No well excuse me, excuse me, hello – reality check here? You can't really be serious can you?

♀LINDA: See, I always knew you were looking at me funny. I always thought you were lesbo curious. But now I know it's just that you appreciate my natural glow!

SUZE: I think you've got just the sort of face they're looking for.

♂TOM: Oh yes, and what about the body? Do you think Alexander McQueen is gonna relish the sight of his hot pants being worn by the bloated sasquatch over here?

♀LINDA: Ah shuddup you jealous Nancy!

♂TOM: Oh you shut up! You demented great heifer! Oh I was born to be in a West End musical you know, I almost was the dresser in 'Les Mis'.

JEZ: Ah but you see Tom, the most important thing is, can you sing?

♂TOM: Can I si... can I si... of course I can bloody sing! I was head chorister at Our Lady Of The Wrap-Over Blouse. It was my first taste of the limelight. Oh, they were halogen days.

♀LINDA: Oh shut up! My new best friend needs more wine.

♂TOM: Oh God, there was that musical wasn't there – you know, where he changed the water into wine. And he was really famous, and he had a rock group or something. Oh Jesus, what was it called? Oh Christ – I'll remember it in a minute.

SUZE: Actually I think we should probably be making a move. Now Linda. I don't want you letting me down on Friday. Remember you need plenty of rest, drink lots of water and eat healthily.

♀LINDA: Yes Suze. I promise Suze. I love you Suze.

JEZ: And Linda remember, your body is a temple.

♂TOM: Yep, the Taj Mahal. That's about the size of it...

LINDA'S BEDROOM.

linda gazes in her mirror.

♀LINDA: It was bound to happen sooner or later, and now the world can share the beauty of Lindy.....

dream sequence linda in the make-up chair with camp make-up artist with a lisp, louie.

LOUIE: You're beautiful babes. No you are, you're beautiful. Ain't she beautiful Candice? People say to me, they say 'Louie, you are the best make-up artist in the business!' And they're not wrong. I'm like Jordan, I've done everyone. The stories these brushes could tell. I done Emma Bunton last week. Without make-up? Bella Emberg. See she ain't got your natural sparkle babe. And that don't come out o'no tube. Actually. D'you know what you are Linda? You're special. I think we will go for that turquoise eyeliner after all. Candice? Can you mix me up a turquoise please? I thank you.

TOM'S BEDROOM

tom on the phone.

♂TOM: Hello! I was wondering if you were taking on any new singing students? My name? Does this voice need an explanation? Dear heart – it's Thomas T. Farrell –henpecked Peregrine with castanetson 'The Cazalets'. How much do you charge?

And who else do you teach? Sorry – did you say Sheila B. Devotion and The Pet Shop Boys? I think I'm breaking up.

tom switches phone off and looks through paper again

♂ TOM: Oh. (Dials number) Hello? Miss Honeycomb? Miss Heidi Honeycomb? I think this could be your lucky gay...day!

LINDA'S BEDROOM

linda pretends she is in an advert.

LINDA: Hi. My name's Linda La Hughes, and I'm the most beautiful woman in the world. How do I do it? Simple. Every day I cleanse, tone and clench. But, I also have one other little beauty secret that I want to share with you – egg. Yes, if you crack an egg on your face every day, not only will your skin feel the benefits, but, if you shove your face under a grill, you've also get yourself a handy, healthy little omelette in case you get peckish.

she turns – sees suze.

SUZE: Ready for catwalk practice Linda?

BATHROOM

tom gargling, then singing.

♂ TOM: Oh, you are a mucky kid Dirty as a dustbin lid...

LIVING ROOM

suze stands by the stereo. she has drawn a line across the centre of the room.

SUZE: Ready? Now follow the line and don't forget to smile... okay, go!!

suze puts a cd on. linda tries to follow the line she can't.

♀ LINDA: Aaagh... no!
SUZE: Linda. How hard is it to walk in a straight line?
♀ LINDA: Well I can do it when I'm on me own, but it's when you're watching me. You're pressurising me Suze, you're pressurising me.

SUZE: But I've stuck a line on the carpet. Try looking at it. Okay?
♀ LINDA: I need toilets.
SUZE: Shut up! And remember – one foot in front of the other. And go!! (Puts CD On)

she tries again. tom comes in in a kimono, pushing a lectern. linda messes up again.

♀ LINDA: He put me off that time! You put me off!
♂ TOM: What, what, what?
♀ LINDA: What are you wearing?
♂ TOM: My special singing outfit. D'you know who gave this to me?
♀ LINDA: Demis Roussos?
♂ TOM: My late great Aunty Daphne. The only Geisha to come from Cheadle Hume. Rumour has it she sang for Chairman Miaow.
SUZE: Linda, if you can't walk in a straight line, you can't be a model.
♀ LINDA: Well can't I have a piggy back or something?
SUZE: Vivien Westwood's doing piggybacks. Alexander McQueen needs walkers! (Exits)
♀ LINDA: Oh, I wish I'd never agreed to be a bloody model now. Why weren't I born a dog?!
♂ TOM: Linda you cannot hang around here all day like some menopausal wombat. Heidi Honeycomb's on her way over.

LINDA

'Hi. My name's Linda La Hughes and I'm the most beautiful woman in the world. How do I do it? Simple. Every day I cleanse, tone and clench.'

GIMME GIMME GIMME 175

⚲ LINDA: Who?

♂ TOM: My new singing teacher.. She told me to leave the latch off and slip into something loose.

⚲ LINDA: Well don't look at me mate; I'm tighter than a condom on a beach ball.

off. the bewitching voice of heidi honeycomb. singing.

HEIDI: 'Something in the way he moves, attracts me like no other lover. Something in the way he moves me...'

⚲ LINDA: You did that without moving your lips.

HEIDI: 'I don't want to leave him now, you know I believe in how...'

♂ TOM: Oh, that must be Miss Honeycomb! Come through Miss Honeycomb.

heidi honeycomb comes in still singing. she is linda's doppelganger.

♂ TOM: Yes, yes, yes, yes, yes – all right, all right you can stop now.

he gasps on realising she's the double of linda. linda gasps too. heidi is equally amazed.

HEIDI: Which one of you's Tom?

♂ TOM: 'Tis I, 'tis I Miss Honeycomb. Linda, shut your mouth, we are not a codfish.

⚲ LINDA: Don't you think she looks like...

♂ TOM: It's rude to stare Linda. Though I have to admit the likeness is uncanny.

⚲ LINDA: Are you Catherine Zeta Jones? People have always mistaken me for you. 'Ere don't take this the wrong, but that cat suit you wore in 'Entrapment'? I could read your lips.

HEIDI: I am Heidi Honeycomb. Singing teacher to the stars!

⚲ LINDA: Oh Heidi, hi!

HEIDI: Name me any pop sensation and bet I've taught 'em!

♂ TOM: Erm... Atomic Kitten!

HEIDI: Erm..

⚲ LINDA: 'Pop Stars'! Danny from 'Pop Stars'!

HEIDI: Er. Gerry and the Pacemakers! Yes! I taught them! Thank you!

♂ TOM: Right Linda – I'm going to have to ask you to vacate this room.

⚲ LINDA: Why? Do I smell?

♂ TOM: No. Well yes you do. But that's not the point. I need to commence my tutelage.

⚲ LINDA: Oh please let me stay Tom, please! She's gorgeous. She's making me come over all Navratilova.

HEIDI: I need lubrication.

⚲ LINDA: I've heard him shout that out in the middle of the night!

HEIDI: Fetch me a small scotch!

♂ TOM: Jeannette Krankie?!

HEIDI: Hey – me and Jeannette Krankie are so close Linda. She phones me up at three in the morning. Gagging for me to let her do her C sharp minor scales. But I say 'Jeannette? Sweet, sweet boy-impersonating Jeannette. Heidi needs to sleep.'

♂ TOM: (Passes drink) There you go Miss Honeycomb. One Gail Porter – mountain – climbing – scotch on the rocks!

HEIDI: I can't abide her. She does me head in.

⚲ LINDA: Oh I know.

HEIDI: The things you see when you haven't got a gun! I was slagging Elaine Paige off to Clodagh Rogers only the other day...

♂ TOM: Excuse me, Heidi, – It's... it's me you've come to teach, all right? I even wore my special singing outfit. And look I can do geisha dancing. (Dances)

⚲ LINDA: Go on, you were telling me about Elaine thingamebob..

HEIDI: Paige. That pint-sized minx with a gob like a claxon's took all my work over the years.

⚲ LINDA: Really?

HEIDI: 'Evita'. 'Starlight'. 'Cats'. I was born to play those parts.

⚲ LINDA: Ah, I'm gonna go round there and knock her out.

HEIDI: My only drawback is I'm of average height and I can't do accents. It's so unfair. Evita coulda come from Nottingham. (Drinks) More Scotch!

♂ TOM: Look what else I can do Heidi, look. Moonwalk Kabuki!

he moonwalks for her and pours her a drink.

♀ LINDA: 'Ere, I love the way you do your hair babe.

HEIDI: I'll take that as a compliment coming from a princess like you.

♂ TOM: So... Quick recap Heidi? I'm up for 'Titus Androgynous' and I need a quick refresher course.

HEIDI: Stand close... and let me feel your voicebox.

♂ TOM: My old singing coach never used to lay a finger on me.

HEIDI: I'm very hands-on with all my boys.

♂ TOM: Oh no, I tell a lie. We once shared a Z-bed. And he taught me a technique for widening my throat.

heidi runs her hands from tom's throat to his groin.

♀ LINDA: Cor! Go for it girl! 'Ere, I should-a been a singing teacher.

HEIDI: And cough!

tom coughs.

HEIDI: Just as I thought – mezzo soprano. (Sings) 'We're walking in the air!'

♀ LINDA: (Lifts skirt) Ere, d'you wanna feel what I am Heidi?

HEIDI: Now, before we go any further can I scotch them rumours. I never laid a finger on Aled Jones. All I did was teach him Delilah. 'My my my, Delilah!' Come on, come on, come on...

LINDA/TOM/HEIDI: (Sing) 'Why why why?'

♀ LINDA: Delilah!

HEIDI: More scotch!

♂ TOM: I nearly worked with Aled Jones once. When I did 'The Snowman' at Pevensey Rep. Only, we couldn't get Aled, so we got Vinnie Jones instead.

HEIDI: I mean Aled's a nice fella. But we're only chums, Linda, chums! But you try telling my fella that.

♀ LINDA: I bet your fella's gorgeous inne Heid? Is he a right bastard?

HEIDI: He's none other than the glove puppet maestro, Hal Frigley.

♂ TOM: Hal Frigley? Hal Frigley?! He was my puppet teacher at drama school! We did 'Riverdance' with sixteen Nookie the Bears! How is the old braggart? I...

HEIDI: I get these urges Linda. But what Hal, God love him, doesn't understand, is he's not man enough for me. (Sings) 'What's she gonna look like with a chimney on her?' Come on, come on, come on.

HEIDI/LINDA: 'What's she gonna look like with a chimney on her?'

HEIDI: You should hear Moira Stuart singing that. Dynamite! (Sits)

♂ TOM: So when do we actually start this lesson, hmm? Time is money Heidi!

HEIDI: (Stands) Now Thomas. Thomas. Imagine your voicebox is a tight-stomached eighteen-year-old with baby lotion all over him. You've got to caress him into performing for you. Down in one! (Drinks) Repeat after me. 'Fa da ree dee fa da ree dee Fa da ree da da'

♂ TOM: 'Fa da ree dee, fa de ree dur Fa da ra da dee da.'

HEIDI: It's like I've met Rick Astley for the first time all over again. My glass appears to be empty.

♂ TOM: (Gets bottle) Then let me fill you up.

HEIDI: Oh don't tease me Tom. Don't tease me! He's such a tease Linda!

♀ LINDA: I know. I walk around this place in a constant state of arousal, guy!

heidi swigs from bottle.

♂ TOM: Far be it for me to criticise Miss Honeycomb. But any more of that and you shall be drunk.

HEIDI: Drunk I may be, but I've got one thing you'll never have.

♀ LINDA: Thrush? I've had it.

HEIDI: Talent. Is there any more booze in this house?

♂ TOM: Now look here, I'm vastly talented, thank you very much. I've shown you my huge array of dances. And I've got a pretty good singing voice too. Listen, this is the opening line from the last pantomime I was in... (Sings) 'Here in the land of golden showers, meet the mighty people with psychic powers'

HEIDI: Don't talk to me about golden showers.

LINDA
**'Oh, hello. Oh what
a nice warm
handshake
you have!'**
JEZ
**'Actually that's not
my hand.'**

♂ TOM: I am talking Heidi!! The other thing you need to know about me is that I am deeply professional. That was one of the first things we learnt at drama school, apart from learning how to answer the door on 'The Bill'. 'He ain't in. I didn't even know he'd been let out.' The other thing is is that you must never ever ever turn up so drunk that you can't perform. Look there's just no easy way of saying this...

HEIDI: You find me incredibly attractive and it's getting in the way of our lesson. I understand. Unhook my uplift. (Reveals bra)

♂ TOM: No, no no!

HEIDI: You're so like Andi Peters! He likes me to keep it on as well.

♂ TOM: Just, just go, all right, just get out, go on, go on! Shoo! Shoo! You vile be-goggled bog creature!

HEIDI: Oh no Tom! Please, please – I need the money. I'm very good. Ask anybody. Ask her!

♀ LINDA: She's great.

HEIDI: See? Oh Please Tom. I'll behave myself. Sing for me. Sing for Heidi.

♂ TOM: All right, all right, all right, all right. But you've got to take this seriously. Because there's a lot riding on this audition, okay?

HEIDI: Maestro please – warble for Heidi!

♂ TOM: Well they asked me to go for something classical at this audition, so I've plumped for this. Okay. (Clears throat) 'Long ago, High on a mountain in Mexico, Stood a young shepherd boy Angelo, And met his wife and he loved her so...'

HEIDI: She intrigues me Thomas. What was her financial situation?

♂ TOM: (Sings) 'Rich was she, Came from a very high family...'

TOM'S BEDROOM

*tom sits on bed drinking a glass
of green sludge.
linda comes in.*

♀ LINDA: Well – here it is, the big day. You're gonna be a top singer and I'm gonna be a top model. Oh, I'm so excited! I haven't been this excited since Jimmy Saville came to our open day at school and sat on my Face.

♂ TOM: Oh, God! Oh!

♀ LINDA: Face! It was the name of our school donkey! So, how did you sleep?

♂ TOM: Funny dreams again. Michael Portillo in denim hot pants and a gingham cowboy hat, you know.

♀ LINDA: Oh well – at least this time he was dressed.

♂ TOM: He's got very big lips hasn't he?

♀ LINDA: My Daddy had big lips. Used to get stuck to windows. Mummy had to prise him off with a backscratch.

♂ TOM: Still, You know what they say about people with big lips, don't you? They make very sensuous lovers.

♀ LINDA: I've got me mother's lips downstairs.

♂ TOM: Oh God! What's the matter with you!

♀ LINDA: In the cellar!

♂ TOM: Oh, oh, in the cellar.

♀ LINDA: She donated them to medical silence only I haven't sent 'em off yet. Ah. Eugh, whassat?

♂ TOM: This is my special pre-audition drink. It's algae, spinach, seaweed, garlic, a squid, and a veritable alphabet of vitamins. Elton John swears by it.

♀ LINDA: Eurgh – his farts must be rank, guy! His poor wife. No wonder she left him. Oh well, I can't sit around 'ere chitty chatting. I've gotta go and be a top model, 'cos I am gorgeous! Oh, can I borrow some of your gay spray? (Sprays Herself) 'Cos I'm gorgeous! I'm gorgeous! I'm gorgeous!

I'm G.O...gorgeous. (Sings) 'I'm gorgeous'.
D'you want some?

♂ TOM: No I don't really want any...
I don't want...

♀ LINDA: 'I'd do anything for you'.

she sprays it over him.

♂ TOM: Linda don't, don't cos it's going in
my mouth and I...! (Coughs he can't speak)
(Mouths) You stupid fucking bitch! Look
what you've gone and done!

♀ LINDA: I can't hear you.

♂ TOM: (Mouthed) I've lost my voice!!

♀ LINDA: You're weird guy! I dunno.

♂ TOM: (Mouthed) You have sprayed that into
my mouth and now I've lost my voice. Well
thanks a lot, Lindy! You evil, evil witch!!

♀ LINDA: You're scaring me Tom. Mime it.
Go on. Mime it. You upset about something?

tom points to his eye.

♀ LINDA: Tom, have you gone blind?

he points to eye again.

♀ LINDA: Eye! Eye! Eye!

he mimes driving a car.

♀ LINDA: Quirky seventies disco dance?

tom mimes driving again.

♀ LINDA: Car!!

he agrees.

♀ LINDA: Eye Car. I Claudius!

tom shakes his head. tom walks.

♀ LINDA: Mince?

tom walks again.

♀ LINDA: Walk?

he nods – makes letter 't'.

♀ LINDA: Walk 't'. Walk't. Walk't. Talk!
Eye car talk.

tom looks hopeful.

♀ LINDA: Eye car talk. Eye car talk.
Eye car talk.

tom nods encouragement.

♀ LINDA: Ah, nah, I dunno what your bloody
trying to say.

linda walks out.

*tom jumps on the bed in
exasperation.*

SHARED HALLWAY.

*suze practising a speech with jez.
linda listening in.*

JEZ: Enunciate darling! Roll your R's.

SUZE: The main focus of this show is
the models. Who says models have to
be attractive? For far too long designers
have been criticised for chucking skinny
pre-pubescent girls down the catwalk.
And life just isn't like that.

tom appears by linda.

SUZE: Which is why we have chosen
some of the ugliest people around to
model Alexander's clothes today. (Giggles)
We have gone out of our way to find the
most revolting looking people in London.
Be challenged. Be horrified. And please
get your sick bags at the ready and
welcome.. Dogs In Togs!

jez applauds. tom laughs.

♂ TOM: (Mouthed) Stupid fucking bitch!!

♀ LINDA: She's a c...

*tom sprays her mouth. she can't
speak either. they strangle each other
in silence.*

Episode Six
DECOY

dream sequence documentary.
linda tottering down the street.

NARRATOR: Although she only looks sixteen, Linda La Hughes is in fact twenty-three. She's attractive, funny, and happy-go-lucky. But as she walks sexily down this ordinary come-day go-day North London street, she hides an amazing secret. She is... a pop star's girlfriend.

the title of the documentary appears across the screen it says 'pop star's girlfriend'.

LINDA'S BEDROOM

linda talking to camera.

♀ LINDA: And then he got through to Birmingham. And he said to me 'This time next week I could be a pop star'. Promise me you'll never leave me. Promise me that even if I make it to the top, you'll always be there by my side' I said 'Danny, baby. This bitch ain't going nowhere.'

INTERVIEWER: Do you ever get jealous of his female fans?

♀ LINDA: No Bing Bong, I don't. And I'll tell you for why. I got the morals of an hooker. In fact, I'm a slut. And I mean to say why is he going to go looking for Wotsits when he's got double egg and chips at home? D'you know what I'm saying?

LINDA'S BEDROOM

in her sleep linda has wrapped her legs around tom's neck. he peers over her dressed as a bellboy. she wakes up and screams.

♂ TOM: Top o'the morning to you lady. Half a crown and I'll stick your carpet bags right up your hackney carriage!

♀ LINDA: How long you been there, you freak?

♂ TOM: About an hour. You, Mistress Vile have been daydreaming. Kept licking your lips and saying 'Prise apart my curtains Danny!'

♀ LINDA: I dreamt I was in a haberdashery.

♂ TOM: Ask me how my audition went! Ask me how my audition went! ASK ME HOW MY AUDITION WENT!!

♀ LINDA: How did your audition went?

♂ TOM: Read all about it! Read all about it! Me audition was blinding governor! I've just gotta practise with these.

picks up two suitcases.

The Executive Suite? Uh. Right away. Stay close to my rear, sir. (Exits)

LIVING ROOM.

linda comes in to find tom practising on the phone.

♂ TOM: Hello, 'Crossroads' – how can I help you? Billy the Bellboy speaking!

♀ LINDA: What was it you went up for again?

♂ TOM: Here's a clue! (Picks up phone) Hello, Crossroads Motel speaking, how can I be serviced by you?

♀ LINDA: What's a motel?

♂ TOM: It's a hotel with a moat around it. I'm up for this really interesting character. Billy the Bellboy. But he's not just any old bellboy.

♀ LINDA: Is a moat like a boat?

♂ TOM: He's this really talented artist. And they hold a painting competition. And he scoops top prize with his shocking portrayal of a naked Nora Batty.

♀ LINDA: Is a moat like a boat?

♂ TOM: No! It's like a... It's like a big, big wet patch. I need to watch something on television so shush. (Zaps **TV** Remote)

♀ LINDA: What's this shit?

♂ TOM: 'Watercolour Challenge'. Hosted by the lovely Hannah 'Mine's a Haggis' Gordon. 'Easy strokes there, lads and lasses. Easy strokes!'

♀ LINDA: Cor, look at the state of her tatty old bush. 'Ere, what are them long things?

♂ TOM: They're brushes! What else d'you expect them to paint with?

♀ LINDA: Potatoes!! When I did Art in me unit, Miss Understood said to me 'Special people paint with potatoes Linda, and you are a special person!'

♂ TOM: (Looking at a newspaper) If I'm going to learn how to paint convincingly, I'll have to get in some practice. Maybe there's a course at the local night school or something Oh! Here's one for you Lindy. 'Lesbians With Learning Difficulties: Lifting The Veil'.

♀ LINDA: Vile!

♂ TOM: I should get myself a hobby. As a boy I used to collect milk bottle tops. Sewed them onto my country dancing outfits like sequins.

♀ LINDA: There was a boy in our flats like you. Sadie May. Wore his mother's wig and pushed a bulldog round in a pram. He was always nicking my dollies. Did you play with dollies?

♂ TOM: I was more likely to be found with my fist up an Orville, actually.

♀ LINDA: Aah, my poor Barbie. She had such an hard life. 'Ere.

♂ TOM: What, what?

♀ LINDA: Sushhh. She took an overdose.

♂ TOM: Linda. We're talking about a dolly.

♀ LINDA: Shortly after she started to self-harm.

♂ TOM: Oh shut up! (Picks up phone)

♀ LINDA: Well, there's no point in trying to phone her Tom. She dead!

♂ TOM: I'm just practising. Make a phone noise, for me.

♀ LINDA: Brrr, brrr. Brrr, brrr...

♂ TOM: (Answers phone) 'Hello, Billy the Bellboy speaking – how can I... Can you? You can stop ringing... stop ringing now.

linda stops ringing.

♂ TOM: 'Hello Billy the bellboy. Can I help? Yes, I'll just put you through. 'You sir, are most welcome.'

linda claps.

♂ TOM: I did a whole term of phone answering at Drama School. I can answer the phone in distress. 'Oh you're poisoning me mind Bertie, with your constant telephonic nuisances!' Thank you. Um, or I can do it in the style of a soft core porn line. 'I should have known by the way he looked at me in the locker room that Coach Telford had an ulterior motive when he suggested a jockstrap inspection.'

♀ LINDA: I was just getting into that.

♂ TOM: I'm so gifted. My talent knows no end. Oh! Why won't anyone employ me?

♀ LINDA: Ah shut up you miserable old fruit. I'm gonna play with me laptop.

♂ TOM: This isn't what I envisaged for myself at all. When I was eight, Madame Puddifer from the Maison D'Arcy School of Disco, Cheam... asked me what I wanted to be when I grew up. And d'you know what I said?

♀ LINDA: A topless waitress on roller boots. That's what I wanted to be. I still do.

♂ TOM: No, I said 'A star, Madame Puddifer. A star!' I never thought I'd end up in this dreadful position.

♀ LINDA: Funny you should say that. When I was eight I found Mummy's 'Joy of Sex'. And I must admit, I had a little flick. And I thought to myself, I don't wanna end up in

that dreadful position'. I think it was
the wheelbarrow.

♂ TOM: Life is so unfair! Why can't my life be
wonderful? Hmm? Why can't you be nice?

♀ LINDA: (Looks around) Who?

♂ TOM: You! I wonder what it would be
like eh Lindy? I wonder what it would
be like?

DREAM SEQUENCE.

the pair of them in a gorgeous flat.

♂ TOM: So, how was it at the office
today girlfriend?

♀ LINDA: So-so bordering on fair, I guess.
Handed in my presentation to Microsoft
Slingback, really hammered home a few
points. How was your lunch?

♂ TOM: Ah, Trevor Nunn is such a sweetie,
you know. Doing 'The Dream' at the Nash.
kept begging me to show him my Frisky
Puck. He said to me 'You can keep your
Berkoffs, your McKellans, your Jacobis. No-
one can hold a torch to you Thomas.'

♀ LINDA: Well, I agree. I think you're one of
the finest actors of your generation.

♂ TOM: Yeah, well, of any generation, I like to
think.

♀ LINDA: Yes, so true.

knock on door.

suze and jez enter, they are scruffy junkies.

♀ LINDA: Oh Tom look, it's our dysfunctional
subplot neighbours from downstairs. Hi!

LINDA

'I got the morals of an hooker... I mean to say why is he going to go looking for Wotsits when he's got double egg and chips at home?'

SUZE: Oh lend us a fiver Linda.

JEZ: Yeah, go on (Snorts) you're loaded.

SUZE: Yeah, it's only for a bit o'skunk, innit.

JEZ: Innit.

SUZE: Innit.

JEZ: Innit.

SUZE: Innit.

♀ LINDA: (To Tom) Do you think I should?

♂ TOM: Well, I mean it's the Christianly thing
to do Linds, yeah.

♀ LINDA: Oh, you're so right – God,
thanks Tom.

♂ TOM: That's okay Linda.

♀ LINDA: (Passes money) Here you go.

SUZE: Oh cheers Linda.

JEZ: Yeah cheers treacle.

SUZE: You're the best people in these flats.

JEZ: Innit.

SUZE: Yeah, anyone gives you any hassle –
you send 'em to me.

JEZ: Come on bitch, shagging time.

jez and suze leave.

♀ LINDA: It's not their fault Tom.

♂ TOM: I know.

tom's face suddenly clouds over.

♀ LINDA: Hey Tom. You seem sad. You still
upset about the absence of a life partner?

♂ TOM: Yeah, kind of, I guess.

♀ LINDA: Oh look don't worry. Mr. Right could
come along at any moment, you know and
nobody deserves a bit of happiness more
than you do.

♂ TOM: Thanks Linds. Gosh you know you're
right. You really are my best friend.

♀ LINDA: Oh you too. I think you're great.

♂ TOM: Thanks

beryl enters.

♂ TOM: Oh God – look Linda... It's our quirky
old lady who lives upstairs, Beryl. Oh I adore
the elderly and the infirm.

BERYL: I'm just gonna collect me pension,
dear. Do a bit of shopping at the cheapo
store. I hope you don't mind my using your
gaff as a thoroughfare.

♂ TOM: Not at all Beryl, no.

♀ LINDA: Bye Beryl!

beryl exits.

♀LINDA: (Contd.) Oh, isn't she lovely?

♂TOM: She's one of life's troupers Linds!

♀LINDA: Yeah.

LIVING ROOM

beryl comes through with 2 lads and some stolen videos.

BERYL: These are hot, so I don't want the fuzz to see. That's why I prefer to slip in the back way!

♀LINDA: (To Tom) What's your excuse?

LIVING ROOM, LATER

tom is going through his dressing up box. linda and beryl watching.

♂TOM: Oh my god! Oh this was from when we did 'Crystal Tips and Alistair Go To Ibiza'. (Puts on wig) 'I'm gonna go to Ibiza and get seriously off my nut, boy!' And you remember who played Alistair, don't you?

♀LINDA: Well 'ard from EastEnders.

♂TOM: He's a wonderful actor, isn't he? So organic, so inventive!

♀LINDA: He's so licky! He licked me all the way up my legs!

♂TOM: You know whose fault it is that I'm single, don't you?

BERYL: Your parents 'cos they're plain?

♂TOM: No, It's showbiz's fault. Maybe if I get this part on Crossroads I'll be able to get myself a boyfriend.

♀LINDA: That's what you said when you had three lines in 'Dangermouse'.

♂TOM: 'Field', 'Dangerfield', you pre-menstrual papoose! And what happened?

♀LINDA: You got arrested for spotting them little houses! I mean, what's the world coming to, eh? You're working in a picturesque part of the countryside, of course you're gonna wanna go out cottaging – any man in his right mind would!

suze rushes in crying.

SUZE: Turn that off!!

tom zaps tv remote.

BERYL: Oh my word, I'm having a psychic moment! D'you think she's upset about something?

SUZE: It's Jez. He's leaving me.

BERYL: Suze? A word. Your husband's left you. And you're the wrong side of thirty. Your looks are going. You feel isolated And you haven't worked through your personal hygiene issues yet. Do you know what you need? A new video. I'll give you this for a one-er.

SUZE: He hasn't left me yet!!

BERYL: When he does, you'll be wanting to watch a few videos. Look, I'll bung in 'Porky's 2' for a fiver.

SUZE: I know he's going to leave me. I just know it. It's since we've had the baby. He's really changed. It's like he's having some sort of mid-life crisis. Did you ever have one of those Beryl?

BERYL: I did imagine I was having an affair with Patricia Routledge.

SUZE: What about you Linda?

♀LINDA: What?

SUZE: Did you ever have a mid-life crisis?

♀LINDA: No. Piss off!

SUZE: He's started drinking every night. Partying with the lads. Oh and then to cap it all he goes and gets a modelling job.

♂TOM: Is he doing sort of... catalogue modelling? Because I love the underwear sections in those.

♀LINDA: Oooh – me an'all.

♂TOM: It was the nearest thing I could find to gay porn as a teenager. All those packages. All those buns.

♀LINDA: I've got a famous botty. I have. When I walk down the road people say: 'Your arse is massive!' (Flicks fingers)

GIMME GIMME GIMME   183

SUZE: He's going to sit at a local painting class and people will paint him.

♂TOM: In the nuddy wuddy?

SUZE: Yes.

♀LINDA: With potatoes?

SUZE: He's not mentioned them.

♂TOM: I really ought to get myself down there, you know, just to help me get this part in Crossroads.

suze starts to bawl again

♂TOM: Oh for goodness sake, would somebody shut her up please.

♀LINDA: I know. She's doing my brain in guy!

BERYL: Methinks I have a cunning stunt. What we need is a woman. A woman who is loose and of easy virtue.

they all look at linda.

♀LINDA: What?!

BERYL: How do you fancy throwing yourself at Jez, Linda?

♀LINDA: I'll do it!

BERYL: You may need to wear a disguise.

♀LINDA: Put me in what you like.

♂TOM: Might I suggest a body bag then?

♀LINDA: I don't mind what I wear, as long as it's nipple pink.

STREET

beryl and suze outside the house by a taxi.

BERYL: By the end of tonight, you'll know if Jez would stray if temptation came his way. Linda'll act as a decoy. She'll try it on with him.

SUZE: He'd never shag her though. She looks like Eddie The Eagle Edwards in a sports bra.

BERYL: That's why she's in disguise. Now she is wearing a look he finds a turn on, isn't she?

SUZE: Oh yes. By jiminy yes.

tom comes running out of the house dressed as a painter.

BERYL: Oh God she looks gorge!

♂TOM: No no no no – it's me. I'm throwing myself into the part of the wannabe artist!

BERYL: How's Linda looking?

♂TOM: She has never looked so good! Linda!

linda comes out in a nipple pink yashmak.

♀LINDA: I can't see where I'm bloody well going in this thing! How the bloody hell am I gonna smoke?

♂TOM: Get in the taxi. Get in the taxi. We're going to be late! (Gets into taxi)

BERYL: Good luck Linda!

SUZE: Yes. Don't do anything I wouldn't do.

♀LINDA: Well that don't leave much, you dirty whore! (Gets into taxi)

♂TOM: (To driver) Right – to the City Lit please. This is my penpal. Fatwa.

♀LINDA: (To driver) Stop looking at my tits! You rotten bugger!

ART CLASS

tom and linda peer around their easels. a naked jez is posing.

ART TEACHER: What a strangely shaped penis Tom.

♂TOM: Oh crikes – have I come out again? Oh – oh, sorry. Yes well actually that's a banana but she's used all the yellow, so...

ART TEACHER: Great. Great.

jez is putting his robe on

ART TEACHER: Oh Jez, please remain seated.

JEZ: Hi Tom, I thought it was you. Put it there!

♂TOM: Oh. Jez. Is that you? I had no idea.

JEZ: I didn't know you were into painting.

♂TOM: Yes – I'm into most things pubic. Er cubic! Yeah – I'm up for the part of Billy the Bellboy in Crossroads so this is all in the

name of research. Have you met my penpal...
Fatwa? Fatwa this is Jez. The model.

JEZ: Gosh. What a devilishly sexy look. Hi.

♀ LINDA: Oh hello. Oh. What a nice warm handshake you have!

JEZ: Actually that's not my hand.

♀ LINDA: Oh. You like disco dance? D'you wanna come a disco dance with me-a?

LINDA

'Tom, if we're never going to see each other again will you kiss me? Like you mean it. Go on. Pretend I'm a boy.'

CLUB

jez and linda dancing.

LIVING ROOM

suze crying. beryl and tom attending to her.

♂ TOM: Oh Suze. Weep not my delicate little dingleberry. Jez and Linda going to a club. Well. It's a bit like all the stuff that comes out of Geri Halliwell's mouth, isn't it? Really doesn't mean anything at all.

SUZE: I may as well face facts. He'd rather go out with a stranger in a yashmak than spend any real time with his wife. I can't bear it. I'm going to be a single mum.

BERYL: Slut!! Hussy! Whore!

♂ TOM: Beryl. Beryl! It's not a stigmata any more you know.

BERYL: Oh. Isn't it?

♂ TOM: No!

BERYL: Oh, sorry Suze, I didn't know. Really?

♂ TOM: God! It's not as if people are going to go up to her on the street and go 'Bitch! Silly bitch, haven't got a man, don't deserve to have a man!' They're not gonna punch her little child and shout 'Bastard! You little bastard! Haven't got a dad. Don't deserve a dad!' I mean, they're not gonna string it up

on the street are they, and paint the word 'devil child' across its scrawny little chest in turkey blood. You know what I'd do? Leave it on a step somewhere, or, or, or in a box. Or 'Chuck it into canal! Yeah, chuck it in friggin' canal, wrap it in friggin' chip paper and chuck it in piggin' canal'!!

beryl and suze are looking at tom quite fearfully now.

♂ TOM: What?! What?

LIVING ROOM

jez and linda slow dancing. linda still in the yashmak.

JEZ: How convenient that Linda's out for the night, and you're using her room.

♀ LINDA: You know who you-a like? You like-a Danny from-a Popstars. They very big up my country.

JEZ: Oh Fatwa. You're such a good dancer.

♀ LINDA: Up my country I am national disco dance champion. I can dance this way. But I can also dance-a this-a way too. (Rubs her bum against his groin) My feet are killing me guy. My friggin' bunions guy. Arrgh, I'm shagged guy.

linda sits on the couch.

JEZ: Fatwa. You're the hottest minx I've met in yonks. But, you know, recently I've felt old. I thought I just wanted one last fling. One last run around the block. With the windows down and the car radio on full blast. But you know, tonight I have realised that I want to do all those things with Suze. Yashmak or no yashmak. She's the hottest honey on the block. So you see, Fatwa. (Linda has fallen asleep) Fatwa? Damn. A furtive fondle on your front bottom would've been fun. But, oh well. (Stands) Goodnight (Kisses Linda) Fatty bum bum.

he leaves, slamming door.

♀ LINDA: (Wakes) Jez? Jez?! I let you into a little secret. Underneath-a this dress? I no wear-a the pants.

tom has come in

♀ LINDA: (Taking head-dress off) Where did he go? God, I only nodded off for five seconds. Blimey, I'm surprised I didn't nod off sooner. He is so bloody boring!

TOM: Do you know what time it is? It's five o'bloody clock! Suze is going out of her mind. I had to stun her with a whale gun. She's been like that ever since she's had the baby. I think it's post-coital depression.

LINDA: Men can get that can't they? The amount of men I've shagged that have just cried their eyes out afterwards. And during.

TOM: Oh – what's this?

LINDA: It's a telephone.

TOM: No, no, no – there's a message on the answering machine. How did I miss that? How? (Presses button)

NORMA: (Voice-over) Tom dear it's Norma.

TOM: Oh it's my agent! What?!

NORMA: (Voice-over) Good news darling. You've got the part. You're Billy the Bellboy in Crossroads. Now for the bad news.

TOM: Oh God, this is a wind up. Oh I don't believe it. What a cruel prank!

NORMA: (Voice-over) You start tomorrow morning. You have to get up to Nottingham by noon and they want you to live there permanently. Enjoy darling. Well done. Ciao.

they are stunned.

LINDA: Well you can't do it Tom. Well you can't. I mean you're crap. You'll be a right show-up.

TOM: Lindy, Lindy, I have just got a leading role in one of Britain's top-rated soaps.

LINDA: No, Tom, it's Crossroads.

TOM: I am going and there's nothing you can do to stop me!!

LINDA: You wanna bet?

she punches him – he falls onto sofa.

LINDA: You can't leave me Tom, you can't!

TOM: Get away from me, devil woman!! (He kicks her in the chin)

LINDA: You can't leave me Thomas, you can't leave me.

TOM: Give me one good reason why I should stay!

LINDA: Because… I is dying.

TOM: What?

LINDA: Don't make me say it again.

TOM: But… but c'mon Lindy, this is sick.

LINDA: No Tom. I'm sick. I didn't wanna tell you before. But, I've only got three weeks to live. I've got an horrible infectious disease what no-one else has ever had.

TOM: What's it called?

LINDA: Gastro-ginger-vivian-itis.

TOM: Oh Lindy.

LINDA: Hold me Thomas.

TOM: Actually, you do smell diseased.

LINDA: Don't leave me, Tommy.

TOM: Oh, oh Lindy I had no idea. Is this why you went to the gynaecologist the other day? But you came back with a huge smile on your face.

LINDA: Looks like you're not the only one who can act, baby.

TOM: I'm gonna turn down the part on Crossroads. I'll phone Norma. Tell them to offer it to Jude Law. We're spookily similar. Oh. I couldn't (Kisses her) wouldn't ever leave you now.

LINDA: Oh Tommy. Oh, that feels good.

TOM: Oh does it?

LINDA: Yeah. If you just rub here that eases the pain.

she guides his hand to her crotch.

TOM: Where – here? Like that?

LINDA: Just there.

TOM: Okay – there we go…there we…

tom twigs she's having him on.

TOM: I think I'm looking at Leonie Liar.

LINDA: Eh?

TOM: You evil evil bat. How dare you toy with my emotions thus.

LINDA: Eh?

TOM: I knew a lady once who made up the state of her health. And do you know what happened to her? She turned into a lesbian.

LINDA: Well maybe I didn't mean three weeks, maybe I meant three decades.

TOM: I think I'd better go and pack.

he leaves.

LINDA: No!

she cries.

LINDA'S BEDROOM

Linda sits forlornly. Tom comes in with suitcases – he puts them down

♂ **TOM:** Well... I can't believe how low you'd stoop. Inventing a life-threatening disease just to stop me from leaving you.

♀ **LINDA:** It worked for Angie Watts.

♂ **TOM:** Den and Angie were married!

♀ **LINDA:** Well so are we. We live together. We row all the time. We don't have sex. What's the difference?

♂ **TOM:** Linda, look, I have just got to go. I have made up my mind. So. Goodbye (Exits)

Linda looks sad.

♂ **TOM:** (Re-enters) I don't want to go, I don't want to go.

♀ **LINDA:** Well don't then, you twit!

♂ **TOM:** But there's a very small part of me that's like a small little child called Humphrey. Afraid of stepping into the kindergarten, afraid of stepping out into the big bad world.

outside a taxi horn toots.

♀ **LINDA:** I've just had a premonition. If you get in that taxi it'll crash. Don't go, Tom!

♂ **TOM:** No. I have to go Lindy. I mustn't be afraid!

♀ **LINDA:** Please don't go Tom. I'll promise I'll never be vile to you again.

♂ **TOM:** Lindy. It's time.

♀ **LINDA:** Well you don't have to move to Nottingham permanent like. You could always stay here and compute.

♂ **TOM:** This might be my one and only chance, Linda. You can always come and visit me you know.

♀ **LINDA:** No – I get lost on trains unless I've got a label.

♂ **TOM:** But, you know, Lindy this... this isn't goodbye. It's just auf weidhersein pet.

♀ **LINDA:** I thought you said it was Crossroads. You're confusing me Tom, you're confusing me!

♂ **TOM:** Lindy. Lindy. I have to go. Give me your blessing and kiss my ring, my child.

♀ **LINDA:** Good luck baby.

TOM
'Den and Angie were married!'
LINDA
'Well so are we. We live together. We row all the time. We don't have sex. What's the difference?'

they hug.

♂ **TOM:** I hope you find a man brave enough to take you on, Lindy. Someone who'll fancy you for you. Love you for you.

♀ **LINDA:** But I want that man to be you. Tom, if we're never gonna see each other again – will you kiss me? Like you mean it. Go on. Pretend I'm a boy.

tom looks around.

tom kisses linda. the kiss continues – finally they break.

♀ **LINDA:** Oh, Tom.

♂ **TOM:** It's just my mobile phone.

♀ **LINDA:** Oh – we had a laugh didn't we, Thomas? I mean, I know nobody else did, but we had a laugh didn't we?

♂ **TOM:** I have to admit Linda, you're the only one who could keep my pecker up.

linda cries – her nose runs.

tom pushes her face away.

♂ **TOM:** I can't look at you anymore.

tom picks up cases, exits. linda crosses to look from window. she sees him going down the path – he opens the taxi door. he turns back to look up at linda. linda looks thoroughly miserable. tom looks equally sad then gets into the taxi.

TAXI

tom sitting down.

♂ **TOM:** Er – Crossroads Motel, please.
   DRIVER: Where?

♂ **TOM:** Oh no, no – erm...Kings Cross Station please. Thank you.

as the taxi pulls away, tom looks from the window. linda watches – she sighs heavily. tom looks away – he too sighs.

LINDA'S BEDROOM

linda turns and walks away from the window.

she scratches her head then pulls at her hair, it comes off. it's a wig. she throws it onto the dressing table and gets into bed. she pulls a tea cosy onto her bald head, she sucks her thumb and switches off the light. she is all alone.

NOTES TO ASPIRING SITCOM WRITERS

AN APOLOGY TO VICTORIA WOOD

One of the problems whilst writing Gimme Gimme Gimme was that about three weeks into recording the first series I thought I was going slightly mad. Every single person I met in the course of my working day had an opinion on what I had written and how funny each and every word was (or was not). I started analysing everything I heard for 'how funny it was'.

I had to give myself a good talking to and then have a very long lie down in a darkened room. When I later emerged from that room, I read an interview with Victoria Wood in the Radio Times. In it she described her experience writing the series 'Dinnerladies' and described a similar feeling of going bonkers. I actually burst out crying! Someone else understood the strain I was under.

Unfortunately for Ms Wood, I bumped into her at that year's Comedy Awards. She was sober and trying to join the queue for the hot snacks buffet, I was drunk and trying to stop her. I kept her talking — or rather, kept her there, talking at her — for what felt like six days, though in reality was probably about twenty minutes, with me repeating over and over again, **'OH GOD, YOU DON'T REALISE HOW MUCH THAT MEANT TO ME! OH MY GOD, YOU UNDERSTAND ME!'** The poor woman. I wouldn't let her go. So can I take this opportunity of apologising to Ms Wood. There was free drink and I was over-excited at being nominated for an award. The fact that I like the sound of my own voice has, of course, nothing to do with it.

I also want to take this opportunity of warning other writers that penning a sitcom isn't a complete bed of roses. If you are thinking of writing a sitcom, you must be prepared for the following:

1. THERE IS JUST ONE CRITERION IN A SITCOM — IS IT FUNNY?

No one is interested in whether you can tell your story efficiently or dramatically, all they care about is whether it makes them laugh. Every single line you write will be analysed by producers/directors/actors/the cleaner for one thing alone: Is it funny? And if not, they will say the following things:

* Could you not think of anything even mildly amusing here, Jonathan?
* That joke... It doesn't really wash it's face, does it?
* Jonathan? Could you gag that speech up for me?
* Cut that line, it's not funny.
* Will people really remember who Crystal Tips and Alastair were?
* I'm not saying that, it's shit. (Hmmm, that sounds dangerously like Kathy Burke.)
* So show me the lines in this episode that are supposed to be funny. (Hmmm, that sounds dangerously like James Dreyfus.)
* I won't be rehearsing this scene. It's not funny enough.
* Could you not think of anything better here then?
* That's a very old joke.
* Obviously this will have to be re-written.
* I'm just the feed. Can I have a joke please?

2. YOU WILL BE PAID A LOT OF MONEY

But you will have to work very hard for it. Not only will you have done various drafts of each script, but once you're in the rehearsal room you will be re-writing daily. You will only stop re-writing the minute the cameras start rolling.

3. YOU WILL HAVE TO HOLD A MILLION THINGS IN YOUR HEAD

Not only will you be re-writing that week's script, but at the same time you will be re-writing the following week's and the week after's depending on your schedule. Some bits are filmed out of sequence at a thing called a Pre-Record. This is usually quick stuff or difficult stuff that can be played into the audience when they come in to save time. We often pre-recorded stuff that took place in the hallway, as this was a part of the set that was hidden from the audience, so wasn't that interesting to watch. We'd also pre-record short scenes. In any one week you could be rehearsing one episode, pre-recording bits from that episode and the week after's, and then in the middle of it all you'd have a read-through for the week after that's episode. They say it's to give you more time to re-write – take no notice.
IT'S JUST TO CONFUSE YOU!

4. WHILE THE ACTORS ARE LYING IN BED, YOU WILL BE WORKING

Although they say that they spend their day off learning their lines (show me the proof!), it is a well-known fact that actors never get out of bed until eight in the evening and then go out partying to six in the morning with Tracey Shaw, and the likes. The writer, meanwhile, will be sat at his/her laptop, desperately shouting out to their boyfriend/girfriend/dog 'Give me a funny name beginning with N! Quickly!' or 'What's funnier? Mouldy Old Dough by Lieutenant Pigeon or Feels Like I'm In Love by Kelly-Marie? QUICKLY!'

5. THE PRESS WILL RIP YOU TO SHREDS

When Gimme first came out the press were merciless. Then when we were doing a second series people were a bit kinder. Once we'd made it to a third series they started being nicer still – presumably because we'd stuck it out for so long. I kind of have more respect for the press who hated it on first viewing, and hate it even more now!

6. FRIENDS WILL AVOID DISCUSSING IT

If they hate it, it just won't get mentioned. It's as if it doesn't exist. Then those with two year olds will complain that their beloved toddler loves the show 'for the colours'. Then the next week the same two year old will have asked Mummy 'What's a vibrator?'

7. WHEN YOU GET NOMINATED FOR A GOLDEN ROSE OF MONTREUX AWARD...

Your boyfriend will be convinced someone who really hates your guts is winding you up. He will be quite distressed about it. He will take some convincing that it is not a joke.

8. YOU WILL NEVER SLAG OFF ANOTHER SITCOM AGAIN

Once you've been through the process – and seen how much hard work it is – only to then have people slagging off your hard work, you start to see the good in even really shit sitcoms. Like Babes In The Wood. I would never ever say anything bad about that. Ever.

GIMME GIMME GIMME

AVAILABLE TO BUY ON VHS AND DVD
FROM NOVEMBER 2002